THE BIRD BIOGRAPHIES OF

John James Audubon

THE MACMILLAN COMPANY
NEW YORK • CHICAGO
DALLAS • ATLANTA • SAN FRANCISCO
LONDON • MANILA

BRETT-MACMILLAN LTD.
TORONTO

Phytolacca decandra

No 26

April 27th 1812. Pennᵃ   White throated Sparow A. W.
drawn by J.J. Audubon   Fringilla Albicolis

THE
BIRD BIOGRAPHIES
OF
John James Audubon

SELECTED AND EDITED BY
ALICE FORD

THE MACMILLAN COMPANY · NEW YORK

· 1957 ·

The editor and publisher wish to express their
thanks to Harvard College Library and to the
Museum of Comparative Zoology of Harvard University, who have granted permission to reproduce,
from their collections, the illustrations in this volume.

Library of Congress catalog card number: 56–7286

Editor's Foreword

It is more than a hundred years since the first publication of *Ornithological Biography*, the volumes written by Audubon as text to his great Folio, *The Birds of America*. These bird biographies, absorbing as pioneer ornithology, constantly reveal their author's adventures as a naturalist, and unroll the wide panorama of our frontier past. They belong among our classics, whether scientific or literary, for good and all.

Ornithological Biography was published in five volumes between 1831 and 1839. From 1840 to 1844 Audubon and his sons brought out a miniature edition of *The Birds of America* in seven volumes, illustrated with hand-colored lithographs in imitation of the large Folio aquatints. The text of this smaller, octavo work was that of *Ornithological Biography*, with minor deletions, with additions which included much borrowed observation; and without the delightful but irrelevant frontier "episodes." Species were rearranged and in many cases the names corrected according to Audubon's *Synopsis* of 1839, an index to Folio and text. That *Ornithological Biography* should become the standard was Audubon's hope. Completed just twenty-six years after the death of "the father of American ornithology," Scots-born Alexander Wilson, these descriptions did in fact enjoy preeminence during the so-called "Audubonian period," or to the close of the painter's life.

Before dawn of November 24, 1826, Audubon wrote the first lines of what was to prove for him an immense and excruciating task. Still unwashed and unshaven, he "sat to" at his table in an Edinburgh rooming house to tell of the Wild Turkey. He wished to have something "to lay on the table of the Exhibition Room for the use of the public" which was about to view his newly finished oil of a group of these birds. His journal relates how his pen carried him off to the Arkansas River, to the point where he could not, when his breakfast arrived, eat a "morsel." He wrote feverishly until a caller interrupted, heard the composition read aloud, and advised him to go to John Wilson, the famous editor of *Blackwood's Magazine,* "to have it put in good English." Audubon seized his hat and rushed forth in slippers and lounging clothes to Wilson's house. He told a servant to advise his master that "Mr. Audubon from America wished to speak to him." Wilson, amused by such ingenuousness, agreed to read the piece.

Three weeks later, again in a state of agitation, the artist took a paper on the Carrion Crow to the even more distinguished David Brewster and read aloud to him in a "cold sweat" of terror. He was all too conscious of his rhetorical shortcomings and of the fact that he had, for his part, "never looked into an English grammar." Next day he and Brewster corrected a proof of the Crow paper together, so that the author's meaning should not be smothered in alterations.

Until now, Audubon's jottings in ledgers and old journals—made mostly for his own satisfaction—had seemed to him of little importance. They had served to fire and also discipline his painted inspiration. Maturer judgment and the palm of authority, pressed on him by his new English and Scottish associates, suddenly made him see their value. If he was not a born writer, he prided himself on his unique knowledge and profound feeling for nature. He used his notes, ledgers, and intimate journals as a point of departure to seek supremacy as a field observer. He was not long in his grave before new facts and voices, fresh techniques of search, study, and reporting, began to vie for his established place. Yet the fact remains that what he wrote of the wilderness has no exact counterpart in all our literature. Not even his idol, James Fenimore Cooper, describes it more vividly.

Audubon dropped clues of his progress as he struggled with composition. His journal for October 16, 1830, announces:

I know that I am a poor writer, that I scarcely can manage to scribble a tolerable English letter, and not a much better one in French, though that is easier to me. I know that I am not a scholar, but meantime I am aware that no man living knows better than I do the habits of our birds; no man living has studied them as much as I have done, and with the assistance of my old journals and memorandum-books which were written on the spot, I can at least put down plain truths, which may be useful and perhaps interesting, so I shall set to at once. I cannot, however, give *scientific* descriptions, and here must have assistance.

At the suggestion of James Wilson, the naturalist, brother of John Wilson of *Blackwood's,* he engaged thirty-four-year-old William Mac-Gillivray, Edinburgh scientist, professor, artist, and writer, to smooth his "asperities" and "correct" as well as condense his scripts. (The well known zoologist William Swainson would have been appointed had he not demanded to appear as co-author and for a sum beyond Audubon's means.) Besides his editing, MacGillivray prepared technical data to follow each bird biography and drew the internal structure of certain species. For a modest but acceptable retainer paid at intervals, he carried the task through to completion, regardless of other activities that later won him recognition in his own right.

It must be confessed that comparison of some of the unedited biographies with the printed versions reveals MacGillivray's remarkable editorial restraint. One sentence in the Humming Bird that stood at 190 words in the original still runs on to a breathless 139. A published sentence of the Brown Thrush (Thrasher) contains a sentence of 145 words—more than twice the length of the Lord's Prayer—succeeded by one of 245 words, almost as long as the Gettysburg Address. Such effusions, extreme examples to be sure, suggest the dilemma of the editor confronted by a torrent of ideas, misleading punctuation, and paragraphs often obdurately long and in doubtful sequence. Again and again, both manuscript and printed rendering call to mind certain of Audubon's unfinished drawings. Strong, often masterful, always impressive, they nonetheless cry out for the long, close labor that their hard-pressed creator could not spare them. It is not surprising, then, that he should have quoted and borrowed from contemporaries, accepted editorial emendation, and sought the help of many students of nature. Foremost of these was the Reverend John Bachman, of Charleston, South Carolina—savant and friend—two of whose daughters married the painter's sons. To Bachman, who aided importantly with *Ornithological Biography,* Audubon wrote in 1834: "God preserve you, and save you the trouble of ever publishing books on natural science. For my part I would rather go without a shirt, or any inexpressibles, through the whole of the Florida swamps in mosquito time than labor as I have hitherto done with the pen."

Yet MacGillivray encouraged him after the first two volumes had reached completion: "I am sure that with your celebrity, knowledge, and enthusiasm you have it in your power to become more *popular* than your glorious pictures can ever make you of themselves, they being too aristocratic and exclusive." Although he noted no marked improvement in the writing, he took "great pleasure in reading."

Early in 1835 Audubon again wrote Bachman:

"What a treat for me . . . to disclose things unknown to all the world before me. . . . I must ask you . . . to assist all you can, and merely enable me to publish *no trash,* but pure, clean truths, and nothing but facts—which makes me stand so proud in my own estimation for what I have already done. My work, I feel sure, will be a standard one for ages to come, for I feel sure that with the exception of some few errors, the truths and facts contained in my writings and in my figures of Birds will become more apparent to every student of nature.

However, three months later he was groaning: "I have labored probably as hard, if not harder, than I ever did in my whole life. . . . I sat to writing and finished in one month, one fourth of the biographies of my third volume. This rendered me *puffy.* I could scarcely breathe. My appetite was gone. . . ."

Ornithological Biography was printed in Edinburgh in an edition of 750 sets. The indifference of the booksellers forced Audubon to become his own publisher. Folio subscribers paid twenty-one shillings per volume, others twenty-five. With all her native patience and precision Mrs. Audubon copied the manuscript of the first two volumes as edited, then posted it to America for publication and copyright. But these two single volumes, printed in Philadelphia and Boston—500 copies in all —were the beginning and end of the American edition.

Audubon took pride in being first to present purely technical as well as general descriptions, thanks to MacGillivray's erudition. "Nothing has been done on it," he wrote Bachman in 1835. "If I can, through my friends, introduce the anatomy of the principal parts of all our birds, the nature of this publication will put at defiance all that can be done in ornithology."

Many more species are known today than in Audubon's time, and guides to the birds are almost as numerous as the birds themselves. Yet his score of 508, of which 474 remain in good standing, surpassed all of his contemporaries—and all but one, Charles Lucien Bonaparte, by far. Of these, it is asserted that he himself saw 385.

With readability, value, and interest for a rule of thumb, but not with the conventional manual in mind, the present editor drew the best from the two original Audubon editions. Audubon's wish was for "a pleasing book as well as an instructive one." The present edition is designed for the modern reader to place beside *The Birds of America*. Careful comparison of both texts preceded the final choice of what was to be left in and what left out. Where, in the editor's view, the octavo edition sacrificed the charm of *Ornithological Biography*, the deleted passages were restored. Any new, pertinent facts in the octavo edition were preserved. Only truly lively, useful observations from Audubon's collaborators were admitted. Specific references had here and there to be supplied. Paragraphs and sentences were divided and occasionally transposed for clarity and logic, as MacGillivray had done on the original at Audubon's request. Expert ornithological opinion recommended exclusion of the MacGillivray data and anatomical drawings. The frontier "episodes" threaded through *Ornithological Biography*, while delightful, had no more place there than they have here, and in any case they are not unfamiliar to the public.

The omission of what may seem vital sections of the original is deliberate. More than one third of *Ornithological Biography* is unrelieved anatomical data. By admission, because he never crossed the Rockies, Audubon did not see for himself many birds he described from skins and secondary observation. Of his grand total, seventeen that he named as separate species have proved to be immatures, females, or color phases. Seventeen others are not recognized today: ten birds, perhaps casuals, were from outside our territories; two were hybrid; five he alone had seen, rendering them doubtful. Scores of the biographies are less than a page long, and scores more only somewhat less fragmentary. Concerned above all that the present generation should be made aware of Audubon's great contribution, the present editor nevertheless felt obliged to omit histories relatively limited in interest—even those of such universal favorites as the Robins, Warblers, and Finches. The Hawks become repetitious. The appalling account of the barbarity of hunters who visited extinction on the Great Auk, like other passages, would offend the squeamish and outrage the conservationist. The unpleasant, familiar enough habits of the Vultures did not seem to merit reconsideration; and Audubon's experiments with their olfactory powers are still debated. On the other hand, the tragic details of the painting of the Golden Eagle, omitted in the octavo edition, have been restored. Some readers may wish to turn back to the old pages for such as the Snowy and Night Herons and the Reddish Egret.

Even while Audubon wrote, ranges were everywhere changing, as he well knew. A table based on the last official *Check-list* of the American Ornithologists' Union is offered in place of facts that time has altered.

For the first time in the more than a century and a half since Audubon began to paint birds in America, a group of his *originals*—not the familiar engravings—are here reproduced, and with notable fidelity. The courtesy of Harvard University has made this possible. The Brown Thrasher is from the Museum of Comparative Zoology; the other drawings are from Harvard College, Houghton Library, the bequest of Joseph Y. Jeanes who acquired them from the estate of Audubon's benefactor, Edward Harris. These bird portraits are to be reckoned great by any standards, and, by their sensitivity of design, they challenge the best efforts of the Chinese masters. Ornithologists who have passed severe judgment on the elaborations of *The Birds of America* will find reason to prefer the bird portraits in this volume to those of identical species in the Folio. Free from the Folio's ornate accessories and sometimes strained attitudes, they are the work of Audubon alone, unassisted, from pencil outline to final brush stroke. Thanks to the excellence of modern reproduction, the present plates entirely escape that "scaliness" of feathering against which Audubon protested eternally to his engraver.

To repeat, it is not to be imagined that *Ornithological Biography* and the text of the octavo much differ, or that this selection departs wantonly from either. Here is the vision, matchless and moving, of an incomparable observer, who catches the beauty and drama, the wonder and mystery of the birds.

ALICE FORD

Contents

Illustrations

THE name as given by Audubon is followed by the modern vernacular name, then by the modern scientific name as in *Check List of North American Birds,* 4th edition, 1931, with revisions in *The Auk* through July, 1955.

Audubon's handwriting, transcribed from left to right, is given as it appears on each illustration. Figures in the original water-color and pastel drawings are natural size.

All drawings are from the Harvard College Library collection, except the Brown Thrasher which is from the Museum of Comparative Zoology, Harvard University.

PASSENGER PIGEON [Passenger Pigeon (extinct). *Ectopistes migratorius*]

Inscribed: "No. 109. Chute de L'Ohio. Decemb. 11, 1809. 12 pennes à la queue tres étagée. appelé ici Wild Pigeon, J. Audubon. Passenger Pigeon, A. W.—Columba Migratoria."

CAROLINA PARROT [Louisiana Paroquet (subspecies of Carolina Paroquet: both extinct; virtually identical but for range). *Conuropsis carolinensis ludovicianus*]

Inscribed: "No. 207. Henderson June 9th 1811—poor imitation of colour the natural Bird being extremely glossy and rich. Carolina Parrot, A. Willson—Psittacus Carolinensis. Juglans oliveformis, drawn by J. J. Audubon."

YELLOW-BILLED CUCKOO [Yellow-Billed Cuckoo. *Coccyzus americanus americanus*]

Inscribed: "No. 106. Yellow-Billed Cuckoo, A. W.—Cuculus Carolinensis. Le Coucou de la Caroline, Buffon—drawn by J. J. Audubon."

RED OWL [Screech Owl (red phase). *Otus asio* (subspecies uncertain)]

Inscribed: "No. 188. drawn by J. J. Audubon. Red Owl, A. W. —Strix Asio."

WHIPPOORWILL [Eastern Whippoorwill. *Caprimulgus vociferus vociferus*]

Inscribed: "No. 11. May 7th 1812 Penns^a. Caprimulgus Vociferus. Whippoorwill femelle, A. W."

BELTED KING FISHER [Eastern Belted Kingfisher. *Megaceryle alcyon alcyon*]

Inscribed: "No. 110. 6me penne de l'aile d'interieur comptée comme premiere—vue de patte Intérieurement—1re penne queue interieure. Belted King Fisher, A. W.—S. A. Alcedo Alcion. L'Alcion d'Amerique Septentrionale, Buffon. King Fisher, Chute de L'Ohio July 15, 1808, drawn by J. J. Audubon." Under tail: "12 pennes à la queue."

Pied-Billed Grebe

I HAD the good fortune, one late June day while I lived in Henderson, Kentucky, to stumble upon a nest of this bird near the Wabash River banks above Vincennes, Indiana. This was not many miles distant from my home. The nest was large for the bird, several inches above the muddy and reedy shores of a pond, only a few feet from the water, and made of decayed weeds, rushes, earth. It was not attached to the strong reeds that surrounded it. When the sitting bird saw me, she slid over the mud and along a path to the water, dived in, and was seen no more for about twenty minutes. The five eggs—smooth, rather rounded, light greenish white—measured an inch and a quarter by seven-and-a-half eighths. Before I departed I saw the bird, apparently the female, swimming low at a distance. I could not discover its mate, and walked away to allow it to resume its occupation.

Few birds plunge with more rapidity. While submerged it uses its wings to propel itself, as I once saw when some of them passed under a boat in which I was pursuing them. To catch them on the water is almost impossible. Their curious habit of sinking gradually backward in the water before an enemy is pleasing to watch. Not a ripple do they leave on the spot.

While I was in Philadelphia, a friend of mine received two Pied-Billed Grebes alive. They had been caught in a fishing net on Brandywine Creek. We placed them in a large tub of water where we could watch their underwater swimming. They swam round the sides of the tub like Puffins, their wings moving in rhythm with their feet. They continued under water much longer than we supposed possible. They would come up to breathe, then plunge again with astonishing speed. We took them out and placed them on the carpet. They ran awkwardly, half erect, for a few feet, tumbled over and scrambled along with the aid of their wings. Nothing could induce them to eat; after a day or two the little creatures were taken to the Delaware and set at liberty.

This bird rests on the floating beds of rushes or on the edge of the shores. You may see it sitting upright and dressing its plumage in the sunshine. Dobchicks are extremely unwilling to take wing except during migration, or when chasing each other at the mating season which begins in March, a time when they show a good deal of pugnacity. The fighting males fly, dive, and rise again, much like the Foolish Guillemot. They pass rapidly through the air while travelling, and at a considerable height, their wings sounding like those of a swooping Hawk. They migrate in parties of six or seven, but never by water as certain *authors* have absurdly suggested! How long would it take a Dobchick to swim from the mouths of the Mississippi to the headwaters of the Ohio? And after six or seven weeks of paddling, how would he proceed farther? But it is well known that they breed farther north, and that they are generally on southern waters early in October.

The food of the Pied-Billed Dobchick consists of small fry, plants, seeds, aquatic insects and snails, digested with the aid of gravel. They seem to form a particular attachment to certain ponds or small lakes on which, until these are closed by ice, you may always observe a pair or a family. Opposite Henderson I regularly saw a couple every autumn. They seem to dislike swift-running streams; when they are on them they keep to the eddies along the shores.

The curious double pectination on the hind part of their tarsi seems to help them greatly as they sit upright on the broad leaves of water lilies; I have seen impressions on these leaves after the birds had plunged from them into the water. The young differ from the adults in color. The mature males and females resemble each other, except that the males are the larger.

Brown Pelican

In 1832, while cruising the Florida Keys aboard the revenue cutter *Marion*, I found the Pelicans pretty numerous, especially at Key West. The *Marion* lay at anchor several days near this island. Scarcely an hour of daylight passed without our having Pelicans around us . . . some fishing, some slumbering on the water or on the mangrove branches. The vicinity all around for forty miles seemed to be a favorite resort of these birds, and I had excellent opportunities to observe their habits.

The Brown Pelican can remain on the wing for hours at a time, despite its heavy appearance, and perform its beautiful evolutions at a great height. After easy flappings and sailings, alternately, for twenty to thirty yards, they glide along with much speed, either in flocks or singly. Their undulating line passes high, low, over water or land: they do not deviate from their course on reaching a key or land. You will see them "troughing" when the waves run high, directing their course along the hollows. On the wing they draw their heads between their shoulders, stretch their broad webbed feet to their whole extent, and proceed in perfect silence.

During the love season flock after flock will rise a mile in the air in broad circles, gracefully glide and course round one another on expanded wings for an hour or more at a time, then zigzag downward with remarkable velocity to settle on the water, on sandbars or the mangroves. These aerial evolutions are interesting beyond description to observe.

Dextrously they wield their large bills to trim their plumage as they stand on a burning sandbar. Well do they know the time of each return of the tide. Though, a short time before it, they may be sound asleep, they suddenly open their eyelids without bell or warning, and all leave their roosts the instant the quiet waters move again. They possess knowledge beyond *this*; they can judge weather changes more accurately than can men. If you see them fishing all together in retired bays, you may be sure that a storm is due that day. But if they pursue the finny tribe far out to sea, the weather will be fine. Most sea birds are good weather prophets, according to their necessities, especially the Pelican, Wild Goose, Gannet, and *Lestris*.

A flock will leave its resting place, proceed over the waters in search of fish, and, on seeing a shoal, separate at once. From a height of fifteen to twenty-five feet they will plunge obliquely in a somewhat winding fashion, open their pouches to the full stretch as they reach the water, and suddenly scoop up a fish. They may immerse their heads and necks —and sometimes their bodies—for an instant. After swallowing their prey, they rise, plunge for another fish, devour it, and continue thus for perhaps eight or ten well-aimed plunges. Once they are filled, they rest on the water for a while, unless they have broods to which they must immediately return. The idea that Pelicans keep fish or water in their pouches to carry to their young is quite erroneous. They force the water from their pouches at once, after plunging, swallow the fish instantly unless it is very large, and afterwards disgorge it for the benefit of the young, either whole or in pieces, depending on the age and size of the brood. Of all this I have satisfied myself by watching within less than twenty yards of the birds as they were fishing. I never saw them fly without the pouch well closed, and doubt that they could do so with a burden of fish and water. They rarely seize fishes longer than their bills.

The Pelicans follow porpoises pursuing prey, and as the flying fishes rise towards the surface the Pelicans come in cunningly for their share of the shoal. But a most curious trait of the Pelican is its unwitting service to the Gulls as a sort of purveyor in the way that the porpoises serve Pelicans. The Gull alights on the bill or head of the Pelican and seizes the fish just as the Pelican expels the water from its pouch. How little do we yet know of the operations of the Divine Power, or of those faculties which Nature has bestowed on animals and which we consider mere instinct! The Pelicans appeared not in the least angry towards the Gulls. I have found more than a hundred fishes, two or three inches long, in the stomach of a Pelican.

The Brown Pelican is by no means active on the ground, for it walks heavily. When it runs in play, or during courtship, it looks extremely awkward, with outstretched neck and partly open wings as if it might fall at every reeling step.

This species keeps in flocks throughout the year. These seldom exceed fifty or sixty members of both sexes and various ages. About mid-April the old males and females separate from the rest and fly off to the inner keys or to large estuaries where large mangroves abound. The more numerous younger birds remain along the seashore, except in gales.

Skirmishes take place between the stronger adult males at the mating time. They snap their bills loudly, tug at their rival's neck and head, strike him with their wings, and drive off the weaker who must content themselves with the less-prized belles. The females, though quiet and gentle ordinarily, are now more courageous than the males. The male Pelican helps build the nest on the southwest side of a mangrove tree, where the benefit of all the heat of that sultry climate is assured. The birds fly dry sticks in their bills from the trees to build a strong platform, to which they add roots and withered plants to form a basin that will hold the eggs. All of the nests are placed high, and many are close together in trees of close proximity. There are never more than three eggs —elliptical, thick-shelled and rough—pure white with a few faint rosy streaks, and blotches of very pale blue from the center towards the crown. The male helps with incubation and also feeds his sitting mate.

The bills and feet of the cream-colored, downy young are disproportionately large. So abundantly are they fed that masses of food lie round them—most offensively, to the observer. As the young progress, their parents bring larger fish to them. But at first the food is dropped in a well-macerated state into their outstretched throats. Next, they receive the fish entire; and finally the parents merely place it on the edge of the nest. When the young are half fledged, they seem a mere mass of fat— utterly unable to walk. Their wings droop by their sides. At this stage the Vultures often fall upon them while their parents are absent. The Crows suck the eggs of the Pelican. If a young bird falls from the nest, it is sure to be seized by some quadruped, or devoured by a shark or barracuda. Indians and others carry them off in quantities. After extensive depredations of the kind the Pelicans abandon these breeding places and do not return to them. In fact they are retiring more and more from man's vicinity. If a few shots are fired on a settlement, the birds all abandon the place, and leave their young.

These Pelicans retire to deeper waters in winter; they flock over the

Gulf of Mexico and between the Florida reefs and the isles opposite, to fish for mullets, a favorite dish of theirs and mine. They are very sensible to cold and are tender birds. Their sight probably equals that of any Hawk in keenness, and their hearing is also very acute. Their loud, rough grunt, uttered during excitement, is far from musical; they are very silent ordinarily.

The young take two years to attain maturity. I believe that but one brood is raised in the season.* The body of the Brown Pelican is much inflated by large air cells. Their bones, though strong, are very light. The female is considerably larger than the male, and resembles him in color, except that all her neck is yellowish white without brown, and her feathers are stiff and not downy like the male's. The bill is more than twice the length of the head, rather stout, straight, and depressed towards the end.

* But breeding intervals are less than one year apart.

Gannets

COMMON GANNET

ON THE morning of June 14, 1833, the white sails of our schooner *Ripley* were spread before a propitious breeze. She might be seen gaily wending her way with me and the members of my Labrador expedition towards the north. We had already explored the Magdalen Islands, and were anxious to visit the Great Gannet Rock, where, according to our pilot, the birds from which it derives its name breed. For several days I had seen numerous files of the Common Gannet heading northward, and I studied their mode of flight as they travelled over. My anxiety to reach the spot increased as our bark dashed through the heaving billows. Finally, about ten o'clock, we saw a white speck in the distance—the celebrated rock of our wishes. After a while I could distinctly see its top from the deck; it appeared to be still covered with snow several feet deep. As we approached, I imagined the atmosphere around it to be filled with snowflakes; but my pilot, who smiled at my simplicity, assured me that I was merely seeing the Gannets returning home. I rubbed my eyes, took up my glass, and saw that the strange dimness of the air was caused by innumerable birds, whose white bodies and black-tipped pinions produced a blended tint of light gray.

When we advanced to within half a mile, this magnificent veil of floating Gannets, plainly seen, now shot upwards into the sky, then descended as if to join the feathered masses below, and again veered off to either side and swept over the surface of the ocean. The *Ripley* now partially furled her sails and lay to, all on board being eager to satisfy their curiosity by scaling the steep sides of the mountain isle.

Imagine our disappointment when the beautiful weather suddenly changed to a fearful storm which assailed us. However, the whale boat was hoisted over the side and manned by four sturdy "down-easters," along with Thomas Lincoln of Dennisville, Maine, and my son John Woodhouse. I myself remained on board to begin my observations.

An hour elapsed. The boat, which for a while we lost sight of, came in view again. The rowers were exerting themselves amid the high waves blown by the hurricane winds, until it seemed that each successive billow might overwhelm their fragile bark. My anxiety was intense as I stood watching with my friends and the crew. Now the boat balanced on the very crest of a rolling and foaming wave, now sunk far into the deep trough. How eagerly yet calmly the boys were pulling! My son stood erect, steering with a long oar. Young Lincoln bailed the water, which was gaining on him because of the spray that kept dashing over the bow. But they drew near enough for a rope to be thrown to them, and the whale boat was hauled close under our lee. In a moment all were safe on deck, the helm was turned round, the schooner was put to, and the sails were made fast as the *Ripley* scudded towards Labrador.

Thomas Lincoln and my son were much exhausted. The sailors required a double allowance of grog. Several birds and a quantity of eggs had been brought back by the party, who reported that wherever there was not enough room on the rock for a Gannet's nest, one or two Guillemots occupied the spot. The Kittiwakes lay thick as snowflakes on the lower ledges. The cries of the countless multitudes drowned the report of the guns, which had no effect beyond causing the killed and wounded birds to fall into the water. The confusion on and around the rock was represented as baffling all description. Except that it was in some measure a sight painful to me, for I had not been able to land on this great breeding place, I felt that to see that mass now gradually fading in the distance, as we moved onward, was worth crossing an ocean.

Mr. Godwin, our pilot, said that the top of the main rock is a quarter of a mile wide from north to south, but narrower in the other direction. "The surf beats its base with great violence except in calm, and landing on it and ascending to the top or platform is extremely difficult," he told me. "The top is entirely covered with nests about two feet apart in regular lines that run from north to south like furrows." He described the havoc wrought among the birds by fishermen and eggers. By May 20 the rock is covered with nesting Gannets. The young are hatched a month later.

The nests, eight or ten inches high, are formed of seaweed and other rubbish in a hole scratched by the birds to a depth of a few inches. Each female Gannet lays one egg, pure white and no larger than a good-sized hen's. The newly hatched young are bluish-black, but gradually, after about two weeks, they become downy white, until at five or six weeks they look like large lumps of carded wool.

The young Gannets which the boys brought on board weighed rather more than seven pounds. By the time they are almost ready to fly they weigh eight or nine pounds.

As to the extent of the Gannet's migration, I have seen it on the Gulf of Mexico in late autumn and winter, and also where the Sabine River enters the Gulf. This maritime species never travels inland except when forced there by violent gales. My friend John Bachman saw a flock of Gannets—fifty to a hundred—on the Sea Islands off South Carolina on July 2, 1836, all of the color of the one in *The Birds of America,* which was shown in its first winter plumage. He also mentioned that an acquaintance of his, Mr. Giles, saw a pair going to and returning from a nest in a tree of that region. That agrees with a report of Captain Napoleon Costé who commanded the U.S. revenue cutter *Campbell* placed at my disposal during my visit to Texas. He stated that he had found a breeding place on the coast of Georgia occupied by a flock of old, and therefore white Gannets, all of whose nests were placed on trees. No one can be surprised at these reports who knows, as I do, that the Brown Gannet breeds both on trees and on dry elevated sandbars. I have seen single birds far out from shore, sometimes beyond what mariners call soundings; but young ones generally keep much nearer shore, feeding in shallower water.

The flight of the Gannet is powerful, well sustained, and at times extremely elegant. While travelling, whether in fine or foul weather, they fly low over the surface of the water, flapping their wings thirty or forty times in succession, then sailing about an equal distance with wings at right angles to their body and with the neck extended. It will plunge through the air like a meteor to snatch a fish it has sighted from on high, and either swallow it at once or munch on it while sitting bouyantly on the bosom of the ocean.

I have seen the Gannet propelling itself against the gale and sweeping along almost sideways, and then obliquely—by turns—like the Petrel and Guillemot. It seemed to move with more velocity then than at any other time, except when plunging after its prey. I have also seen it remain under the surface of the water for at least one minute after it plunged. Once I shot one just as it emerged; it held a fish firmly in its bill and had two others half-way down its throat, a circumstance which has made me wonder whether it may sometimes follow its prey in the water and seize several in succession. Other times I have watched them scarcely enter the water amid a shoal of launces, swimming, or you might call it running, on the surface and striking to right and left until they were satiated, their wings raised upwards all the while. On the Gulf of Mexico I wounded a Gannet which fell on the water and then swam so fast before our boat that we rowed for about a quarter of a mile before we came up to it. Suddenly it turned towards us, then opened its bill as if to defend itself. Sometimes, when wounded in the wings, they will float and allow themselves to be taken without any attempt to escape.

As the Gannet rises from its rocks, about to fly, it raises its head, throws it backward, opens its bill and sounds a loud, wolfish, prolonged cry. After waddling very awkwardly for a few paces with wings open to keep its balance, it launches into the air, at first downward, then up, as its wings beat between smooth sailings. They like to open their wings when the sun shines, and beat them while shaking their heads rather violently to their uncouth *cara, karew, karow*. By the time they reach their breeding rock they are usually already paired, and may be seen billing, like Cormorants, and copulating, but never on the water like the latter. Though then quite gregarious, the Gannets show animosity towards their near Gannet neighbors as soon as incubation commences. One of them may lazily find it easier to rob the nest of his friend of weeds and sod than bring them from a distant place. The result will be some well-directed thrusts of their strong bills, in full view of the other interested Gannets, sitting in their rows and passing the news along until all are apprized of the quarrel.

The patient mother plucks a few feathers from deep beneath her breast to warm her only egg. If the weather be fine she spreads her wings as she sits, passing her bill along the roots of the wing feathers to destroy insects. Should a gale or a thick cold fog mar the day, she gathers her feathers close around her and shrinks deeper into the nest, taking care to protect the egg from rain. Now and then her mate returns with loaded bill, singling her out from among the thousand beauties all equally anxious for the arrival of their lords! He alights gently, presents her repast, perhaps talks cheeringly to her, before spreading his broad wings to depart in search of a shoal of herrings. He assists her in incubating, though he sits far less than she; the free bird supplies the other with food.

At length the little black fledgling crawls out of its shell. What a strange contrast to the almost pure white of the parent! The female waits for a bit before feeding it, due to its tender state, but then with exceeding care she drops some well-macerated morsels into its open mouth. So well prepared is this food that there is no instance on record of a Gannet's having suffered from dyspepsia or indigestion, even at that tender age. The abdomen of the naked blue-black young one is extremely large, its neck thin, its head large, its eyes as yet sightless, and its wings but slightly developed. Gannets do not all lay on the same day, so that one may see them at different stages on their grounds, where the once well-fashioned nests of the great eyrie are trampled down, making it appear as if common property. The lazy-looking young birds stand everywhere and anywhere, with a look of nonchalance which I have never observed in any other species, until you might think they cared as little about the present as the future, paying no attention to the old ones who, about once or so a day, drop fish for them. The Gannets eat codlings as well as herring, and sometimes very large mackerel. The young never leave the grounds until they are well able to fly. Then they separate from the old birds and do not rejoin them for at least a year. All the birds then leave the breeding place till the next season. Although I have found a few young ones still patched with dark gray and with most of their primary quills still black, I am confident that they do not acquire their full plumage until the end of two years. I have seen some with one wing and tail almost pure black, others with only the tail black, and several with pure black feathers interspersed among the general white plumage.

I know of no other bird with so few formidable enemies. Not one of the Jaegers with which I am acquainted attempts to molest it. Nor have I seen the Frigate Pelican [Man-o'-War], in quest of food, ever injure the Gannet. On its island rocks it is not accessible to quadrupeds. The

Great Black-Backed Gull and the Glaucous Gull are the only creatures, so far as I know, that feed on the eggs or young. The Skua is said to pursue the Gannet at times, but that species does not exist in North America. I am inclined to doubt the truth of this statement. I have never seen a *Lestris* (or Jaeger) attack any bird of its own size and strength.

Although this bird is easily kept in captivity, it is far from a pleasant pet. It is malodorous and awkward, and its pale, owl-like eyes glare at you with an unfriendly expression. Add to this the expense of feeding it, and I can easily imagine that you will not give it a place in your aviary, unless for the amusement of seeing it catch its food like a dog.

The feathers of the lower parts of the Gannet differ from those of most other birds in that they are extremely convex externally. This gives the bird the appearance of being covered beneath with light shell-work, an exceedingly difficult effect to represent in a drawing.

What shall we say to those who have pretended that the American bird differs from the European? Merely this, compare the two, outside and inside, show us the differences, and then we shall judge if they are sufficient to indicate different species. But until you have done this, do not imagine that a mere difference in scientific names is enough to satisfy the world on this or any similar point.

WHITE-BELLIED BOOBY

I AM unable to find a good reason for this Gannet's having been called the *Booby*. Authors, it is true, generally represent them as extremely stupid, but to me the word is utterly inapplicable to any bird with which I am acquainted. The Woodcock, too, is said to be stupid, as are many other birds. My opinion, founded on pretty extensive observation, is that birds manifest that kind of *ignorance* or *innocence* called *stupidity* only when the species is unacquainted with man. A little acquaintance with him soon enables them to guess enough of his character to induce them to keep aloof and not be imposed upon. This I observed in the Booby Gannet, and in certain land birds of which I have spoken.

After my first visit to Booby Island in the Tortugas in 1832, the Gannets had already become very shy and wary. Before our revenue cutter, the *Marion*, sailed away from those peaceful retreats of the wandering sea birds, the Boobies had become so knowing that the most expert marksman of our party could not get within shot of them.

As the *Marion* was nearing the curious little Florida islands of the Tortugas, one bird particularly attracted my notice. The nearer we approached the land, the more numerous did this species become, arousing the hope that I should have an opportunity to study its habits. As night came on, some of these birds alighted on our top-yard, seeming to prefer to roost at as great a height as possible above their surroundings, and disputing over the privilege.

The first we shot at next day had alighted on the prong of a tree that had floated and caught on a rocky shallow, well out from shore, in quite rough, shark-filled waters about four feet deep. I was too anxious to take this bird to be overcome by such obstacles. In an instant the pilot and I were over the sides, our guns cocked and ready, while the yawl and its crew awaited the results. After we struggled through the turbulent waters for about a hundred yards, my companion raised his gun and fired. But away flew the bird with a broken leg, and we saw no more of it that day. Next day, however, at the same hour, the Booby was perching on the very same prong, resting. After about three hours it made for the open sea, doubtless in search of food.

About eight miles northeast of the Tortugas lighthouse lies Booby Island, a small sandbar of a few acres to which these birds resort during the breeding season. We found it covered with Boobies basking in the sunshine, pluming themselves. But they all flew off when we came within fifty yards of shore. We landed, nevertheless, and scattered after sending the *Marion* away. We lay as flat as possible in the sand to await their return. Although none of them alighted when they ventured back again, we easily obtained thirty of both sexes and different ages as they flew over us. The wounded ones which reached the water swam off with such buoyancy and rapidity that it took much rowing to overtake them. Most of those that fell directly into the sea, with only a wing broken, escaped.

In the evening of the same day we landed on Noddy Island, where thousands of those Terns called the Noddy resort to breed. It was thickly covered with bushes and low trees. We also saw a great many Boobies, perched on the top branches of the trees where they had nests, and we again obtained as many as we desired. They flew close over our heads, eyeing us with dismay but in silence. Indeed not one emitted a cry except when they rose from their perches or from the sand, their note harsh and guttural, resembling *hork, hork.*

The large flat nest of dry sticks, covered and matted with seaweed, is placed on the top of a bush four to ten feet high, I have no doubt the Booby returns to it, like the Common Gannet, for many years in succession, repairing it as it may happen to require. I found only one egg in each of the nests which I examined—dull white and about the size of a common hen's, but more elongated.* Sometimes the egg was covered with filth from the parent, in the manner of the Florida Cormorant. The uncouth-looking young were covered with down. Their bills and feet were deep blue or indigo. If touched they turned away their heads but did not cry. A great quantity of putrefying fish lay beneath the trees, proving how abundantly the parents supplied their young. Indeed there was a constant stream of birds coming in from sea with food—mostly flying-fish and small mullets—which they disgorged in a half macerated state into the open throats of their offspring. Unfortunately, my time on that coast was not sufficient for me to trace their growth. I observed, however, that none of the birds which were still brown in color had nests, and that they roosted apart, particularly on Booby Island, where many barren ones were also to be seen, basking on the sunny sands.

The flight of the Booby is graceful and extremely protracted. They pass swiftly above the water's surface at a height of twenty yards to a foot or two, often following the troughs of the waves for some distance with their wings extended at right angles to the body. Then without apparent effort they rise and let the rolling waters break beneath them, before tacking about and sweeping along in the opposite direction in search of food, much like true Petrels. The Booby will suddenly stop short, plunge headlong into the water, pierce a fish with its powerful beak, and emerge again with incredible ease. After a short distance it rises on the wing, performs a few wide circles, and makes off toward some shore. At this time its flight is different in that it is done by flapping the wings for twenty or thirty paces, with alternate sailings of more than twice that extent. When it is overloaded with food, the bird

* Two. Usually only one chick is reared.

. 14 .

alights on the water, where, if undisturbed, it may remain for seeming hours at a time, probably until digestion affords relief. Their power seems sufficient to brave the tempest. During fair weather they fly far out to sea; I have seen them fully two hundred miles from land.

Its wide mouth and expanding gullet enable it to swallow rather large fishes—mullets seven or eight inches long and weighing fully half a pound each. Numerous air-cells beneath their skin probably assist them in rising and dropping on the wing; perhaps still more so when they are about to plunge for prey.

The principal enemies during the breeding season are the American Crow and Fish Crow, which destroy their eggs, and the Turkey Buzzard, which devours their unfledged young. They breed during May, but I have not been able to ascertain whether they raise more than one brood in a season. During incubation, the adults chase away immature birds, which, incidentally, seem to require several years to attain their perfect state.*

Those taken alive will feed freely, and may be kept any length of time if supplied with fish. I could not tempt them to swallow any other food, except slices of turtle (which they did not seem to relish). I never observed one drinking. Only an expert seaman could secure one when it has alighted on the spar of a vessel.

The Boobies roost on trees in company with the Brown Pelican, I was informed, and also with the Noddy Tern.

The pilot of the *Marion*, an observing man, assured me that while he was in Vera Cruz he saw the fishermen there go to sea and return from afar, simply by following the course of the Boobies for navigation.

The bills and legs of the brown one-or-two-year-olds were dusky blue. These parts become paler until, with maturity, they appear as I have shown them in *The Birds of America*. I noticed no external difference between the sexes in the adult birds, whose dark, tough flesh is scarcely fit for food.

* About one and a half years.

European Cormorant

I STILL see the high rolling billows of the St. Lawrence breaking in foaming masses against the huge Labrador cliffs where the Cormorant places its nest on the shelves. I lay flat on the edge of a precipice, a hundred feet above the turbulent waters. By crawling along carefully I came within a few yards of the spot where the parent bird and her young, quite unconscious of my nearness, were fondling each other.

The mother gently caressed each little one with her bill, as they drew near her and rubbed their heads against hers. Then she looked up, her keen eye met mine, and she croaked, spread her sable wings and launched into the air in terror, leaving her brood at my mercy. Far and near, above and beneath me, she passed and repassed, while performing those actions which birds perform on the ground, or on water, in moments of distressed anxiety for the fate of their beloved young. Her many neighbors well understood her unnatural mode of flight, which was as though she were crippled, and one after another they took to wing until they blackened the air. Meanwhile, in their great alarm, the little ones crawled into a recess and huddled together. I now crawled backwards and left the Cormorants to resume their ordinary peaceful security. I had the pleasure of this experience at about three in the morning on July 3, 1833. I think the strong gale and the dashing of the waves enabled me to remain unseen and unheard for a while so near the birds, as I watched the mother disgorge food into each open mouth, and saw the very happy little ones bill with her and caress her about the breast.

All Cormorant nests that my party, which accompanied me on the vessel *Ripley*, saw in Labrador were placed on high shelves of precipitous rocks fronting the water southward. I saw Ravens and Peregrine Falcons nesting on the same rocks, sometimes quite near the Cormorants' nests. The latter were made of small dry sticks, matted with weeds and moss to a thickness of four or five inches in new nests, and of a foot or more in old ones. Like others of the species this bird repairs and enlarges old tenements, and returns to the same rocks for years in succession. Some of the nests varied from thirty to thirty-six inches in diameter, according to the space on which they rested; others were barely large enough to hold the young. On narrow shelves the nests were crowded together; on wider ones they were placed apart without order. But none were below a certain height, nor were there any on the summit. All were offensive to eye and nose. The three or four eggs (oftener three) averaged two and five-eighths inches in length and one and three-quarters in breadth. The shells were mostly coated over with calcareous matter and were a uniform pale blue-green.

At first the young are a dark, purplish, livid color, and uncouth appearing, with legs and feet seemingly enormous. In two weeks they are covered with brownish black down but for their bare abdomens. They grow fast and are fledged in six or seven weeks. At a month some weighed three pounds; those almost ready to fly weighed six on average. The young of this species, as with most water birds, are much heavier than their parents when they leave the nest.

This Cormorant can swim under water at an astonishing speed, particularly if it apprehends danger. Its head and neck are all that can be seen. Often they swim with the rump elevated and the head under—like the Shoveller Duck—while searching for food in clear shallow water. They dive and pursue their prey under water with their wings partly spread like paddles, while the tail directs their course and checks or accelerates their speed. This is true also of the Florida Cormorant. I have never seen one plunge after its prey from the air; I have often seen them drop from a rock headlong into the sea when I have shot at them in order to observe their reactions.

Like Pelicans, Ducks, and other water birds, the Cormorants clear themselves of vermin by beating up water about their bodies with their wings, or by rubbing and scratching with their feet and claws. Then they spread their wings and tail in the sun, and after a while dress their plumage. After they cleanse themselves by washing, they stretch their wings and flap them in the way that young birds do to try their strength before leaving the nest.

They are extremely regular in returning to the same places to roost towards night . . . hundreds gather along their way. Those that have no broods spend the night apart from the others, and stand nearly erect in files on the highest shelves. But in Boston I observed some roosting singly, immediately over their fishing places—usually eddies under rocky projections. They are shy, wary, and almost impossible to approach. Their flight is strong, swift, remarkably sustained, and usually in long strings, or at angles, fairly high in the air. You may see them on the rocks in the hundreds, looking like a crowd of black dominoes, their necks curved gracefully and resting low between the shoulders.

All of our Cormorants feed principally on various kinds of fish. If they seize one that is too large to swallow entire, they carry it to the shore or to a branch and there thrash or tear it to pieces. Sometimes the fish they have swallowed will discommode them, so that they shake their heads violently and disgorge it, or else manage to pass it downwards into the stomach. All the species are expert at tossing up a fish inconveniently caught—a foot or so above their heads—and receiving it into their open gullet, like the Man-o'-War bird.

The courtship is similar to that of the Florida Cormorant, the males swimming gracefully around the females, raising their wings and tails, drawing their heads over their backs, swelling out their necks for an instant, and uttering a rough guttural note like the grunt of a pig. The female now crouches on the water, and then sinks into it, while the male sinks over her until nothing more than his head is to be seen. Soon both spring up and swim joyously round each other, croaking the while. Twenty or more pairs may be thus engaged at a time. I have seen this courtship occur on the shelves where the nests were placed, also.

The Cormorant waddles and walks at a good pace, but awkwardly. It leaps from stone to stone, assisting itself with its wings, and, at intervals, with its tail which acts as a kind of spring.

No differences appear in the garb of the sexes during their several stages of maturity and growth. Specimens of both are equally beautiful and perfect in the breeding season, and are similar to the male bird portrayed in *The Birds of America*. They breed before they have acquired their final beauty.

The white markings of the old birds, noticeable during courtship, incubation, and the rearing of the young until they can fly (at two and a half months, approximately), begin to disappear from the moment incubation has fairly begun. By the time the young leave them, the parents have scarcely any of this white, except on the sides of the head. In autumn and winter the head feathers are similar to those of the neck; the plumage has lost much of its springtime beauty, and the entire crest falls off. Not until late February do the white markings begin to reappear.

The young do not exhibit the crest until the second spring. The fact that they have *open nostrils* until they are nearly halfgrown may surprise you as much as it surprised me.

I have never seen a Cormorant on a tree, or on fresh water.

Water=Turkey

In external appearance and habits, the Anhinga, Snakebird or Water-Turkey is very closely allied to the Cormorants. The structure of the feet, wings and tail (though the latter is longer in the Water-Turkey) is similar. If one could picture a small Cormorant, elongated and attenuated, its feet rather enlarged and shortened, its head diminished, its bill more like that of a Heron, he would have a pretty correct notion of this bird. Its snakelike neck is also similar to the Heron's; but the rest of its bony structure resembles that of the Cormorants and Pelicans.

The pleasures which I have experienced in this chequered life of mine have been many . . . perhaps many more than I should have had had I not been a devoted lover of the wondrous works of Nature from earliest memory. Among the greatest of these pleasures has been the pursuit and faithful description of our American birds, some of which were previously unknown and little observed. I have passed many sultry summer days in the dismal wooded swamps of Louisiana to watch the curious habits of the Anhinga or Water-Turkey.

I saw the female bird sitting on her eggs in a nest which she built on a long branch of a cypress in the middle of a lake. With keen eyes she watched every motion of the wily Buzzard and cunning Crow, lest either cowardly marauder deprive her of her treasures. Her partner soared high overhead, also vigilant, his wings spread wide and his tail fanlike. Higher and higher he rose until he became a mere dusky speck in the blue sky. But suddenly closing his wings, he shot downwards and in an instant alighted on the edge of the nest, and gazed complacently at his mate.

About three weeks later I noticed that the mother had cast the empty egg shells out of the nest into the green slime of the stagnant water.

I climbed up and saw the tender young ones clad in the softest buff-colored down, their bills black, their feet a yellow-white, and their heads and necks naked. Their necks writhed as they stretched forth their open pouches, as all infants do, to be fed. I then withdrew to a hiding place and saw the mother return with a supply of masticated fishes which she fed to her young by regurgitation.

I watched the growth of the younglings. Many days later I saw them stand—almost erectly—and noticed that the parents, though still affectionate, seemed less attentive. The following week I saw the little ones discharged from the nest and forced into the waters below. It is true that I had previously seen the young trying their wings as they stood upright on the nest, flapping them for minutes at a time. Although convinced that they were ready to provide for themselves, it was not without a feeling of despondency that I saw them hurled into the air, to alight on the water. But Nature had behaved wisely: I afterwards found that the old birds wished to rear another brood there before the coming of unfavorable weather.

This diurnal bird prefers bayous and marshes in low country, retired and secluded. It never plunges or dives from an eminence to take its prey, but, like the Cormorant, drops silently to the water from its perch. I have seen several alight on the dead top branches of the same tall tree to roost over the water for the night, week after week, but they kept a distance of feet or of yards apart. While sleeping they stood almost erect and kept their heads snugly down among their scapulars. At times they wheezed in their breathing.

Despite the suggestion of its large wings and fanlike tail that it is intended by Nature for protracted and powerful flight, the Water-Turkey is a leading fresh-water diver. With miraculous swiftness it disappears beneath the surface, scarcely leaving a ripple. It is astonishing to see it emerge, a hundred yards off, its head just above the water, or its bill alone cutting the surface and drawing a line so fine as to be invisible thirty yards away. All this helps it to evade its pursuers; it swims with its body sunk beneath the surface only when in sight of an enemy, and at other times is as buoyant as any other diver.

It consumes an amazing quantity of fish. One morning I fed a domesticated seven-months-old Water-Turkey a blackfish, the head of which is considerably larger than its body, and which has formidable fins. The bird swallowed it entire, head foremost; in an hour and a half it appeared to have digested it, and was ready for three more smaller ones. Once it swallowed nine fishes in succession, measuring seven and a half inches. Eels were less to its taste and hard to keep down, but the bird finally mastered them.

While I lived near Bayou Sara, Louisiana, by the Mississippi, friends of mine had two young Water-Turkeys which they had raised from the nest . . . perfectly tame and gentle, and much attached to their human foster parents, whom they followed everywhere. They ate shrimps and fish, or else boiled Indian corn. At the age of one year they were allowed to go to the river or pond and fish for themselves, and they regularly returned towards night to roost on top of the house. Both were males, and, in time, fought hard battles; but each met with a female which it enticed to the house-top where all four roosted together for a while. Soon after, they all disappeared and were never seen again. Probably the females had laid eggs in the woods.

The flight is swift, and can be sustained at times. They quite disappear from sight in the upper regions which they reach by beautiful gyrations, varied by zigzag lines in the love season. During migratory expeditions they beat their wings occasionally, much like the Cormorant, or sail like the Turkey Buzzard and some of the Hawks. But this bird moves rather awkwardly along tree branches, its wings extended to help its progress, and its bill sometimes proving useful in the manner of the Parrot's.

While courting on the wing they whistle *eek, eek, eek,* and the first note is the loudest, the second and third diminishing. Their call notes on the water strongly resemble the rough grunting cry of the Florida Cormorant.

The nest of sticks, fresh twigs and other matter is variously placed, according to the region . . . at the top of high trees, or in low bushes, and not more than eight or ten feet above water. They may be seen singly, or amid hundreds or even thousands of nests of various kinds of Herons, especially the Great White and Great Blue Herons. The nests are about two feet in diameter, flat, and similar to the Florida Cormorant's. The number of eggs varies from three to [five]; they are two-and-five-eighths inches long and an inch and a quarter in diameter; and a dull white chalky substance covers the light blue shell of the elongated oval.

Like all flesh-eating and fish-eating birds, the Water-Turkey can go without food for days and nights without too much difficulty.

My friend John Bachman writes thus about this species:

I brought home three young Snake-birds [Water-Turkeys] to domesticate them. I entrusted one to a friend. Another died while I was away from home. It was curious to see the smaller one force its bill into the mouth and throat of the larger one—a male—when it was hungry, and to see the larger allow it to retrieve a fish which its foster parent (actually its brother) had earlier swallowed. The little sister continued to look to the male bird for protection. One of them is still in my possession. It will pick up a fish, toss it in the air, and swallow it head first. My pet was tame from the beginning and followed me about the house, the yard, and the garden, until I thought its peculiar attachment quite troublesome. When it was young I carried it to a pond, believing that it would like the water; but invariably it scrambled to shore as soon as possible, as if in dread of the element in which it was meant to live.

It is a fearless bird and keeps hens, turkeys, and the dogs at bay, dealing blows with its sharp bill to right and left, and occasionally preventing the fowls from taking a morsel of food at the trough until it has tantalized them by first eating all it wants.

Not until my bird—the male—was fully fledged was it anxious or willing to go to the water. But then, whenever it saw me go toward the pond, it went with me as far as the garden gate, seeming to say, "Pray, let me go." And as I opened the gate it waddled after me like a duck. It let itself into the water, not with a plunge, but by dropping from a plank. It swam like a duck, then dipped its long neck down to fish.

Once it escaped and flew about a quarter of a mile into the pond. Some boys who happened to be in a canoe saw a strange creature approaching with open mouth and a head that looked like a snake's. They took alarm and fled to a near-by house. The Water-turkey, hungry and wanting food, had swum to them, followed in their frightened wake, and landed as soon as they did. It also went to the house, and was recognized by members of the family, who sent the bird back to me.

I saw Bachman's pet at his home in Charleston in 1836 on my way to the Gulf of Mexico, and often watched its habits. It was killed by a beautiful retriever dog which the Earl of Derby had presented to me. Its death was the occasion of sorrow for both my friend and myself, as John Bachman had given me the Water-Turkey for that nobleman whom I was soon to see again in England.

Man-o'-War Bird

THIS bird is as gregarious as our Vultures. It moves in small or large flocks, all depending on circumstances. Like the Vulture it spends most of the day on the wing in search of food; and like it, it flocks in numbers to roost or after feeding, fanning itself or sleeping close to its fellows. Lazy, tyrannical, rapacious, they domineer over birds weaker than they are and eat the young of every species when the parents are absent. They are, most truly, marine Vultures.

I have seen them assemble in flocks of fifty to five hundred about mid-May around Indian Key and farther south, high in the air above islands where they have bred for many seasons and now court for hours together. After that they return towards the mangroves, alight, and at once begin repairing old nests or building new ones. They pillage one another's nests for materials, and make excursions for more to the nearest keys. With ease they break off dry twigs with their powerful bills as they pass swiftly through the branches. To see several of them passing and repassing thus is a beautiful sight; their purpose is accomplished as if by magic. I know of only two other birds that do this—the Fork-Tailed Hawk and the Chimney Swallow; neither of these is so expert at it. Should it chance to drop a twig on the way to the nest, it plunges after it and catches it up before it lands.

The nests are usually on the south side of the keys, on both tall and low trees with overhanging branches above the water. There may be several nests in one tree, according to the space. Sometimes one side of an island is crowded with them. They are composed of sticks crossed to a height of about two inches; flattish; but not very large. The long wings and tail extend for more than a foot beyond the nest during incubation. The eggs—two or three, but oftener the latter—are two-and-seven-eighths inches long, two wide, and elongated, with a thick smooth shell of a greenish white color, often soiled by the filth of the nests.* The young are covered with yellow-white down, and look as if they had no feet. They grow tardily, are fed by regurgitation, and do not leave the nest until they can follow their parents on the wing.

The plumage of this species undergoes changes from season to season as the bird matures, and the changes of the female appear the more remarkable. Except for her white head and lower parts, she is transformed gradually from marbled gray and brown to brownish black, until, in the third spring, she is of a purer brownish black combined with a purer white enriched by bronze lights. Her feet—dull yellow at first—become a rich reddish orange, and her bill pale blue. The bird is now capable of breeding, but not until the next moult is her full plumage attained and its final glossiness and whiteness evident. The male is also ready to breed in the third spring.

The power of flight of this bird I conceive superior to that perhaps of any other. It seems mere sport for it to overtake the smaller Gulls or the Jaeger. Our swiftest Hawks sometimes have to pursue their victims—perhaps a Green-Winged Teal or Passenger Pigeon—half a mile at top speed to secure them. But this one gains on his prey like a meteor, darts on either side to cut off all retreat, and with open bill forces the fleeing bird to drop or disgorge the fish that it has caught. The Man-o'-War watches the dolphin pursue the little flying-fishes, then closes his wings, swoops, and rises with one of the tiny things across his bill. Or he may see a porpoise in full chase of the mullet fish, launch towards it, and seize a fish that is trying to escape its dreaded foe. Because the fish is too large for the Man-o'-War's gullet, the bird munches on it as he rises high. Three or four of his species see him and shoot towards him on widespread pinions, rise smoothly in broad circles, reach him, lash him with their wings, and tug at his prey, which may drop from bill to bill in the contest and, perhaps, back into the deep. The hungry birds seem to deserve their disappointment. Such sights you may see every day, if you sail for the Florida Keys.

At Key West I watched a Man-o'-War force a Cayenne Tern to drop a fish which was larger than the Tern—perhaps eight inches long.

* One egg.

The Man-o'-War rose with it across his bill for a short way, then tossed it up; but because he did not catch it at an angle to suit him, he dropped the fish, let it fall several yards, and caught it again. He tossed it a second time and caught it with its head downward in a convenient way, and immediately swallowed it.

I have seen this bird scratch its head while on the wing, and because it drops in air while doing so it proves an easy target.

For years I had been anxious to know the use of the pectinated claws of birds. I examined both feet of this species with a magnifying glass and found the racks crammed with insects such as one finds on the bird's head and especially around the ears. I found its claws longer, flatter and more comblike than any others that I have seen. I am therefore convinced that these pectinated claws are used by the bird to cleanse those parts of its skin which its bill cannot reach.

They chase and jostle one another in a frolic, then veer away on extended wings in a direct course until out of sight. Though their flight is as easy and powerful as I have said, they move with difficulty on the ground. They can rise from a sandbar with ease, nonetheless. The bird then (and on the water's surface) raises its wings almost perpendicularly, spreads its tail half erect, and at the first flap of its wings and stroke of its tail, it bounds away. It rarely stands very erectly on a branch, though it moves sideways along one like some Parrots. It never dives. Its bill is like that of the Cormorant in form; that bird, also, does not plunge or dive. Both dip into the water after dropping from a perch or rock to escape danger, as the Anhingas and some others do. But they are by no means shy. The Man-o'-War will poise with wings high to take a dead fish, a crab, or any floating matter suited to its appetite; it beats its wings until its bill has performed its duty, then at once rises and devours its prey. Its sight is wonderfully keen.

These birds are extremely silent; the only note I have heard them utter is a rough croak. They devour young Brown Pelican nestlings and the young of other birds. But their own young are often seized by the Turkey Buzzard.

In *The Birds of America* I have shown a very beautiful old male Man-o'-War, and also the pectinated claws of a two-or-three-year-old.

Herons

GREAT BLUE HERON

Louisiana has always been my favorite part of the Union, although Kentucky and some other States have divided my affections. Let us pretend ourselves on the banks of the Ohio, to watch the Heron, one of our most interesting waders. Its contour and movement are always graceful, if not elegant. So carefully does the bird place his foot on the moist ground, cautiously suspending it for an interval at each step forward, that his tread is silent. His golden eye glances over his surroundings with the aid of his graceful neck. If satisfied no danger is near, he lays his head on his shoulders, allows his breast feathers to droop, and patiently awaits the approach of his finned prey. You might almost take him for a statue. But now he moves, takes a silent step, and with care advances. His head rises slowly from his shoulders; an instant, and he has caught a perch with his formidable bill. After beating it to death on the ground, he gulps it down with difficulty. He spreads his broad wings and slowly flies to another station.

I have found this Heron in every State where I have travelled, as well as in our "territories." It is well known from Louisiana to Maine, and in the Far West. Not a Heron of any kind did I see or hear of in Newfoundland or Labrador; it seldom occurs farther east than Prince Edward's Island in the Gulf of St. Lawrence.

Strong and hardy, this bird is to its tribe what the Passenger Pigeon is to the family of Doves. Extremely suspicious and shy, it is ever on the watch, its sight as acute as that of any Falcon and its hearing keen also. Ordinarily it is almost hopeless to attempt to approach it, though you may now and then surprise one feeding under the bank of a deep creek or bayou. I have seen many so wary that they take to wing at sight of a man half a mile away. However, in close woods, they can be approached with fair success if they are perched in a tree.

The Blue Heron feeds at all hours of day; at dawn; and, in clear weather, at night, according to appetite. They fly from one part of the country to another, high above the trees, with regularity, under cover of night. Their breeding season varies according to latitude. In Florida it occurs about early March, in the middle districts about mid-May, and in Maine a month later. At the approach of this period, these birds associate in pairs, temporarily abandoning their solitary ways. Except at the breeding time, each one seems to claim a certain district for its feeding ground and chases off every intruder of its own species; each roosts by itself on trees, or on the ground or in the middle of a wide marsh for safety. This unsocial temper probably arises from a desire for an abundance of food such as each one requires.

Its manners are exceedingly interesting as the breeding season approaches and the males look for partners. About sunrise a number alight either on a broad sandbar or on a savannah. They continue to arrive for several hours, until you may see forty or fifty before you. In the Floridas I have seen hundreds collect in this way in a morning, in their full beauty, without young birds among them. The males walk about with great dignity, bidding defiance to their rivals. The females croak their encouragement. Adversary meets adversary with little attention to politeness, as bills open and wings spread, before the rush of the foes. One would think that one well-aimed thrust might inflict death, but the strokes are parried with as much art as an expert swordsman would employ. Although I have watched these encounters for half an hour at a time, I never saw one killed in combat; but I have often seen one trampled upon, even after the incubation period had begun. Finally, the males and females leave in pairs, mated for the season—or so I believe, as I never saw them assemble twice on the same ground. After mating they become comparatively peaceable.

It is by no means their constant practice to breed in communities; I have found many pairs breeding apart. Nor do they always choose trees in the interior of a swamp. I have found heronries in the Florida pine barrens more than ten miles from any marsh, pond or river, and I have seen nests in the tops of the tallest trees, as well as only a few feet above ground, or on the ground itself, or on cactuses.

Imagine, if you can, a hundred acres overgrown with huge mingling cypress trees, the trunks of which stand fifty feet high before they send off a branch above the dark muddy waters. No sunbeam penetrates the dark canopy. Fallen logs cover the mire where matted grasses and lichens grow, and where, farther in, nymphae and other aquatic plants spread. The Congo snake and water moccasin glide along. Hundreds of turtles drop from the floating trunks of fallen trees. The sullen alligator plunges into the dismal pool. The pestilential air, alive with mosquitoes and other insects, is extremely injurious to the health of humans. Frogs croak. The Anhingas [Water-Turkeys] and Herons scream. The sounds form fit music for the scene. If the intruder, knee-deep in mire, discharges a gun, the frightened birds, breeding high above, make a deafening noise and cross one another confusedly in their flight. The young attempt to cling to safety, but some fall into the water with a splash. A shower whirls down from the tree-tops, and the observer is glad to make his retreat. Not only the Blue Heron, but the White also, and sometimes the Night Heron are found in such places, to which they return year after year unless they have been cruelly disturbed.

The nest of the Blue Heron is large and flat. The outside is composed of dry sticks. The inside is matted with weeds and mosses to a considerable thickness. You may see several in one tree that is large and convenient. I have never found more than three eggs;* this is true of all the large Heron species with which I am acquainted. The smaller ones lay more as they diminish in size, the Louisiana Heron often laying four† and the Green Heron five or even six.‡ The eggs of the Great Blue Heron are very small for its size; two and a half inches by one and seven-twelfths—dullish white, rather rough, and oval.

The male and female sit alternately. Each feeds the other by turns, with affection for each other as marked as for their young, whom they feed so abundantly while quite small that it is not uncommon to find the nest containing fish and other food, both fresh and putrefying. As the young advance they are less frequently fed except when copious supplies are available. I have seen them standing in low nests and crying in vain for food. The exertions of the old birds appear insufficient at times, owing to the quantity demanded by their charges, which

* Four eggs.
† Four or five.
‡ Four or five.

do not fend for themselves until able to fly. Then their parents chase them off by force, but owing to their inexperience at procuring food they become quite poor. Their food is mostly fish, but they devour frogs, lizards, snakes, birds, and such small quadrupeds as shrews, meadow mice and young rats. They strike at moths, butterflies and Libellulae like expert flycatchers, whether these are on the wing or in repose. I never saw one catch a fiddler crab. The only seeds I have known them to eat are those of the great water lily of the South. I do not believe that, in the wild state, this Heron ever eats dead fish, or indeed any food not killed by itself. Now and then it strikes at fish so large as to endanger its own life. I once saw one on the Florida coast strike a fish while standing erect, and then be dragged along for several yards on the surface of the water, and again beneath. Only after a severe struggle did it disengage itself. Afterward, quite overcome, it stood still, near the shore with its head turned away from the sea, as if afraid to try another such experiment. Some Herons which I kept on board the *Marion* in the Tortugas would swallow a bucketful of young mullets in half an hour's time. They would eat several pounds of green turtle flesh at a meal. I have no doubt that one of them could devour several hundreds of small fishes in a day.

A Heron caught alive by us near Key West looked so emaciated that I had her killed to discover the cause of her miserable condition. She had bred that spring. Her belly was in a state of mortification. We found the head of a fish measuring several inches, which, undigested, had lodged among her entrails.

I took a pair of these young Herons to Charleston and had them placed in a large coop on the deck of the boat with four White Herons, who immediately attacked them so violently that I had to turn them loose on the deck. I had observed the antipathy between the two species in the wild state, but was surprised to see it in young birds which had never seen each other's kind. Not even in a large yard on land did their dislike abate. The White Herons attacked the Blue and kept them completely under. The latter became much tamer and more attached to each other. They caught pieces of turtle flesh and gobbled them in an instant; as they became tamer they ate biscuits, cheese and bacon rind.

Woe to the man or dog who carelessly comes within reach of the powerful bill of a wounded Great Blue Heron!

I have seen this bird give chase to a Fish-Hawk that was flying along with a fish in its talons and, at the first lunge, make the Hawk drop its quarry, which the Heron retrieved from the ground. Once I saw a Hawk drop its fish in the water; the Heron, as if vexed, continued to follow and harass the Hawk and force it into the woods.

The flight is even, powerful, and capable of great distances. It flies silently from its perch for eight or ten yards with neck extended and legs dangling, then it draws back its neck, extends its feet in a straight line behind it, and with easy, measured flappings continues its course. At times it flies low over the marshes, or, if suspecting danger, high over land or forest. It travels from one pond or creek, or even one marsh to another without any deviation except on apprehending danger. Before alighting it now and then circles until it is near its destination, where it extends its legs and keeps its wings spread wide to effect a footing. It alights on a tree in the same way, but with less ease than on the ground. If an enemy surprises it, it will utter several loud and discordant notes, then mute the moment it flies off.

This species takes three years for full maturity, and even afterward its size and weight increase. It is very uncouth when just hatched. Bill, legs and neck are then very long. By the end of a week the head and neck are covered sparingly with long tufts of silky, dark gray down; the young feathers have quills with soft blue sheaths. The tibio-tarsal joints appear monstrous; the leg bones are so soft that they may be bent without breaking. At the end of four weeks, body and wings are well covered with dark slate-colored feathers, and broadly margined with ferruginous, which shows on thighs and flexures of the wings. By then the bill has grown wonderfully; the legs would not easily bend now; and the bird is able to stand erect on the nest or near it. Almost as if their parents wished to teach them to subsist in later life on little sustenance when need be, they are seldom fed oftener, now, than once a day. At six or seven weeks they fly off in search of food, each Heron by itself.

The following spring they are larger, and their long breast and shoulder feathers are to be seen. The pendent crest of the male becomes visible; the top of the head is now white. I have not been able to discover that they breed at this age. The second spring finds them handsome, with their upper feathers light, their black and white marks much purer, and their crests three or four inches long. Some breed at this stage. The third spring, the Great Blue Heron appears as I drew him for *The Birds of America*.

Though the males are somewhat the larger, there is little difference between the sexes in external appearance. This Heron moults in the South about the first of May, or as soon as the young are hatched. A month later the pendent crest is dropped; much of the beauty of the bird is gone for the season. In good condition a full-grown Heron will weigh about eight pounds, though this is variable—some will not exceed six.

A friend of mine who visited Prince Edward's Island in the Gulf of the St. Lawrence found it extremely difficult to obtain specimens for his collection, though this is a fine breeding place of the bird. At length he thought of covering himself with the hide of an ox, and under this disguise he obtained some Herons which were completely deceived by the stratagem.

LOUISIANA HERON

I never see this interesting, graceful, delicately formed and beautifully feathered Heron without calling it the "Lady of the Waters." Its light step leaves no impression on the sand of the Florida coast. It is at all seasons a social bird and moves about in company with the Blue Heron or White Egret (and others, at its breeding places). The Louisiana Herons are in full livery in Florida by the end of February, and by April 5 in Charleston. Though timid they are easier to approach than other species of Herons. They have alighted a few yards from me and gazed as if to discover my intentions. The flight is light, rather irregular, and swifter than that of the other Herons. They usually move in long undulating files, rather widely separated, with constant flappings (and high on their migrations). Because they pass and repass their roosting place before alighting, they prove an easy target for the hunter.

On April 29, while I was wading around a beautiful key of the Floridas, in search of cray-fish, I suddenly came upon one of the breeding places of the Louisiana Heron. Among low trees and bushes, matted together by creeping plants also supported by cactuses, I saw hundreds of pairs of these lovely birds with their nests close together, low and easy to peer into. The nests were of small dried sticks; flat; and sparsely lined. There were three nearly elliptical, pale blue, smooth, thin-shelled eggs in each, measuring an inch and six-twelfths in length and an inch and a quarter in breadth.* Incubation is twenty-one days, and occurs but once in a season.

During summer and autumn, after the old have left their young, both ages are seen in the Carolina rice fields, and they are then unusually gentle and easily approached. The Louisiana Heron acquires its full beauty the second year after its birth. Train and crest lengthen for several years until they appear as I have painted them. It requires care to obtain specimens in such complete plumage; this state does not last many days after pairing has taken place. By the time the young are hatched much of this fine plumage has dropped. By autumn only a few of the long barbs remain; in winter they cannot be seen.

GREAT WHITE HERON

THIS bird is the largest Heron found in the United States. I saw many between Indian Key and Key West while sailing along the numerous islands. Some were in pairs, others were single, and still others were in flocks. Within a few weeks I procured more than a dozen of different ages, as well as nests and eggs; and my party and I carefully noted their habits.

One morning at three I paddled with a companion as silently as possible over some narrow and tortuous inlets about eight miles from our harbor. We expected to find many White Herons, but for a long time our labor was almost hopeless, as none came near us. After six or seven hours of searching, we saw a Heron which flew directly over us. It proved to be a female. Her belly was bare either from sitting on eggs or from recently hatching her young. After procuring her, we breakfasted on biscuit soaked in molasses and water, and rested in the shade of some mangroves where the mosquitoes had a good opportunity to break their fast also. Then we went about from key to key, saw many White Herons, and by night reached our vessel, the *Marion*, rather exhausted and having but the one bird.

* Normal: four or five eggs.

That night at midnight we returned with our Captain to the last key we had visited. The moon shone bright as we rowed. The state of the tide was against us, and we had to drag our boats several miles over the soapy shallows. But at last, in a deep channel under hanging mangroves of a large key where we had seen Herons roosting earlier, we lay quietly till daybreak. But the mosquitoes and sandflies! At dawn our boats parted company, to meet on the other side of the key.

A Heron sprang from its perch almost directly over our heads, but escaped, croaking loudly and rousing hundreds of these Herons, which flew from the mangroves and sailed over and round us in the gray light like spectres. I almost despaired. The tide was rising; now we must wait till full tide, because the birds had gone to their feeding grounds. Mr. Egan pointed to a nest with two small young ones standing on it. He waited for two hours for the old birds to return to it, but in vain, while I proceeded into a narrow bayou. I found the Captain's boat and saw that he had obtained two Herons of this species. We went back for Mr. Egan. Now it was nearly high water. About a mile from us, more than a hundred Herons stood on a mud-bar up to their bellies. We divided, and I myself went to the lowest end of the key, where I had the pleasure of observing all the Herons take to wing, one after another, in quick succession. I aimed, but my Heron pursued its course. Not another bird came near, although many had alighted on the neighboring key and stood perched like so many newly finished statues of purest alabaster, finely contrasting with the deep blue sky. Mr. Egan took one bird, the Captain another, and I was empty-handed until we reached the next key, where I found the bird which I had shot earlier but had not brought down. From it I drew the Great White Heron of *The Birds of America*.

This species begins to pair early in March, but many do not lay their eggs until mid-April. Their courtship, I am told, resembles that of the Great Blue Heron; their nests are placed farther apart, however, and seldom more than a few feet above high water mark, which in Florida is so low as to look as if but a yard or two above the tree roots. The large flat, unlined nests, about three feet in diameter, are made of sticks. The three eggs, measuring two and three-quarters inches in length and one and eight-twelfths in breadth, have a rather thick shell of a light bluish green color. I was told that incubation continues for about thirty days. Both birds sit with legs outstretched before them, in the same manner as the young when two or three weeks old. The brood are pure white, slightly tinged with cream color, and without signs of a crest. I am unable to say how long it is before they attain their full plumage as I painted them.

Sedate, quiet, they walk majestically and with elegance. They flock at their feeding grounds, sometimes a hundred or more of them. They stand motionless on the banks and rarely move towards their prey, but instead wait until it comes near, then strike it and swallow it live; or, if it is large, they beat it on the water or shake it violently, biting it severely the while. Only the tide drives them from these grounds; they wait for it to reach their bodies. So wary are they that, though they may return to the same key, they rarely alight on trees resorted to before. If repeatedly disturbed, they do not return—for many weeks at least. They generally roost on one foot, with the other drawn up; unlike the Ibis, they are never seen lying flat on trees. However, they draw in their long necks and place their heads under their wings.

I was often surprised to see that by day one or more stood with out-stretched neck while others of the flock rested. These were keenly eyeing all the sea around, now and then starting suddenly at sight of a porpoise or shark in pursuit of some fish. They never fly inland if surprised, but instead cruise along the shores. Their flight is firm, regular and capable of long distance by slow flaps; the head is drawn in after the first few yards and their legs are extended backward like the other species of Herons. Now and then they rise high and sail in wide circles. They never alight without circling, except when going to feeding grounds on which other individuals have already settled.

When my party reached Charleston, four of these Herons, all young ones, were still alive. My friend John Bachman kept two for many months, but as they swallowed a bucketful of mullets in a few minutes it was difficult to keep them fed. They roosted in a beautiful arbor in his garden, where at night they looked like beings of another world in their pure white plumage. The points of their bills, which had been broken, grew again and were as regular at the end of six months as if nothing had happened to them. In the evening or early morning they would set, like pointer dogs, at moths which hovered over the flowers, then with a well-directed stroke of their bill seize and swallow their prey. They also struck at chicks and grown fowls and ducks, not to mention a sleeping cat, with disastrous results. At last they began to pursue the younger children of the place and after that had to be banished. One is now in the Charleston Museum, beautifully mounted.

I presented a skin of this Heron to the Academy of Natural Sciences, Philadelphia; two to the Duke of Sussex who gave them to the British Museum; and one to the Zoological Society of London.

Least Bittern

ONE morning in 1819 while I was employed at the Cincinnati Museum a woman came in with a live Least Bittern in her apron. She said it had fallen down her chimney the night before and that when she awoke at daybreak it was the first thing she saw—perched on a bedpost. I placed this young bird of delicate species on a table in front of me and drew from it the figure which appears on the left of the plate in *The Birds of America*. It stood perfectly still for two hours, but when I touched it with my pencil after my drawing was done, it flew off and alighted on a window cornice. I put it back on the table and took two books which I arranged so as to leave a passage of an inch and a half for the Bittern. It walked through with ease. Then I reduced the passage to an inch. Again the bird made its way between without moving either book. Although it measured two inches and a quarter in width, it could contract its breadth to an extraordinary degree.

When I was in Philadelphia in 1832 a gentleman presented me with a pair of live adults in perfect plumage, caught in a meadow outside the city. For several days I fed them on small fish and thin strips of pork. They were expert at seizing flies, and also ate caterpillars and other insects. My wife admired their gentle deportment. Even when teased they would merely spread their wings, ruffle their feathers and draw back their heads as if to strike, yet suffer themselves to be touched by anyone without pecking his hand. As they attempted to escape, they climbed again and again with ease from the floor to the top of the window curtain by means of feet and claws. I repeated the experiment with books for a passage, and succeeded as at Cincinnati. At the approach of night they became much livelier, and walked gracefully about with much agility, close together. I drew both of them in the attitudes seen in their portrait.

I have found this species as far east as New Brunswick, on our larger lakes, and in the interior, but seldom more than one or two at a time. In the Floridas and Carolinas they are known to breed in small communities of four or five pairs. Although found in salt marshes, the bird prefers the edges of ponds, lakes or fresh-water bayous. It nests in secluded situations of this kind, sometimes on the ground amid the rankest grasses, but oftener several inches above it. If off the ground, the flat nest of dried or rotten weeds is attached to the stems of grasses. The three or four eggs* are yellowish green, an inch and a quarter long, and almost equal in size at both ends. In one instance I found one such nest in a thicket near several of the Boat-Tailed Grackle and one of the Green Heron, with all the birds on friendly terms it appeared. I approached and could have taken the female with the hand, but the male flew away. Both cried *quā* and eyed me intently as I drew near. Their ordinary cry is a rough croak.

The young are covered with large reddish tufts of down; their bills are very short; and they sit on the rump with legs extended on each side before their body, like the young Herons. At two weeks they will leave the nest if disturbed, and scramble quickly through the grass, clinging to the blades with their sharp claws when necessary. At a later period they await their parents' return with food impatiently, calling with a low croak for half an hour at a time. As they learn to fly, they often take to the branches to escape such enemies as minks and snakes. The latter destroy many of their number.

This Bittern's flight is apparently weak by day, when it seldom moves more than a hundred yards at a time, even after fright. If much alarmed, it will fall among the grasses like the Rail. But I have seen it passing steadily along, fifty yards or more on high, in the dusk of the evening, its neck retracted and its legs stretched backward like the larger Herons. At that hour it sounds its peculiar cry at short intervals as it proceeds, with several others perhaps, in search of breeding grounds or on a migratory expedition. When it walks it shoots its head forward at every step, as if about to thrust its bill into some substance. If you try to seize it when it is disabled it is apt to inflict a painful wound.

* Four or five.

Its food consists of snails, slugs, tadpoles, young frogs and water lizards, as well as small shrews and field mice on occasion. Although more nocturnal than diurnal, it moves about a good deal by day in search of food. About noon the Least Bitterns may be seen standing erect on one foot, much fatigued and so sound asleep as to be caught by hand with ease if cautiously approached. This remarkable habit of our Bitterns has brought the undeserved charge of stupidity against them among the Creoles of Louisiana. But my own opinion is that the animal truly deserving to be called stupid yet remains to be discovered; the quality indicated by that epithet occurs nowhere else than among individuals of that species which so thoughtlessly applies the opprobrium.

White Ibis

SANDY ISLAND, Florida, is remarkable as a breeding place for various kinds of water and land birds. It is about a mile long, not more than a hundred yards broad, and resembles a horseshoe, its inner curve facing Cape Sable, six miles distant. At low tide it is surrounded for a great distance by mud flats that abound in food for wading and swimming birds—plants, fruits, and insects. Besides the White Ibis, I found the Brown Pelican, the Purple Heron, the Louisiana Heron, the White and the Green Herons, two kinds of Gallinules, the Cardinal Grosbeak, and Pigeons breeding there.

There are a few tall mangroves, thousands of wild plum trees, cactus sometimes nearly as thick as a man's body and more than twenty feet high, smilax, grape-vines, cane, palmettoes, Spanish bayonets, and the rankest nettles I ever saw. It is all so tangled together that I leave you to guess how difficult it was for my companions and myself to force our way through in search of birds' nests. We did so, however, although the heat was excessive and the stench of dead birds, putrid eggs, and the natural effluvia of the Ibises nearly insufferable. But the White Ibis was there in thousands. Although I already knew the bird, I wished to study its manners once more, that I might be able to present this account of them for you, despite the pain of cactus scratches and lacerations of my legs that this necessitated.

As we entered, we saw nests on every bush, cactus and tree. Whether the number was one thousand or ten thousand I cannot say, but I know that I counted forty-seven on a single plum tree. These nests of the White Ibis are about fifteen inches in diameter, and are formed of dry twigs intermixed with fibrous roots and green branches, which this bird easily breaks from the trees with its bill. The interior of the nest is flat, and finished with leaves of cane and other plants.

The bird breeds only once a year, and lays three eggs* two and a quarter inches long and an inch and five-eighths in diameter. They are rough to the touch, though not granulated, a dull white, blotched with pale yellow, and spotted with deep reddish brown. The young birds are at first covered with thick, dark gray down. They are fed by regurgitation. In about five weeks they can fly, but they leave the nest at the end of three weeks and stand on the branches or on the ground, awaiting the arrival of their parents with food, mostly small fiddler crabs and cray-fish. At this age I have found them miles away from the breeding place. Then they are easily caught. As soon as they are able to provide for themselves, the old birds leave them, and they are seen searching for their own food.

These Ibises are extremely gentle and unwary while nesting or in the act of incubation, unless they have been much disturbed. They will almost allow you to touch them on the nest. All the while the females are silent, but the mates show their displeasure by sounds resembling *crooh, croo, croo*. The report of a gun scarcely alarms them at first, although at all other periods they are shy and vigilant in the highest degree.

During the breeding season a change occurs in the coloring of the bill, legs and feet of this bird. The bill is then deep orange-red, and the legs and feet nearly carmine; the males have the gular pouch of a rich orange color. During winter, these parts are of a dull flesh color. The irides or irises of the eyes lose much of their clear blue, and resume something of the umber color of the young birds. I am thus particular in stating these matters, because it is doubtful if anyone else has ever paid attention to them.

The White Ibises go a great distance in search of food for their young, flying in flocks of several hundreds, waiting for low tide before they depart. They travel twenty or thirty miles to the great mud flats, where they collect an abundance of food; they return the moment the tide begins to flow. They feed by night as well as by day, at whatever hour the tides may be low. Some went to the keys near the Atlantic, a distance of more than forty miles. Others flew to the Everglades. But they

* Four.

never went off singly. They rose with one accord from the breeding ground, formed themselves in lines often a mile long, and soon disappeared from view. Soon after the turn of the tide we saw them approaching again in the same order. Not a note could be heard then. But if you disturb them when they are far from their nests, they utter loud, hoarse cries resembling the syllables, *hunk, hunk, hunk,* either while on the ground or as they fly off.

The flight of the White Ibis is rapid and long. These birds pass through the air with alternate flappings and sailings, according to the mode of the leader of the flock. With the most perfect regularity, each Ibis follows the motion of the one before it, so that constant, regular undulations wave through the whole line. If one bird is shot at, the whole line immediately breaks up, and for a few minutes all is disorder; but as they continue their course they resume their former arrangement. The wounded bird never attempts to bite, or to defend itself in any manner. But if it is only winged, it will run off with more speed than is pleasing to the pursuer.

At times the White Ibis, like the Red and the Wood Ibises, rises to an immense height in the air, where it performs beautiful evolutions. After amusing themselves thus for some time, they glide down with astonishing speed and alight either on trees or on the ground. Should the sun be shining, they appear in their full beauty, and the glossy black tips of their wings contrast admirably with the yellowish white of the rest of their plumage.

The White Ibis is as fond of ponds, bayous, or woodland lakes as the Wood Ibis. I have found it breeding in such spots at a distance of more than three hundred miles from the sea, and in the midst of the densest forests, until driven off to warmer latitudes by the approach of winter. When disturbed in swampy forest, these Ibises fly at once to the tallest tree-tops, sound their hoarse *hunk,* and watch the motions of the intruder so carefully that it is extremely difficult to get within shot of them.

Its manner of searching for food is very curious. The Woodcock and the Snipe are, it is true, also probers, but their task takes less ingenuity. The White Ibis frequently seizes small crabs, slugs and snails, and even at times flying insects, but its usual mode of taking its food proves that cunning is the principal ingredient of its instinct. For instance, the cray-fish often burrows down three or four feet in hot, dry weather to reach water and find comfort, and at a time when the Ibis is most hard pressed for food. The bird walks with remarkable care towards the mud mounds which the cray-fish has thrown up while forming its hole. Then it breaks up the upper part of the mound, causing the fragments to fall into the cavity made by the animal. After that it retires a single step and patiently awaits the result. The cray-fish, disturbed by the load of earth, instantly sets to work anew, and at last reaches the entrance of its burrow. But the moment it comes in sight, the Ibis seizes it with his bill.

While I was at Indian Key, I saw an immense quantity of beautiful tree snails. They were pyramidal or shortly conical in form, some of pure white, others curiously marked with spiral lines of bright red, yellow and black. They were crawling vigorously on every branch of each bush, where there was not a nest of the White Ibis. But wherever that bird had its habitation not a live snail was to be seen, although hundreds lay dead beneath. Was this caused by the corrosive quality of the bird's ordure?

There is a curious difference, as to plumage, between the sexes. Five of the bird's primaries or large wing feathers are tipped with glossy black for several inches. The female, which is only a little smaller than the male, has but four marked in this manner. On examining more than a hundred individuals of each sex, I found only four exceptions. These occurred in very old females which, as happens in other kinds of birds, might have been undergoing the interesting change sometimes seen in Ducks, Pheasants and other species when the aged females sometimes assume the livery of males.

Much has been said respecting the "oil bags" of birds. I dislike controversy, simply because I never saw the least indication of it in the ways of the Almighty Creator. Should I err, forgive me, but my opinion is that these organs were not made without a purpose. Why should they consist of matter so conveniently placed as to issue under the least pressure through well-defined tubes? When in full health, the White Ibis as well as other Ibises has these oil bags of great size. If my eyes have not deceived me, they make much use of the contents. If you feel anxious to satisfy yourself as to this, I urge you to keep some Ibises alive for several weeks, as I have done. You will then have an opportunity to judge. You will tell me, if the fat contained in these bags is not the very best *lip salve* obtainable!

If a wounded Ibis falls into the water, it swims tolerably well. But

I have never seen any take to the water and swim either by choice or to escape pursuit. One morning I chanced to be on the look-out for White Ibises in a swamp not many miles from Bayou Sara, Louisiana. The time was the end of summer. All around me was pure and calm as the clear sky, whose bright azure the lake reflected. The trees had already changed their verdure for more varied and mellower tints, and their pods and acorns dropped from the boughs. Some of the Warblers had begun to think of removing farther south. The Night Hawk, in company with the Chimney Swallow, was passing swiftly towards the land of their winter residence. The Ibises had all departed for the Florida coast, except for a few of the white species, one of which we spied.

The bird was perched about fifty yards from us almost in the center of the pool, and as our guns echoed among the tall cypresses, down to the water it fell, broken-winged. Its exertions to reach the shore roused the half-torpid alligators that lay in the deep mud at the bottom of the pool. One showed his head above the water, then a second and a third. All gave chase to the poor wounded bird which, on seeing its dreaded and deadly foes, made with double speed towards the very spot where we stood. I was surprised to see how much faster the bird swam than the reptiles, which, with widely opened jaws, urged their heavy bodies through the water. The Ibis was now within a few yards of us. It was the alligator's last chance. Springing forward, he raised his body almost out of the water, and his jaws nearly touched the terrified bird. We pulled three triggers at once, and fired into the throat of the monster. Thrashing his tail furiously and rolling his body in agony, the alligator at last sank into the mud. The Ibis walked to our very feet, as if in gratitude; there, lying down, it surrendered itself to us. I kept this bird until the succeeding spring. I had the pleasure of seeing its broken wing perfectly mended by care and good nursing. But then I restored it to liberty in the midst of its loved swamps and woods, after its long captivity.

A young White Ibis which I kept alive for some time fed freely, after a few days of captivity, on soaked Indian cornmeal, but showed great pleasure when cray-fishes were offered to it. It was fond of lying on its side in the sun for an hour or so at a time, pluming its body and nursing a sore wing. It walked lightly and very gracefully, though not so much so as the Heron. It did not molest its companions and became very gentle and tame, following those who fed it like a common fowl.

Trumpeter Swan

THE history of the American Swans has been but very slightly traced. Few records of the habits of these majestic, elegant, and useful birds exist, on which much reliance can be placed. Their geographical range still remains an unsolved problem. One species has been mistaken for another, and this by ornithologists who are said to be of the first order.* We may have more than two species within the limits of North America, but I am at present acquainted with only the one which is the subject of this article, and the smaller one which Sharpless named *Cygnus americanus.*

In a note in the journals of Lewis and Clark, written in the course of the expedition of these daring travellers across the Rocky Mountains, it is stated: "The Swans are of two kinds, the large and small. The large Swan is the same as the one common in the Atlantic States. The small differs from the large only in size and note; it is about one-fourth less, and its note is entirely different. These birds were first found below the great narrows of the Columbia River, near the Chilluckittequaw Indian nation. They are very abundant in this neighborhood, and remained with the party all winter, and in number they exceed those of the larger species five to one." These observations are partly correct and partly erroneous. The smaller Swan of the two, the one named by Sharpless, is the only one abundant in the middle districts of our Atlantic coast. The larger Swan, the Trumpeter, is rarely if ever seen east of the mouths of the Mississippi. A perfect specimen of the small Swan mentioned by Lewis and Clark has been sent to me from the Columbia River by Mr. Townsend. [Dr. J. K. Townsend provided

---

* Bewick's Swan of Great Britain had been given as North American in Richardson's *Fauna Boreali-Americana;* C. L. Bonaparte called the American Swan the Whistling Swan in his Synopsis of the birds of North America.

upwards of seventy bird skins for the completion of *The Birds of America.*—Ed.]

The Trumpeter Swans make their appearance on the lower Ohio about the end of October. At once they plunge into the larger ponds or lakes at no great distance from the river, displaying a marked preference for those which are surrounded by dense, tall canebrakes. There they remain until the water is closed by ice, when they are forced to move southward. During mild winters I have seen a few of them in the ponds around Henderson, Kentucky, until the beginning of March, probably wounded birds which have remained there to recover. On the arrival of intense cold, most of the flocks which visited the Ohio would fly on down the Mississippi just ahead of the weather, and return if its severity decreased. It has appeared to me that neither very intense cold nor great heat suits these birds as well as a medium temperature.

The waters of the Arkansas and its tributaries are also annually supplied with Trumpeter Swans. The largest which I have examined was shot on a lake near the junction of the Arkansas with the Mississippi. It measured nearly ten feet in alar extent,* and weighed above thirty-eight pounds. The quills, which I used in drawing the feet and claws of many small birds, were so hard, and yet so elastic, that the best steel pen of the present day might have blushed, if it could, to be compared with them.

I have traced their winter migrations as far southward as Texas where they are abundant at times. There I saw a pair of young ones in captivity, and quite domesticated, that had been caught in the winter of 1836. They were about two years old and pure white, although much smaller than even the younger one represented in *The Birds of America,* having perhaps been stinted in food, or having suffered from their wounds, as both had been shot. The sound of their familiar notes reminded me of the days of my youth, when I was in the company of this species half the year.

At New Orleans, where I made the drawing of the young bird which appears in *The Birds of America,* on December 16, 1822, Trumpeters are frequently sold in the markets. They are taken on the ponds of the interior and on the great lakes leading to the Gulf of Mexico. My friend the Reverend John Bachman has never seen or

* Wing-spread.

heard of one in South Carolina where he has lived for twenty years, though in hard winters the smaller American Swan is not uncommon there. It does not often migrate farther south than that State.

Once while I was encamped in the Tawapatee Bottom during a fur-trading voyage, our keel boat was hauled close under the eastern shore of the Mississippi and our valuables were all taken off. Then I had a partner in trade. Our party consisted of twelve or fourteen French Canadians, all of whom were pretty good hunters. As game was extremely abundant in those days, the supply of deer, bear, raccoons and opossums far exceeded our demands. Wild Turkeys, Grouse and Pigeons were hanging all around us. The ice-bound lakes afforded an ample supply of excellent fish, if one struck a strong blow with an axe on the ice just above the fish and pulled it out through the hole. The great stream was so firmly frozen that we made a practice of crossing it daily from shore to shore.

No sooner did the gloom of night become discernible through the gray twilight than the loud notes of hundreds of Trumpeters would burst upon our ears. As I gazed over the ice-bound river, flock after flock would be seen coming from afar and in various directions, alighting towards the middle of the stream opposite our camp. After pluming themselves awhile they would quietly settle on the ice. Through the dim light I could still discern the graceful curve of their necks as they gently turned them backwards to allow their heads to repose upon the softest and warmest of pillows. Just a dot of black, as it were, could be observed on the snowy mass. That dot was about half an inch of the base of the upper mandible or part of the bill, which was exposed, I think, to enable the bird to breathe with ease. Not a single Trumpeter did I observe acting as a sentinel among them. I have since wondered whether their sense of hearing was not so acute as to enable them to detect the approach of their enemies. Darkness closed in. No more could be seen until the dawn. But as often as the howlings of the numerous wolves that prowled through the surrounding woods, were heard, the clanging cries of the Swans would fill the air.

If the morning proved fair, the flocks would rise on their feet and trim their plumage. As they ran, with wings extended as if they were racing each other, the patter of their feet would come on the ear like the noise of great muffled drums, accompanied by the loud, clear sounds of their voices. After running fifty yards or so to windward, they would all be on the wing. If, instead, the weather was thick, drizzly and cold, or if there were indications of a fall of snow, they would remain on the ice—walking, standing, or lying down until signs of better weather became apparent. Then they would all start off.

One such drizzly morning our men formed a plot against the Swans. They separated into two parties, one above the birds, the other below them, on the ice. At a signal they walked slowly from the camp towards the unsuspecting birds which, having become acquainted with the sight of us because of our frequent crossings on the ice, remained as they were until the boatmen were within a hundred and fifty yards of them. Then they all rose to their feet, stretched their necks, shook their heads, and showed strong signs of apprehension. The gunners meanwhile advanced. One of their guns went off by accident, and the Swans were thrown into confusion. They scampered off in various directions and took to wing, some flying up and some down the stream, others making directly towards the shores. The muskets now blazed, and about a dozen birds were felled, some crippled, others quite dead. That evening they alighted about a mile above our camp. We never went after them again. I have been on hand for the killing of several of these Swans. I can assure you that unless you have a good gun well loaded with large buckshot, you may shoot at them without much effect, for they are strong, tough birds.

For a perfect conception of their beauty and elegance, you must observe them when they are not aware of your proximity, as they glide over the waters of some secluded inland pond. The neck, which at other times is held stiffly upright, moves in graceful curves, now bent forward, now inclined backwards over the body. The head, with an extended scooping movement, dips beneath the water, then with a sudden effort it throws a flood over its back and wings, while the sparkling globules roll off like so many large pearls. The bird then shakes its wings, beats the water, and, as if giddy with delight, shoots away, gliding over and beneath the surface of the stream with surprising agility and grace. Imagine a flock of fifty Swans thus sporting before you. I have more than once seen them, and you will feel, as I have felt, happier and freer of care than I can describe.

The body of the Swan is buoyant when it is swimming, but when the bird is apprehensive of danger, it sinks considerably lower. If it is resting and basking in the sunshine, it draws one foot, curiously expanded, towards the back, and often remains in that posture for half an hour at a time. When it is making off swiftly, its tarsal or knee joint is seen about an inch above the water, which passes over the lower part of its neck and along the sides of its body in wavelets, just as water undulates on the planks of a vessel gliding with a gentle breeze. Only during the courting season, or while it was passing its mate, have I ever seen a Swan with wings raised and expanded, as it is said to do, to profit by the breeze that may assist its progress. Yet I have pursued some in canoes to a considerable distance, without overtaking them or obliging them to take to wing. You and all the world have seen Swans laboring along on foot; therefore I will not trouble you with a description of their mode of walking, especially as it is not much to be admired.

Its flight is firm, and at times greatly elevated and sustained. It passes through the air by regular beats of its wings as Geese do, its neck and feet stretched full length, the latter projecting beyond its tail. When Swans are passing low, I have frequently thought I heard a rustling sound from the feathered motion of their wings. They group themselves in angular lines when bound for a distant place. The leader of the flock is likely to be one of the oldest of the males, but of this I am not at all sure, because once I saw a gray bird, which must have been a young one of that year, at the head of a line.

This Swan feeds principally by partly immersing its body and extending its neck under water, like Ducks and some Geese, while working its feet in the air as if this helped it keep its balance. Often, however, it resorts to the land, where it picks at the herbage—not sidewise as Geese do, but more in the manner of Ducks and poultry. Its food consists of roots of different vegetables, leaves, seeds, various aquatic insects, land snails, small reptiles and quadrupeds. The flesh of a cygnet is pretty good eating, but that of an old bird is dry and tough.

I kept a male alive for upwards of two years while I was residing at Henderson in Kentucky. It had been slightly wounded in the tip of the wing, and was caught after a long pursuit in a pond from which it could not escape. Its size, weight, and strength rendered the task of carrying it nearly two miles by no means easy. But as I knew that it would please my wife and my then very young children, I persevered. Although at first it was extremely shy, it gradually became accustomed to the servants, who fed it abundantly, and at length it proved so gentle as to come to my wife's call to receive bread from her hand. "Trumpeter," as we named our bird, now assumed a character which until then had been unexpected. Laying aside its timidity, it became so bold at times as to give chase to my favorite Wild Turkey cock, my dogs, children, and servants.

Whenever the gates of our yard happened to be open, the Swan would at once make for the Ohio, and it was not without difficulty that he was driven home again. On one occasion he was absent a whole night, and I thought he had left us for good. But word came of his having travelled to a pond not far distant. Accompanied by my miller and six or seven of my servants, I betook myself to the pond, and there we saw our Swan swimming buoyantly about as if in defiance of us all. Only with a great deal of trouble did we succeed in driving it ashore. Pet birds, no matter what their species, seldom pass their lives in accordance with the wishes of their possessors. In the course of a dark and rainy night, one of the servants having left the gate open, "Trumpeter" made his escape, and was never again heard of.

With the manners of the Trumpeter Swan during the breeding season, its mode of constructing its nest, the number of its eggs,* and the appearance of its young, I am utterly unacquainted.

* Seven or eight dull white eggs.

Canada Goose

It is my opinion that all Canada Geese pair in our territories before they depart for the distant North. No doubt this results from the fact that the clement season of Labrador and that general region is too short for them to bring up their young, and to renew their own plumage there before the rigors of advancing winter force them to leave for milder country. My opinion is founded on certain facts.

I have, for instance, frequently seen large flocks of Geese in ponds, on marshy grounds, or even on dry sandbars, and noted mating birds renewing their courtship as early as January. Some of the flock would be contending or coquetting for hours every day until all seemed satisfied with their choice; after that they were careful to keep in pairs. I have noticed also that the older the birds, the shorter were the preliminaries of courtship. As for the barren birds, these were altogether indifferent to the show of love and affection displayed around them. The bachelors and old maids, whether from regret, or from not caring to be disturbed by the bustle, quietly moved aside and lay down in the grass or sand at some distance from the rest. Whenever the flocks rose on the wing or betook themselves to the water, these forlorn ones always kept behind.

On reaching the place chosen for their summer residence, the Geese of the flock separate in pairs, which build their nests and rear their young at a considerable distance from each other.

It is extremely amusing to witness the courtship of the Canada Goose in all its stages. Let me assure you that although a gander does not strut before his beloved with the pomposity of a Wild Turkey, or with the grace of a Dove, his ways are quite as agreeable to the female of his choice. Picture a gander who has just accomplished the defeat of another male after a struggle of half an hour or more. He advances gallantly towards the female, his head scarcely an inch from the ground, his bill open to the full stretch, his fleshy tongue raised, and his eyes darting fiery glances. As he moves, he hisses loudly, while the emotion which he experiences causes his quills to shake and his feathers to rustle. Now he is close to her who, in his eyes, is all loveliness. His neck bends gracefully in all directions, passes all around her, and occasionally touches her body. As she congratulates him on his victory and acknowledges his affection, they move their necks in a hundred curious ways.

However, fierce jealousy urges the defeated gander to renew his efforts to obtain his love. He advances, his eye glowing with rage, shakes his broad wings, ruffles up all his plumage, and, as he rushes on the foe, hisses with the intensity of his anger. The whole flock stands by, amazed; opening up a space, the birds gather round to view the combat. The bold gander who had been caressing his mate scarcely deigns to take notice of his foe, but seems to send only scornful glances towards him. He of the mortified feelings, however, raises his body, half opens his sinewy wings, and with a powerful blow sends forth his defiance. In the presence of so large an audience, the affront cannot be borne. Nor is there, indeed, much disposition to bear it in any circumstances. The blow is returned with vigor. The aggressor reels for a moment, but soon recovers. The combat rages on. Were the weapons more deadly, feats of chivalry would now be performed. As it is, thrust and blow succeed each other like strokes of hammers driven by sturdy forgers. The mated gander catches hold of his antagonist's head with his bill; no bull-dog could cling faster to his victim. He squeezes him with all his energy, lashes him with his powerful wings, and at length drives him away, spreads out his pinions, runs with joy to his mate, and fills the air with cries of exultation.

But look yonder—not a couple, but half a dozen ganders, are engaged in battle! Some desperado, it seems, has fallen upon a mated bird. Several bystanders, as if sensible of the impropriety of such conduct, rush to the assistance of the wronged one. How they strive and tug—biting and striking with their wings! How their feathers fly about! Exhausted, abashed, and mortified, the presumptuous intruder retreats in disgrace. There he lies, almost breathless, on the sand!

Such are the conflicts of these ardent lovers. So full of courage and affection towards their females are they that the approach of a male invariably ruffles their tempers, as well as their feathers. No sooner has the goose laid her first egg than her bold mate stands almost erect by her side, watching even the rustling sound of the breeze. The least noise brings from him a sound of anger. Should he spy a raccoon making its way among the grass, he walks up to him undauntedly, hurls a vigorous blow at him, and drives him away instantly. Indeed I doubt if a man, unarmed, would come off unscathed in such an encounter. If imminent danger excites him, the gander urges his mate to fly off, and resolutely remains near the nest until he is assured of her safety. Then he himself flies forth, to mock his disappointed rival by his notes.

Suppose all to be peace and quiet around the fond pair, and the female sitting on her eggs. Picture the nest near the bank of a noble stream or lake. The clear sky spreads over the scene, bright sunbeams glitter on the waters, and a thousand fragrant flowers give beauty to the swamp which, till lately, was so dismal. The gander passes to and fro over the stream, moving as if lord of the waters. Now he inclines his head with a graceful curve, now he sips to quench his thirst. As noontide arrives he paddles towards the shore to relieve his affectionate and patient consort for a while. The lisping sounds of their offspring are heard through the shell. Their little bills have begun to break the walls that enclose them, and in a moment they come forth full of life and beauty in their downy covering. With tottering steps they follow their cautious parent towards the water after a day or so. By the time they reach the edge of the stream, their mother is already floating. One after another they follow her. All now glide gently along, and what a beautiful sight!

The mother slowly leads her innocent younglings close in to a grassy margin. To one of them she shows the seed of the floating grass, to another she points out the crawling slug. She keeps a watchful eye on the cruel turtle, the garfish, and the pike that lurk about for their prey. She glances up at the Eagle and Gull that hover over the water in search of food. Just then, a ferocious bird dashes at her young ones. Instantly she plunges beneath the surface, and in the twinkling of an eye her brood disappears after her. Soon they come up among the thick rushes, with nothing above water but their little bills. The mother marches towards land, lisping to her brood in accents so gentle that none but they and her mate can understand what she is saying. All take safe cover until the Eagle and Gull fly away disappointed.

More than six weeks elapse. The soft, tufty down of the goslings has become coarse and hairlike, their wings are edged with quills, and their bodies bristle with feathers. They have grown, and living in the midst of abundance has made them fat, so that on shore they waddle along with difficulty. As they are not yet able to fly, the greatest care is taken to save them from their numerous enemies. But by the end of the burning days of August they have grown apace and can fly with ease from one shore of the stream to another.

When the hoarfrosts cover the countryside and the streams begin to freeze over with ice, the family of Canada Geese is joined by others. The ganders spy an advancing snowstorm, and with one accord they sound the order for the departure of all. After much wide circling upwards, the flock rises high in the thin air. An hour or more is devoted to teaching the young the order in which they are to move during migration. When the whole flock has been marshaled, off it starts. As it proceeds, it is now an extended front, now a single long file; then again it may array itself in an angular formation. Should one of the young feel fatigued, his position in the ranks is changed, and he assumes his place in the wake of another who cleaves the air before him. The parent bird may fly by his side for a while to encourage him.

Two, three, or more days elapse before they reach a secure resting place. The fat with which they are loaded at their departure has rapidly wasted. They are fatigued, and feel the keen gnawings of hunger. Spying a wide estuary, they direct their course towards the water, alight on it, swim to the beach, and stand and gaze around them. The young are full of joy, but the old, who are well aware that many foes have been awaiting their arrival, are full of fear. All night the flock remains silent though not inactive. Carefully they approach the grassy shores where they feed and regain their wasted strength. As early dawn lights the surface of the water, they rise into the air, extend their lines, and proceed southward. Finally, they reach a place which they think may afford rest and security during the winter. At length they joyfully perceive the return of spring, and prepare to fly away from their greatest enemy, man, after his many annoyances.

The Canada Goose often arrives as early as the beginning of September, and does not by any means confine itself to the seashore. During my residence in Kentucky I never spent a winter without seeing immense flocks of them, especially around Henderson where I have killed many hundreds, as well as on the Falls of the Ohio at Louisville and the vicinity, which abounds in ponds overgrown with grasses whose seeds they greedily feed on.

It seems to me probable that this bird must have bred in numbers in the temperate parts of North America before the white population began to spread itself over these regions. This opinion is founded on the experience of many old and respected citizens of our country, General George Clark in particular. He was one of the first settlers on the banks of the Ohio, and he assured me at a very advanced age that, fifty years before our conversation took place, or about 1760, wild Geese were so plentiful the year round that he had them shot to feed his soldiers, who were then garrisoned near what is now Vincennes, Indiana. My father, who travelled down the Ohio shortly after Braddock's defeat, told me much the same thing. I myself and many persons now residing in Louisville in Kentucky well remember that it was quite easy, twenty-five or thirty years ago, to obtain young Canada Geese in the ponds of the neighborhood. As late as 1819 I came upon the nests, eggs, and young of this species near Henderson. However, as I have already said, the greater number remove far north to breed. Indeed the extreme heat of our Southern States is so uncongenial to their constitution that attempts to rear them there in a domesticated state very rarely succeed.

The Canada Goose, when it remains with us to breed, begins to form its nest in March in some retired place not far from water, usually among the rankest grass, and not infrequently under a bush. It is large and flat, elevated several inches, and carefully built of various kinds of dry plants. Only once have I found the nest off the ground; in that case it was on the stump of a large tree in the center of a small but very secluded pond. The stump was about twenty feet high. I counted five eggs in the nest. I did not disturb the parent birds, wishing to see how they would convey the young to the water after incubation. But in this I was disappointed, for on returning to the nest at what I thought to be the proper time, I was mortified to find that a raccoon or some other animal had destroyed the eggs. The birds had abandoned the place.

The largest number of eggs I have found in the nest of this Goose is nine, which I think is more by three than they usually lay in a wild state.* In the nests of the domesticated Canada Goose I have counted as many as eleven, but of these, several usually prove unproductive. The thick-shelled, rather smooth, dull yellowish green eggs, which measure three and one-half by two and one-half inches, hatch in twenty-eight days. Unless the eggs are removed from the nest or broken at an early stage, there is but one brood in a season. The young follow their parents to the water a day or two after they have issued from the egg, as I have said earlier. They usually return to land to rest in the sunshine in the evening, and they pass the night there under their mother. She takes every care imaginable for their comfort and safety, as does her mate. He never leaves her during the incubation longer than necessary to obtain food, and he takes her place on the nest at intervals. Both remain with their brood until the following spring.

It is during the breeding season that the gander displays his courage and strength to the greatest advantage, as we have seen. I knew one that appeared larger than usual, with its lower parts a rich cream color. It returned three years in succession to a large pond a few miles from the mouth of the Green River in Kentucky. Whenever I visited the nest it seemed to look upon me with utter contempt. It would stand in a stately attitude until I was within a few yards of the nest. Then it would suddenly lower its head, shake it as if it were dislocated from the neck, open its wings, and launch into the air, flying directly at me. So daring was this fine fellow that in two instances he struck me a blow with one of his wings on my right arm, with such force that for an instant I thought it was broken. Immediately after this effort to defend his nest and mate, he ran swiftly towards them, passed his head and neck several times over and around the female, and again assumed his attitude of defiance.

Always intent on making experiments, I thought of trying to conciliate this bold son of the waters. I took with me several ears of corn, shelled them and threw the kernels towards him. But they remained untouched for several days. At last I succeeded, however, and before the end of the week both birds fed freely on the grain even in my sight! I felt much pleasure at this, and repeated my visit daily. I found, before the eggs were hatched, that the Geese would allow me to approach within a few feet of them, although they never suffered me to touch

* Normal: five.

them. Whenever I attempted to, the male met my fingers with his bill and bit me so severely that I gave up.

The great beauty and courage of this male made me want to possess him. I had marked the time when his young were likely to appear, and on the preceding day I baited a large twine coop with corn and waited for him to enter it. In he walked. I drew the string, and he was my prisoner. Next morning when the female was about to lead her offspring to the river which was nearly half a mile away, I caught her and all her young. She came within my reach while attempting to rescue one of her brood. I took them home, pinioned each of them on the side to prevent their escape, and turned them loose in my garden, where I had a small but convenient artificial pond.

For more than a fortnight both the old birds appeared completely cowed. Indeed, for some days, I felt apprehensive lest they abandon the care of the young ones. However, with much attention to them, I succeeded in rearing the goslings by feeding them abundantly on the larvae of locusts, which they ate greedily, as well as on cornmeal moistened with water. The whole flock of eleven Geese prospered.

In December the weather became intensely cold, and I saw that now and then the gander would spread his wings and sound a loud note, to which the female first, then all the young ones in succession, would respond. They would all run as far as the ground allowed them to do, in a southerly direction, and attempt to fly off. I kept the whole flock three years. The old pair never bred while in my possession, but two pairs of the young ones did, one of them raising three, the other seven. They all bore a special enmity to dogs, and they showed dislike for cats, but still more animosity towards an old Swan and a Wild Turkey cock which I had. I found them useful in clearing the garden of slugs and snails. Although they now and then nipped the vegetables, I liked their company. When I left Henderson, my flock of Geese was given away, and I have not since heard how they have fared.

On one of my shooting excursions in the same neighborhood, I chanced one day to kill a wild Canada Goose, which, on my return, was sent to the kitchen. The cook, while dressing it, found an egg in it ready to be laid. I placed the egg under a common hen, and in due time it hatched. Two years later the bird mated and produced a brood. This goose was so gentle that she would suffer any person to caress her, and would readily feed from the hand. She was smaller than usual, but in every respect as perfect as any I have ever seen. At the period of migration she showed less desire to fly off than any other I have known. But her mate who had once been free did not share her apathy.

I have not been able to discover why many of these Geese were so averse to reproducing when reared from the egg, or when brought up in captivity, unless they were naturally sterile. I have seen several kept for more than eight years without ever mating, and yet others that had young in the second spring after their birth. I have also known an impatient male to abandon a female of his own species in captivity and pay his addresses to a common tame goose, by which a brood would in due time be brought up and thrive. That such tardiness of the female is not known in its wild state I feel pretty confident, because I have observed Canada Geese having broods of their own when, judging by their size, the dullness of their plumage and other such signs, they could not have been more than fifteen or sixteen months old. I have therefore decided that this species, like many others, requires long years to counteract the original wild and free state. Indeed it seems probable that our attempts to domesticate many kinds of wild fowls useful to mankind have often been despaired of too soon. A few years more of constant care might have produced the desired effect.

The Canada Goose becomes gregarious immediately after its young have developed, but it does not seem fond of the company of any other kinds of Geese. When other species alight in the same ponds, it forces them to keep at a respectful distance. During its migrations, I have never seen a single bird of any other description within its ranks.

The flight of this Goose is firm, rather rapid, and potentially very long. Once they are high in the air, they move ahead with extreme steadiness and regularity. Before rising from the water or from the ground, they usually run a few feet with outspread wings. But if suddenly surprised, and in full plumage, they can rise on the wing with a single spring of their broad webbed feet. While travelling a considerable distance, they pass through the air about a mile overhead and steadily follow a direct course towards the point for which they are bound. Their notes are distinctly heard, and the various changes made in the arrangement of their ranks are easily seen. But when they are slowly advancing from south to north early in the season, they fly much lower, alight more frequently, and are more likely to be bewildered by sudden banks of fog, or when passing over cities or over arms of the sea where much shipping may be in sight. Great consternation then prevails among them. They crowd together, confused, wheel irregularly, and utter a constant cackling like sounds from a disconcerted mob. Sometimes the flock separates, some proceeding in a direction contrary to that in which they came, but after a while they sail to the ground as if quite confused, alight and appear almost stupefied. They will then let themselves be approached and shot or knocked down with ease. I have witnessed this myself.

Heavy snowstorms also cause them severe distress, and at such times some have been known to fly against beacons and lighthouses, dashing their heads against the walls in mid-day. At night they are attracted by the lights of these buildings, and now and then, when this happens, a whole flock is caught. At other times their migrations northward are suddenly checked by a change of weather. The approach of storms seems well known to them, for they will suddenly wheel and fly back in a southern direction several hundred miles. I have known flocks to return to places which they had left a fortnight before. Even during winter they are keenly sensitive to changes of temperature, flying north or south in search of feeding grounds. So certain is their sense of the coming weather that one may feel sure, when he sees them flying southward in the evening, that the next morning will be cold, and *vice versa*.

The Canada Goose is less shy far inland than on the coast. The smaller the pond or lake to which they resort, the easier it is to approach them. Like Swans and fresh-water Ducks, they feed by plunging their heads towards the bottom of shallow ponds or the borders of lakes and rivers, immersing their fore parts and frequently elevating their legs, feet and posterior into the air. They never dive on such occasions. In the fields or meadows they nip the blades of grass sidewise like the domestic Goose. After rainy weather they rapidly pat the earth with both feet as if to force the earthworms from their burrows. They are extremely fond of alighting in corn fields covered with tender blades, where they often remain through the night and commit great havoc.

Wherever you find them, and no matter how remote from the haunts of man the place may be, they are at all times so vigilant and suspicious that it is extremely hard to surprise them. In keenness of sight and acuteness of hearing, they are perhaps surpassed by no bird whatever. During the hours when the flock is resting, one or more ganders stands on the watch as sentinel. At the sight of cattle, horses, or deer, they are seldom alarmed, but a bear or cougar is instantly announced. If the flock is on the ground near water, the birds immediately flee to the middle of the pond or river and remain there until the danger is over. Should their enemies pursue them into the water, the males utter loud cries, and the flock closes its ranks, and the birds rise simultaneously in a few seconds and fly off in a body, though seldom in lines or in such angles as those they form when travelling a great distance.

So acute is their hearing that they are able to distinguish the different sounds or footsteps of their foes with astonishing accuracy. The breaking of a dry stick by a deer is at once distinguished from the same sound caused by a man. If a dozen large turtles or an alligator drops into the water, making a loud noise in their fall, the wild Geese pay no heed to it. But no matter how faint and distant the sound of an Indian's paddle may be, if the paddle strikes the side of the canoe by accident, it is remarked at once. Every Goose raises its head and looks intently towards the place from which the sound came, and in silence they watch for the movements of their enemy.

These birds are extremely cunning. Should they think themselves unnoticed by an approaching boat which they have seen, they will move silently into the tall grasses at the edge of the water, lower their heads, and lie perfectly quiet until the vessel has passed by. I have seen them walk from a large frozen pond into the woods to avoid being seen by a hunter, and return as soon as he has crossed the pond. But should there be snow on the ice or in the woods, they prefer to watch the intruder and take to wing long before he is within shooting distance, as if aware of the ease with which they could be followed by their tracks over the treacherous surface.

Canada Geese are fond of returning regularly to the place chosen for their rest. This they will continue to do unless they are much molested while there. In spots where they are little disturbed they seldom go farther than the nearest sand-bank or the dry shore where they feed. But in other parts of the country they retire many miles to points of greater security, where they can detect danger long before it can reach them. When such a place is found and proves safe, many flocks resort to it, but they alight apart in separate groups. On some great sandbars of the Ohio, the Mississippi and other large streams, flocks of as many as a thousand individuals may be seen at evening. There they spend the night, lying on the sand within a few feet of each other, every flock having its own sentinel. At dawn the next morning they rise to their feet, arrange and clean their feathers, perhaps walk to the water to drink, and then depart for their feeding grounds.

When I first went to the Falls of the Ohio, where bare rock shelves extend for fully half a mile along the river, thousands of Canada Geese rested there at night. The breadth of the channels that separate the rocky islands from either shore, and the rapidity of the currents which sweep along them, make this place a more secure resort than most others. Now, at the time I write, in the 1830's, the Geese still visit these islands during winter for the same purpose, but their number has become very small. So shy are those birds at present around Louisville that the moment they are disturbed at ponds where they feed each morning, a single gun report will immediately return them to their rocky asylums. Even there they are by no means secure. Not infrequently it happens that a flock alights within half a gunshot of a person concealed in a pile of driftwood; his aim generally proves too true for their peace. In fact I knew a gentleman who had a large mill opposite Rock Island who used to kill the poor Geese from a distance of about a quarter of a mile by means of a small cannon heavily charged with rifle bullets. If I recollect truly, Mr. Tarascon not infrequently obtained a dozen or more Geese at a shot in this manner. This was done at dawn, when the birds were busily engaged in trimming their plumage with the view of flying off in a few minutes to their feeding grounds. But this war of extermination could not last long. The Geese deserted the fatal rock, and the great gun of the mighty miller was used only for a few weeks.

The Canada Goose moves with considerable grace on the water, and resembles the Wild Swan, to which I think it is related. If wounded in the wing, it sometimes dives to a shallow depth and makes off with astonishing speed, always in the direction of the shore. The moment it reaches land, it sneaks through the grass or bushes, its neck extended an inch or so above the ground, and thus proceeds so silently that, unless closely watched, it is pretty sure to escape. If shot at and wounded while on the ice, it immediately walks off in a dignified manner, as if anxious to make you believe that it has not been injured. It sounds a loud note all the while. But the instant it reaches the shore it becomes silent and makes off stealthily.

I was much surprised one day, while on the coast of Labrador, to see how cunningly one of these birds which was moulting, (and consequently quite unable to fly), nevertheless managed to elude pursuit for a while. We first saw it some distance from the shore, and swiftly rowed our boat towards it. It swam before us with great speed, making directly for land; but when we were within a few yards of it, it dived, and nothing could be seen of it for a long time. Every one of the party stood on tiptoe to mark the spot at which it should rise, but all in vain. Then the man at the rudder accidentally looked down over the stern. There he saw the Goose in the water, with only the point of its bill above the surface. Its feet were busily propelling it, that it might keep pace with the boat. The sailor attempted to catch it while we were within a foot or two of the Goose, but, with the swiftness of thought, it shifted from side to side, fore and aft. Delighted at witnessing so much sagacity in a *Goose*, I begged the party to suffer the poor bird to escape.

I have witnessed the killing of many a fine Goose, so I hope you will let me relate one or two anecdotes connected with the shooting of this game. A curious method I have practiced with much success. I have sunk a tight hogshead to within an inch of its upper edge into the sand of the bars where these birds rest at night. Then I have stationed myself within it at the approach of evening and have drawn over me a quantity of brushwood, placed my gun on the sand, and covered it with twigs and leaves. The birds have sometimes alighted very near me, and in this disguise I have killed several at a shot. But the stratagem has answered for only a few nights in the season. During severe winters these birds appear to be able to keep certain portions of the deepest part of a pond quite open and free from ice, by their continuous movement in the water.

I am well acquainted with one of the best sportsmen now living in the Kentucky country, one possessed of strength, activity, courage and patience—qualities of great importance in a gunner. I have frequently seen him mount a capital horse of speed and bottom, at midnight, when the mercury in the thermometer was about at the freezing point, and the ground blanketed with snow, and the trees so covered with ice as to seem made of glass. Picture him going off at a gallop—his steed rough shod—nobody knows whither, but myself, who am by his side. His wallet contains our breakfast, plenty of ammunition, and the necessary implements for the occasion. The night is pitch dark, and dismal enough, but who cares! *He* knows the woods as well as any Kentucky hunter, and in this respect I am not much behind him.

A long interval passes before the first glimpse of day appears in the east. We know quite well where we are, and that we have travelled just twenty miles. Only the Barred Owl's cry interrupts the melancholy silence of the hour. We tie our horses and move cautiously on foot towards a long pond, the feeding place of several flocks of Geese which have not yet arrived. But the whole surface of the open water is covered with Mallards, Widgeons, Pintail Ducks, Blue-Winged and Green-Winged Teals. My friend's gun, like mine, is a long and trusty one, and the opportunity is too tempting. On all fours we cautiously creep to the very edge of the pond, raise ourselves on our knees, level our guns, and let fly. The woods resound with repeated echoes. The air is filled with Ducks of all sorts. Our dogs dash into the half frozen water, and in a few minutes a small heap of game lies at our feet.

Now we retire, separate, go to different sides of the pond. If my companion's fingers are as cold as my own I feel certain that it would be difficult for him to fasten a button. There we are, shivering with contracted feet and chattering teeth. But we know Geese are coming. Their well-known cry, *hauk, hauk, awhawk, awhawk,* resounds through the air. They wheel and wheel for a while, finally alighting gracefully on the water where they play and wash themselves before beginning to look about for food. There must be at least twenty of them. Twenty more soon arrive, and in less than half an hour we have before us a flock of one hundred.

My experienced friend has put a snow-white shirt on over his apparel, and although I am trying hard to see him, I conclude that this is impossible even for the keen eye of the sentinel Goose.

"Bang, bang," quoth my friend's long gun. The birds, in dismay, instantly start up and fly towards the spot where I am hiding. When they approach, I spring to my feet; the Geese shuffle, and instantaneously rise directly upwards. I touch my triggers singly. Two birds come heavily to the ground at my feet, broken-winged and dead. We collect our game, return to our horses, fasten the necks of the Geese and Ducks together and throw them across the saddles, and proceed towards another pond for more hunting.

On another occasion my friend went alone to the Falls of the Ohio. As usual he reached the border of the stream long before daylight. His well-trained steed plunged into the whirling current, and carried his bold rider with some difficulty to the island, landing him there drenched and cold. The horse knew what he had to do as well as his master. While the animal ranged about, nipping the frozen herbage, the hunter carefully approached a pile of driftwood well known to him. There he concealed himself, his famous dog "Nep" staying close at his heels. The dull gray dawn began to give him a dim view of the Geese. He fired, several fell, and one, severely wounded, rose and alighted in the Indian Falls. Neptune dashed after it, but, as the current is powerful, the gunner whistled to his horse which pricked its ears and galloped up. Instantly he vaulted into the saddle and they plunged into the treacherous stream. The wounded game was overtaken, the dog was dragged along, and finally, on the Indiana shore, horse and rider managed a landing. Any man but the one whose exploits I am now faithfully recording would have perished long ago. But it is not half so much for the sake of the game, that he undergoes such labor and danger, as for the gratification it affords his kind heart to distribute it among his numerous friends in Louisville.

On our Eastern shores matters are differently managed. The gunners there shoot Geese for pecuniary gain, attracting them with wooden decoys or with live birds, lying in ambush for hours, and destroying an immense number with long guns. There is little sport in this shooting. I shall say no more about it.

Ducks

GOLDEN-EYE

ONE day as I was approaching the shallow fording place of Canoe Creek, near Henderson in Kentucky, I observed five Golden-Eyed Ducks, or Whistlers, as they are known in that part of the country. They were fishing and swimming about, and allowed me to come within a few yards of them on the shore, before they began to close in, shake their heads, and cry their rough notes. Not wishing to shoot them, I slapped my hands smartly together, saw them all dive, then suddenly rise again, and run over the water for about ten yards, before taking flight and passing and repassing over the ford several times. They alighted on the large branches of a sycamore that hung over the creek, no more than about twenty yards from where I stood.

This was the first time in my life that I had seen Golden-Eyes alight on a tree. I waded to the opposite side and gazed at them with amazement for several minutes. As I was about to move on, one of the Ducks glided down with nearly closed wings, reached the water, and at once dived. The others followed, one after another, somewhat the way Pigeons and Starlings do, as if uncertain whether there might be danger. I left them to themselves, and, soon after, met a family of country people going to Henderson. One of them asked me about the depth of the ford, and I replied that the water was low. I added that they should be careful lest the Ducks there frighten the horses that the women were riding. The good folks, with whom I was well acquainted, laughed and we parted.

About four o'clock, as I was returning with a fine Turkey cock slung to my back, I met the same party, who told me that—sure enough—the

Ducks were still at the ford and that most likely I could have "a good crack at them." There they were, when I reached the spot. I forced them to fly off, but I was no more than fifty yards beyond the creek when I heard their splashings as they again alighted. During the next two weeks I visited the place several times, without once failing to find the five Ducks there. I decided to find out why this was so. I undressed and waded out barefooted, examined the creek bottom, and found it made up of rather hard blue clay that was full of holes bored by cray-fish. To make quite sure that these creatures were what attracted the Ducks, I watched for an opportunity to shoot two of the latter and to examine their stomachs. The examination satisfied me on the subject. Long before this, I had become convinced that an abundant supply of food afforded a powerful attraction to migrating birds. You will note my remarks on this in my biographies of the Wild Turkey and the Passenger Pigeon in these pages. But I had not before, nor have I since, seen such persistent attachment to a particular spot as that shown by the five Golden-Eyes.

The flight of this species is powerful, extremely rapid, and wonderfully protracted. It passes along with a speed equal to that of any of the Duck tribe, enabling it, I believe, to travel ninety miles in an hour. The whistling of its wings may be distinctly heard at a distance of more than half a mile. But this statement contradicts the opinion of probably every previous writer, for it has been generally believed that the greater the wingspread, the more rapid the flight. This is anything but correct.

After flying from the water they proceed for a considerable distance very low, not rising to any height until they have advanced several hundred yards.

The only nest of the Golden-Eye that I have examined I discovered in mid-June, 1824, on the margin of a small creek about eight miles from Green Bay, Ontario. While I sat under the tree where the Ducks were nesting, the female left it—probably to go in search of food. I was thinking of my peculiar circumstances more than about birds of any kind. Besides, I was almost destitute of ammunition, and bent only on returning to my family, then in Louisiana. But how exciting such moments prove to the ardent observer of Nature! In an instant, hunger, fatigue, even the thoughts of my beloved wife and children vanished—in a few minutes I was safely lodged on the tree, thrusting my arm into the cavity of a large broken branch. Nine beautiful, greenish, smooth eggs, almost equally rounded at both ends, were at my disposal. They were laid on some dry grass of the kind that grows on the edges of the creek, and were deeply imbedded in the down of the bird. As I was not then aware of the necessity of measuring and keeping eggs, I roasted them on some embers, found them truly delicious, and soon satisfied my hunger. While I was eating them, the bird returned, but no male was to be seen.

At the approach of spring I have seen their throats and also the feathers of the head swell, while they emit their rough, croaking, frequent notes. The males become very pugnacious, but when the love season is over they proceed northward together, arriving at least a fortnight ahead of the females. They usually spend the autumn and the earlier parts of winter separated from the females. Like the Goosanders, they shake their heads violently on emerging from the water. Their flesh is fishy and, in my opinion, unfit to eat except in case of excessive hunger. On salt water they feed mostly on bivalves and fishes of different kinds. While on fresh water their food consists of various fishes, mollusca, young frogs, tadpoles, cray-fish, and, I believe, some kinds of grasses.

In the extent of its migrations, it at least equals any of the Ducks. It braves the blasts of the North, visiting the highest latitudes in spring and returning southward over the whole country at the approach of winter, as if seeming not to care where it spends its time, provided it finds an abundance of water. Propelling itself gaily, it searches the pebbly or rocky bottom of the Ohio, or dives deep in the broad bays of Massachusetts or the Cheasapeake. Presently, it emerges with a cray-fish or a mussel held firmly in its bill. It shakes its head, while over its flattened back roll large pearly drops of water which cannot penetrate the compact, oily plumage. The bird glances around, swallows the food, and suddenly plunges headlong. Happy being! It is equally fitted for travelling through the air and water as well as for the pleasure of walking on the shore. Its cunning preserves it from many of man's attempts to destroy it. It is instinctively sagacious enough to place its eggs deep in the hollow of a tree, secure from the nocturnal prowler. Under the down of its snowy breast, the eggs are fostered until the expected young come forth. Then, with its own bill, the bird carries its brood to the lake, where, under its tender care, they grow apace. Rapid though the flight of winged marauders may be, they cannot injure the Ducks there; for while the young ones sink into the deep water, the mother bird arises on whistling wings and speeds away, swifter than the Jer Falcon.

EIDER

THIS history of that remarkable Duck, the Eider, must ever be looked upon with great interest by the student of Nature. The singular shape of its bill, the flatness of its body, its beautiful plumage, its valuable down, and the nature of its haunts, render it a remarkable species. I shall try to give you as full an account of it as I have been able to prepare from my own observations.

The comparatively short neck of the Eider, the great expansion of its feet, its flat body, and its exceptional diving power in its search for shell-food set it apart from the other true Ducks. Moreover, its flight is nearer the surface of the water. Rarely does it fly at any considerable height over lakes and streams, or far inland unless driven by storms. Unlike some Ducks, the Eiders like to breed in communities, and often close by one another. They are in general more ready than some to abandon their females the moment incubation has commenced, leaving them with a double responsibility which the females nevertheless meet with a courage equal to the occasion.

Late in October, 1832, the Eiders appeared in considerable numbers in the bay of Boston. A fisherman-gunner in my employ brought me a large bagful. He was formerly a brave tar, but by then advanced in years. I feel some pride in telling you that I assisted him in obtaining a small pension from our Government, an undertaking also supported by two of my Boston friends, the generous Dr. George Parkman and that great statesman, John Quincy Adams. The old man had once served under my father, who had been a French Navy officer. To receive a bagful of Eider Ducks from him was a gratification not easy to describe. Well, there were the Ducks, all turned out on the floor. The young males still resembled their mother; others were a bit more advanced; several males and females were complete in all their parts, except that the bills of the males had lost the orange tint to be seen during the breeding season.

The gunner told me that he and his fellow hunters take this species by anchoring their small vessel about fifty yards from the rocky isles where these birds harbor and feed at this season. There they now and then downed two at a shot as the Ducks passed on the wing, usually in long lines. Sometimes they took the King Eider the same way; the two species are wont to associate during winter. The Eiders were selling at from fifty to seventy-five cents the pair in Boston, being much sought after by epicures.

My Labrador Expedition landed on June 18, 1833. We saw a great number of "Sea Ducks," as the gunners and fishermen of that coast (as well as on our own) call the Eiders. During a visit to an island in Partridge Bay, we took several females which had paid little attention to us, some allowing us to come within a few feet before they left their nests. The nests were so numerous that we could have collected a small boat-load. They were all placed in short grass that grew in rows in the fissures of the rock. There were generally five or six eggs—in several instances eight, and in one ten.* Not a male bird was to be seen. At the first gun report, all the sitting birds flew off and alighted in the sea about a hundred yards off. Then they crowded together, splashed up the water, and washed themselves until our boat left the place. Many of the nests had no down. Some had more than others. Some were quite covered with it, so that the eggs felt warm to the touch. The mosquitoes and flies were as abundant as they are in the Florida swamps.

On June 24, two male Eiders, much in moult, were shot out of a flock made up of males only.

On July 7, we saw two females with their young on the water while we were rambling over the moss-covered shores of a small pond. When they saw us they lowered their heads and swam off with that part of them lying flat on the water. Their young followed so closely as almost to touch them. We fired without shot in our guns, whereupon they all dived at once, but rose again in a moment, the mothers quacking and murmuring. The young dived again, and we saw no more of them. The old birds took to wing, and, flying over the hills, made for the sea a mile distant. How their young were to reach them there was, at that time, a riddle to me, but I learned the sequel afterwards, as you shall see.

On July 9, while I was taking an evening walk, I saw flocks of female Eiders without broods. They were deep in moult, kept close to the shore

* Normal: five.

.69.

in a bay, and were probably sterile birds. On my way back to our schooner, the *Ripley,* our Captain and I started a female from a broad flat rock more than a hundred yards from the water. We went to her nest on the rock's bare surface which had not a blade of grass within five yards of it. It was of the usual bulky construction, with five eggs buried deep in down. The female flew round us until we withdrew, after which we had the pleasure of seeing her alight, walk to her nest, and settle upon it.

Large flocks of males kept apart. They frequented the distant sea islands, although during this moulting season they had to swim from one island to another, unable to fly any distance. But before they began moulting—fully a month earlier—we saw them flying from place to place in long lines around the outermost islands every morning and evening. In that way they protected themselves from their enemies. They roosted in numbers close together for the night on some rock inaccessible to boats.

By August 1, there was scarcely an Eider Duck to be seen on the coast of Labrador. The young were by then able to fly. The old birds had nearly completed their moult. All were moving southward.

None are seen on the coasts of Newfoundland and Labrador in winter. Their appearance in long files about May 1 hails the approach of the summer season. They seem to search the main shores and inner bays for the places where they nested or were hatched. All of them appear to be paired, and they are in perfect plumage. After a few days of rest on the shores facing south, most of them move on to the islands. The rest of them nest along the craggy shores or on the edge of fir woods not far from the water. (A few venture about a mile into the interior.) They begin to build their nests about the end of May. As many as eight nests may be found beneath a single bush; others are to be seen on crags above the high-water mark. The nest is sunk as deeply as possible in the ground. It is formed of seaweed, mosses, and dried twigs, so matted and interlaced as to look neat to the very center of the cavity, which rarely exceeds seven inches in diameter. The eggs are laid early in June, the male attending on the female the whole time. There are usually from five to seven, three inches in length and two inches and one-eighth in breadth—much larger than domestic Duck eggs.* The form is a regular

* See preceding note.

oval, smooth shelled, pale olive-green colored. They afford delicious eating. If the eggs are not removed or destroyed, the female lays but one set to the season. As soon as she begins to sit, the male leaves her. After she has laid all her eggs, she begins to pluck down from the lower parts of her body every day for some time, until the roots of the feathers are not only quite bare as far as she can reach, but as clean as wood from which undergrowth has been cleared away. She puts the down beneath and around the eggs, and when she leaves the nest to go in search of food she places the down over the eggs to keep them warm, and presumably to insure their safety. But the Black-Backed Gull may remove the covering and suck or destroy them.

The newly hatched young are at once led to the water, even when it is a mile distant and the travelling difficult both for parent and brood. Should the nest happen to be among rocks over the water, the Eider, like the Wood Duck, carries the young in her bill to their favorite element, the water. Her care of her young for two or three weeks could not be exceeded. She leads them gently in a close flock in shallow waters where they dive to find food. If they weary when they are some distance from shore, she will sink her body in the water and take them on her back for several minutes. Should the Black-Backed Gull approach, she beats the water with her wings as if to raise the spray around her, while the peculiar sound that she utters causes the young to dive to safety in all directions. She may try to entice the Gull away from them by feigning lameness, or she may leap out of the water and attack her enemy so vigorously that, exhausted and disappointed, he is glad to fly off. After he departs she alights near the rocks where she expects to find her brood, and she calls them to her side. Now and then I saw two females which had formed an attachment to each other, as if for the purpose of more effectively protecting their young. I very seldom saw these prudent mothers bothered by the Gull.

At the age of one week the young were a dark mouse color, very downy. Their feet were very large and strong. By July 20 all seem to be hatched. They grew rapidly, and after a fortnight were taken only with great difficulty, unless stormy weather drove them to accessible rock shelves at the head of shallow bays.

It is by no means difficult to rear them, provided proper care be taken of them. They become quite gentle, and attached to the place set apart for them. A fisherman of Eastport, who carried eight or ten of them from Labrador, kept them several years in a yard close to the bay, where they betook themselves regularly after they were grown, along with some common Ducks, regularly returning towards evening. They were kept until the male birds acquired their perfect plumage and mated. But some gunners who mistook them for wild birds (although none could fly as a result of having been pinioned) shot most of them one winter day.

Should the female be deprived of her eggs, she immediately goes off in search of a mate. She may be seen returning to her nest with a drake the same day. The two swim, fly, and walk side by side, and by the end of ten or twelve days the male takes his leave to rejoin his companions at sea. The female is by then sitting on a new set of eggs. But this happens only early in the season; I observed that as soon as the male began to moult, the female did not seek a mate after her nest was plundered, but instead abandoned the place. A remarkable fact is that the female Eiders with broods moult fully three weeks later than the males, whereas the females which do not breed begin to moult as early as the males.

It seemed very wonderful that in the long lines in which we saw them travelling in Labrador we did not once see a young bird among them, or one not in its mature plumage. The young males, if they breed before acquiring their full coloring, either remain by themselves at this period, it seems, or with the barren females which, as I have said, separate from those that are breeding. I am inclined to think that the old males begin their southward migration before the young or the females, as none were to be seen for about two weeks before the latter started. In winter, in the States, the males and females intermingle. At the approach of spring, the mated pairs travel in great flocks, when you can distinctly see in the orderly lines individuals of both sexes, alternately.

The flight of the Eider is firm, strong, and generally steady. Constant beats of the wings propel these birds, whose lines undulate according to the inequality of the surface produced by the waves over which they pass at a height of a few yards, rarely more than a mile from shore. Their velocity is about eighty miles an hour. They fly much higher above their breeding grounds and also when not travelling a long distance, apparently to avoid their enemy, man. They dive with much agility, and can remain under water for a considerable time, often going down to a depth of eight or ten fathoms or more in search of food, especially shell-fish.

RED-HEAD

THE fine pair of Red-Headed Ducks from which I made the two figures which appear in *The Birds of America* were given me by my friend Daniel Webster of Boston, Massachusetts, whose talents and accomplishments are too well known to require any eulogium from me.

The Honorable Daniel Webster also sent me a fine pair of Pied Ducks killed by himself on the Vineyard Islands, on the coast of Massachusetts, from which I made the drawing for their picture in the *Birds*. The female had not, I believe, been hitherto figured; the one represented was not an old bird.

MALLARD

LOOK at the Mallard as he floats on the lake—see his elevated head glittering with emerald green, his amber eyes gleaming in the light! Even as he marks your approach at a distance and suspects you bear him no good will—for he sees your gun—the wary bird draws his feet under him, opens his wings, and with loud quacks bids you farewell. Now there comes another on the edge of that purling streamlet. How brisk are his motions when compared with those of his domestic brethren that waddle across your poultry yard! How much more graceful is his form, how neat his apparel! The Duck at home is the descendant of a race of slaves, and has lost his spirit. His wings have been so little used that they can hardly raise him from the ground. But the free-born, the untamed Duck of the swamps—see how he springs on the wing and hies himself over the woods.

Some flocks of Mallards, as they arrive in migration from mid-September to early October when the mast is ripe, appear to be guided by an experienced leader as they alight directly on a pond of seed-bearing grasses. The rustling of their wings can only be compared with the noise made by an Eagle swooping on its prey. Other flocks sweep around and above the water several times in perfect silence before they alight, as if uneasy about the safety of the place. But in either case the birds immediately bathe, beat their bodies with their wings, dive in short plunges, and cut so many capers that you might imagine them stark mad. The fact is that all this gaiety is only due to the need they feel of ridding themselves of the insects in their plumage, as well as to their pleasure on reaching a milder climate where food is abundant, after a hard journey of perhaps a day and a night. After washing and preening themselves they are ready for their meal; in this, other travellers would do well to imitate them.

Woe be to the slug or snail that comes their way, as the Ducks advance in straggling parties towards the grassy shores. Some probe the mud for leeches, frogs, or lizards; others fill their crops with beechnuts and acorns, or perhaps wood mice, in the woods. Their cackling would deafen you, but all at once they are silent, their heads erect, their necks outstretched, as they listen. Perhaps the sound is only the bear ploughing up the newly fallen leaves with his muzzle in the search of the mast of which he too is fond, or removing an old rotting log in search of worms.

The Ducks resume their foraging. But now another, more alarming sound is heard. The bear rises on his hind legs, snuffs the air, and with a loud snort he gallops off towards his canebrake. The Ducks retreat to the water, uttering half-stifled notes as they look for the approach of the dreaded enemy as he cunningly advances from behind one tree and then another. He has lost his chance at the bear, but, as he is pushed by hunger, a Mallard will do for the bullet in his trusty rifle. He is an Indian. His flowing black hair has been cut close from the sides of his head, which has a hole cut for it to enter the dearly purchased blanket that serves as a garment—now ragged as horse netting as it flaps to drive off the mosquitoes that suck his life's blood. He takes aim, a curl of smoke rises, and the Ducks all scatter except for a pair hit by the prowler. The Indian judges the depth of the mire, boldly advances into the water, and draws the game to him with a stick. Back in the woods he kindles a fire, and pretty soon feathers fill the air. He takes a quill to clean the touch-hole of his gun in the damp weather, and saves the entrails to bait some trap. Soon after the Indian has swallowed the savory morsels he will be off in pursuit of other game.

The Mallards that remain with us all the year begin to pair in the very heart of winter. The males, like other gay deceivers, offer their regards to the first fair one that attracts their notice, and repeat their offers to the next they meet. The drake proudly shows, first the beauty of his silky head, then the brilliance of his wing-spots. Finally, with honeyed jabberings, he discloses the warmth of his affection. He plays around this one, then around another, until the passion of jealousy is aroused in the breasts of the females. Bickerings arise. The younger duck disdains her elder sister. A third, who conceives herself a great coquette, interposes to invite the caresses of the feathered beau. But ere long the females retire to lay their eggs in a safe place, drawing weeds around them to form a haphazard sort of nest. Around the light green, smooth-shelled eggs—seven to ten* of them—the Ducks place the soft down of their own breasts. Only when food and sustenance compel them to do so do they leave the eggs during the long process of incubation.

In about three weeks the young begin to cheep in the shell, then emerge after a violent struggle. What beautiful creatures! They begin to dry their downy apparel with their little bills. One after another in a long line they follow their mother to the water, and at once take to swimming and diving as if elated to be born. The wearied and emaciated male is far away on some other pond, without a thought to his progeny or the lonely condition of his mate or to her care and anxiety in protecting her flock from danger. She leads them about, teaches them to seize small insects. She warns them to dive from threats on land and to beware of the ravenous fishes and turtles in the water. By the time the leaves have changed their hue, the young Mallards can fly. The old males join the gathering flocks.

I have found the Mallard breeding on large fallen and rotten logs, three feet above the ground, in the center of a canebrake nearly a mile from any water. Once I found a female leading her young through the woods, no doubt conducting them towards the Ohio. When she saw me she squatted flat among the grasses with her brood around her. As I drew nearer she ruffled her feathers and hissed at me like a Goose, while her little ones scampered off in all directions. I had an excellent dog, well trained to catch young birds without injuring them. I ordered him to look for them. At this the mother took wing and flew through the woods as if about to fall down at every yard or so. She passed over the dog again and again, uneasily watching his search. One after another he brought the ducklings back to me. They struggled in my bird-bag. The

* Normal: ten.

distressed parent came to the ground near me, rolled and tumbled about, and so affected me by her despair that I ordered my dog to lie down. Then, with a pleasure that can be felt only by those who are parents themselves, I restored her innocent brood to her and walked off. As I turned round to see her, I really thought I could perceive gratitude in her eye. A happier moment I never felt while rambling through the woods in search of knowledge.

Except where they are likely to be disturbed by gunners, the Mallards feed both by day and night. So numerous were the Mallards while I was at General Hernandez's in East Florida that a single Negro hunter would shoot from fifty to a hundred and twenty in a day, supplying the whole plantation with excellent food.

Its flight is swift, strong, and well sustained. It will rise almost perpendicularly for ten or fifteen yards as it leaves the water at a single spring. Or in a dense wood it will rise above the tallest trees and then move horizontally, quacking only if alarmed on departure. The whistling of the Mallards' wings may be heard a great way off when they are travelling some distance, especially in the quiet of night. I have thought their velocity perhaps a mile and a half a minute; I am confident that they can fly a hundred and twenty miles an hour at full speed on a long journey.

The Mallard is truly omnivorous, eating everything that can possibly satisfy the cravings of its extraordinary appetite. So very greedy is this bird that I have observed a couple of them tugging against each other for the skin of an eel which one had already half swallowed. They are expert flycatchers. To force the worms out of their burrows, they pat the damp ground with their feet.

Besides man, the enemies of the Mallard are the White-Headed Eagle, the Snowy Owl, the Virginia Owl, the raccoon, the lynx, and the snapping turtle.

WOOD DUCK

I HAVE always experienced a peculiar pleasure while studying the habits of that most beautiful bird, the Wood Duck. I have sat beside a gigantic sycamore, on the watch for it. A dark bayou wound tortuously beneath the maples that bordered its muddy shores. A deep thicket of sugar-cane spread along its side. The hum of myriad insects scarcely disturbed the mysterious silence. While the mosquito alighted on my hand I allowed him to draw his fill, that I might observe how dextrously he pierced my skin with his delicate proboscis and pumped the red fluid into his body, before extending his tiny wings and flying off. I watched the ticks scramble over the withered leaves to elude the searching eye of the beautiful lizard. A squirrel eyed me, its body spread flat against a tree trunk. The Warblers, too, peeped from among the twigs. On the water the large bull-frogs were looking for the sun. Suddenly an otter emerged with a fish in its jaws, and I speedily recalled my dog, which plunged after it. At that moment the rustling of wings swept through the woods, and a flock of Wood Ducks overhead filled my heart with delight. Once, twice, three times they swept rapidly over the stream without detecting danger, then alighted while sounding a reassuring note to those still distant.

This beautiful species confines itself entirely to the fresh water of secluded retreats that occur in our woods. Well acquainted with man, it carefully avoids him, except during the breeding season when, if it finds a convenient place to deposit its eggs and raise its young, it will now and then even locate itself near a miller's dam.

Its speed and the ease and elegance with which its flight is performed are remarkable. The Wood Duck passes through the woods and branches of the trees as easily as the Passenger Pigeon. At the approach of night, it shoots over the trees like a meteor, with almost noiseless wings, headed in small flocks for its breeding grounds. I have taken perhaps undue advantage of the movements of these birds to shoot them on the wing by placing myself between their lake haunts and their place of breeding, and keeping myself concealed, thus obtaining a number at twilight.

I never knew one of these birds to nest on the ground or on a tree branch. They prefer the hollow, broken part of some large branch, the hole of our large Woodpecker, or the deserted retreat of the fox squirrel. I have been surprised to see them going in and out of a hole of one of these other creatures, when their bodies on the wing appeared to be nearly half again as large as the opening within which they laid their eggs. Only once did I find a nest (with ten eggs in it) in a fissure of rock on the Kentucky River a few miles below Frankfort. Their holes are usually over deep swamps, or above canebrakes, or on broken sycamore branches, and seldom more than forty or fifty feet from the water.

The smooth, nearly elliptical, greenish buff eggs—from six to fifteen—according to the age of the bird—are placed on dry plants, feathers, and a bit of down, presumably from the breast of the female.* They are two inches long and an inch and a half in diameter.

Like certain others of the species I have described, the female Duck is abandoned by her mate when incubation begins. Not until the young are able to fly do old and young of both sexes come together, and so remain until the next breeding time begins. I have been surprised to find the feathers of other birds (including even the domestic fowl) in the nests, and particularly those of the Wild Goose and Wild Turkey. When the nest is on the broken branch of a tree, it is easy to see it from the ground, owing to the feathers, sticks and grasses around it. But in a hole the eggs are deep down and quite out of sight, and, as usual, covered with down while the female is off the nest and feeding in the vicinity. If the nest is above water, the young scramble to the mouth of the hole the moment they are hatched, launch into the air with their little wings and feet spread out, and drop into their favorite element. If they are hatched at a distance from water, their mother carries them to it, one by one, in her bill, holding them so as not to injure their tender bodies. However, I have noticed several times that when the hole was thirty, forty, or more yards from a bayou or other water, the mother let the young fall on the grasses and dried leaves beneath the tree, afterwards leading them directly to the nearest pool or creek. The newly hatched birds answer their parent's call with a mellow, often and rapidly repeated, *pee, pee, pee.* The mother's low, soft, prolonged call resembles *pe-ēe, pe-ēe.* The watch note of the male resembles *hoe-ēek,* uttered when an enemy alarms him, or when he calls to passing Wood Ducks.

Like the others, the young of this Duck are taught to obtain their food along the shallow, grassy shores, beginning with small aquatic flies, mosquitoes, other insects, and seeds. They dive expertly below the surface when frightened, make for the shore and run for the woods when but a few weeks old. I have used two methods of taking both the old and the young alive—a bag net such as is employed in catching our little Partridge, placed half sunk in the water, and another way I accidentally

* Normal: twelve.

discovered. I was on a shooting excursion one day with an excellent pointer dog. The sight of this faithful animal always immediately frightened the young Ducks to the shore. As they disappeared, the old one, conceiving her brood to be safe, took to wing. The next instant my dog Juno dashed across the bayou or pond to the opposite bank and at once began tracking the Ducklings. In a few moments she returned with one held between her lips, and I took it from her unhurt.

While I was living in Henderson, I thought of taming a number of Wood Ducks. Juno caught as many for me, in the way described above, as I wanted. I took them home in a bag. I placed a dozen or more in empty flour barrels, which I covered over for several hours with a view to thus taming them sooner. I had several of these barrels placed in the yard. Whenever I raised the lids, I found all the little ones hooked by their sharp claws to the very edge of their prisons. The instant I allowed them more room they tumbled over and ran about in all directions. After I put them inside the barrels again, I noticed that they would rise from the bottom to the brim of the cask by moving a few inches at a time up the side, then fix one foot at a time with their tiny hooked claws which had points like a needle. They fed on cornmeal soaked in water and learned, as they grew, to catch flies expertly. When they were half grown I fed them also on the common locust yet unable to fly, gathered by boys from the trunks of trees and "iron weeds" which is a kind of hemp. These I would throw on the water of the artificial pond in my garden. They would scramble and fight for them so eagerly that they always afforded me great amusement. They grew apace. I pinioned them all. Later they bred in boxes which I had placed conveniently over the water, and which had a board or sticks leading to them. I provided an abundant supply of materials for nesting.

During the love season, the great beauty and neatness of the Wood Duck's apparel, and the grace of its motions, afford much pleasure to the observer. I am able to present a full account of their habits at that period. When March returns, and the dogwood expands its pure blossoms to the sun, and the Cranes soar away on their broad wings, bidding us adieu for a season, flocks of water fowl begin their early migrations. The frogs issue from muddy beds to pipe a few notes of languid joy. The Swallow has just arrived, and the Bluebird has returned to his box. The Wood Duck has the pool almost to himself, enabling us to study the ways of his tribe.

The beautiful males chase their rivals. The females coquette with their beaux. A fine drake raises his head and curves his neck gracefully. As he bows before the object of his love he raises his silken crest for a moment. His throat swells as he utters a guttural sound which, to his beloved, is as sweet as the song of the Wood Thrush to his gentle mate. As if unwilling to manifest the desire to please him, which she really feels, the female swims close by his side, now and then caressing him by touching his feathers with her bill. Towards any of her sex that may come near, she shows displeasure. Soon the happy pair separate from the others, repeat their caresses every now and then, and finally, having sealed the conjugal compact, fly off to the woods to search for a large Woodpecker's hole.

Occasionally the males fight with each other at this season, but their combats do not last long, nor is the field ever stained with their blood. The loss of a few feathers or a sharp tug at the rival's head is enough, generally, to decide the contest.

Although the Wood Ducks always form their nests in the hollow of a tree, their caresses are performed exclusively on the water, to which they resort for the purpose, even when their love has been demonstrated beforehand on a branch far above the ground. While the female deposits her eggs, the male flies swiftly past the hole where she is hiding, erects his crest and sends forth his love notes, to which she keeps responding.

On the ground this Duck runs nimbly and with more grace than most other birds of its tribe. On reaching the shore, it at once shakes its tail sidewise, looks around, and begins to search for food. I conceive the sight of thirty or forty of these birds perched on a single sycamore on the bank of a secluded bayou as pleasing a sight as any I have ever enjoyed. There they move with the same apparent ease. They always remind me of the Muscovy Duck, of which they look like a highly finished and flattering miniature. I have seen a whole flock walk out of the water along an inclining log or fallen tree before flying off at the sight of an approaching steamer on the Ohio or Mississippi. When frightened by the appearance of a man on shore, they rise from the water by a single spring, either following the stream or making for the woods. If wounded and closely pursued, they may submerge all but their bill, or run and hide in a canebrake beside a log. When they discover an enemy while they are under the shelter of shrubs or plants, they swim off in silence among the thickest weeds instead of taking to wing. Then they run over a narrow piece of ground to another pond in order to elude the search. I have seen a whole covey standing or sitting on a floating log, pluming and cleaning themselves for hours, a perfect target for the sportsman.

Their food consists of acorns, beech-nuts, grapes, and berries of various sorts, for which they half-dive like the Mallard. Or they search under trees on shore and in the woods, turning over the leaves with dexterity. They also devour insects, snails, tadpoles, and small water lizards, swallowing some sand or gravel at the same time to aid the trituration of their food.

I feel assured that the Wood Duck might be perfectly domesticated, and become as valuable as it is beautiful.

Its sense of hearing is exceedingly acute. It often protects it from the mink, pole-cat and raccoon, not to mention the vile snake—its most pernicious enemy—that creeps into the nest and destroys the eggs. The young have to guard against the snapping turtle, the garfish, and the eel, as well as the lashing tail and tremendous jaws of the alligator.

I have seen hundreds in a single flock, and known fifteen to be killed by a single shot. Ordinarily, unless their eggs are destroyed, they raise only one brood in the season. I find in a journal I wrote in Henderson nearly twenty years ago [c. 1815], that the attachment of a male to a female lasts during only one breeding season, and that the males take a succession of mates. The strongest has first choice, and the weakest contents himself with what remains. The only other habits which I have to mention are: that it dives at once into its hole without first alighting on the tree; that I have never witnessed it taking possession of a Wood-pecker's hole by force; and lastly, that during winter it allows other species of Ducks to associate with its flocks.

My friend Dr. John Bachman of Charleston, South Carolina, has kept a male for several years which after moulting takes on a plain color for six weeks, like that of the young males. Gradually its feathers reassume their bright tints.

GREEN-WINGED TEAL

THE name of Green-Winged Teal is a poor one, in my opinion, for the bird has wings no greener than those of several other species. Indeed, very many birds are strangely named, not less in *pure* Latin than in

English, French and Dutch. Many are receiving, every year, names still stranger than those which they previously bore. For my part I am at present a kind of conservative; I adhere to the old system until I see the "mud" subside that was raised by the "waders." Then I may probe my way with more chance of success.

The Green-Winged Teal is a fresh-water bird, rarely met with in sea bays, creeks, or lagoons where, however, it sometimes spends a few days. Like the Mallard and several other species, it is able to feed with its body half immersed, and has therefore a comparatively long neck. It feeds on grasses, small acorns, fallen grapes or berries, and on aquatic insects, worms and small snails, a more select diet than that of most other Ducks, with the result that its flesh is delicious. I would readily agree with any epicure that after the Teal has fed on wild oats or soaked rice for a few weeks, its flesh is much superior to the Canvas-Back in tenderness, juiciness and flavor. Indeed it is as much superior as the European Quail is to the Capercailzie, or the Sora of the Delaware to the Scolopaceous Courlan of the Florida Everglades.

I have often thought that water birds—Ducks, for example—like land birds, which migrate in flocks, are apt to pass over places where their kind has been before. Pigeons, Starlings, Robins, and other land birds have been observed to do so. Curlews, Cormorants, Plovers, Ducks and Geese are similar in this respect. Their first object, as everyone knows, is to remove from one part of the country to another where there is safety and an abundance of food. I conclude that birds are inclined to return to districts where they have spent a season. The Green-Winged Teals follow each other in flocks either of a few families or of many hundreds of individuals, particularly in autumn, to avoid the rigors of winter. In spring again, many land and water birds migrate either singly or in groups, the males departing before the females and in some cases the young keeping to themselves. This plan is perhaps intended for the greater dispersal of the species.

On land, the Green-Wing moves with more ease and grace than any other species I know, except our beautiful Wood Duck. It can run at a good rate, without entangling its webbed feet as many others do. In this respect, too, there is a marked difference between fresh-water and salt-water Ducks. On the water the Green-Wing moves with ease and at times with much rapidity, and is a good diver. On the wing it has no rival among Ducks. Our two smaller Mergansers are swifter, but exhibit none of the graceful movements of the Green-Wing around fresh water. They rise from the water in a single spring, and so swiftly that none but an expert marksman need attempt to shoot them at a distance of many yards. They feed close together along shores and shallows, often moving from one pool to another on foot unless the distance is considerable. After feeding they retire to a clean part of the shore, or to a sandbar, and rest in perfect harmony, composing their plumage, letting their wings droop slightly, and sunning their breasts for an hour or more, with a sentinel to watch over the safety of those which doze or sleep soundly. In this way they spend the winter months in a mild climate where the vicinity is not too populated by humans, and where there are damp fields, meadows and savannahs.

Their migrations occur more over the land than along the borders of the sea. I have seldom seen this bird associate with other species, although I have often seen Green-Winged Teals on a pond or river not far from other Ducks. It is more shy than the Blue-Winged Teal, but less so than most fresh-water Ducks. Its voice is seldom heard during winter except when one flock is passing over another that has alighted; then a few males call to the voyagers as if to invite them to join them. Before they depart, however, they become noisy. Combats take place among the males while the females coquette around them. Most of the birds are paired before they leave us.

In each of the three instances when I have found the nest of this Teal, it was no nearer the water than five or six yards. I should not have discovered the nest had I not first seen the birds swimming or washing themselves near the spot. But I watched them land and go up their path in a direct line among the rushes. On two occasions I came so near the nest that I almost touched the sitting bird as it rose in fright. While it flew around me, then alighted on the water, I viewed the nest. It consisted of a bed of the bird's own down and feathers, with grasses beneath it intermingled with mud and the stalks of plants, all raised to a height of four or five inches. I found seven, much rounded, dull yellowish eggs in one nest, nine in another, and only five in a third.* The average size was one and three-quarters inches by one inch and three-eighths. The eggs were fresh in only one of the nests. I took two and afterwards ate

* Normal: eleven.

them. I marked one nest's location with a stick, visited it three days in succession, but found that the bird had abandoned it. The other two nests were only about a hundred yards apart; I had handled the eggs in them quite as much, but I had not taken any away, with the result that the females were still sitting. I concluded that although the eggs may be touched or even handled and lifted from the nest, the bird did not take umbrage provided none was taken. But should she miss any, some strong feeling urged her to abandon the rest. I thought further that as incubation had just begun with this particular bird, she cared less about her eggs than the other two whose eggs contained chicks.

Having met with the young Green-Winged Teal only once, and at a time when I was less aware of the necessity of noting observations in writing, I am unwilling to speak of their colors from recollection. All I can say is that I had great trouble in catching four of them, so cunningly did they hide in the grass, and so expert were they at diving.

BLUE-WINGED TEAL

Is it not strange that birds which have been seen as far north as the Fifty-seventh Parallel during the breeding season should also be found breeding at nearly the same period in Texas? It is still stranger that some species should proceed from their winter quarters to those far northern regions without paying any heed to the districts that lie between, which seem as well adapted for breeding because of their convenient, secluded localities. These facts, and many others connected with Nature's wonderful arrangements, increase the Nature lover's desire to study her beautiful and marvelous works.

The habits of the Blue-Winged Teal and certain other birds which I have observed induce me to believe in the existence of what I would term a *double sense of migration* in many species. It is acted upon in spring and in autumn. In the latter period it gives them the power and the desire to move from the higher latitudes to opposite or meridional points. Thus they would seem to enter into the formation of the fauna of different countries, from which they again return to their native haunts. In such a way they appear to diverge towards new sections of the globe equally adapted to their wants. If these observations should prove not unfounded, we need no longer be surprised to find, in various parts of the world, species which were hitherto supposed to inhabit only far distant shores.

In New Orleans, and during spring, this bird, the Blue-Winged Teal, is in full plumage. The Creoles of Louisiana call it "Sarcelle Printempsière" at that season. In autumn, when scarcely one of these Teals retains the beauty of its spring plumage, they call it "Sarcelle Automnière." This double name leads many people to imagine that there are two Blue-Winged Teals.

These are the first Ducks to arrive in that region, where they frequently appear at the beginning of September in large flocks. They are then exceedingly fat. Unlike the Green-Wing which braves the coldest weather there, they depart when the cold is so intense as to form ice. But by late February they are as abundant there as ever, though very lean, and the male plumage is very beautiful again. They remain as late as mid-May.

Their flight is extremely rapid and well sustained, possibly equal to that of the Passenger Pigeon. The blue of their wings glistens like polished steel in clear sunny weather. As they wheel over the place where they intend to alight, their wings are alternately in bright light and shade, so that the glow and varied lustre, even at a distance, draw the eye to them. As they advance against a stiff breeze, they show their upper and lower surfaces by turns. The vivid blue of their mantle resembles the dancing light of a piece of glass suddenly reflected on a distant object. All the while they emit their soft lisping note, which is also heard after they alight and when they are under apprehension of danger. I have seen them passing over the sea at quite a distance from land, but never travelling in company with other Ducks. Like others of the species, they pass and repass a place before alighting, lest there be danger. They swim buoyantly, often close together, sometimes touching each other.

The Blue-Winged Teal is easily kept in captivity, and soon becomes very docile. It feeds on coarse cornmeal in this state. I have no doubt that it could be easily domesticated.

The old males lose the spring plumage of the head almost entirely during much of the autumn and winter, but it sometimes begins to re-appear as early as the beginning of January. The young of both sexes in their first plumage resemble the females, but the males acquire their full beauty before they are one year old.

Osprey, or Fish-Hawk

THE habits of this famed and formidable bird differ so much from those of almost all other Hawks that an accurate description of it cannot fail to interest the student of Nature.

With the exception of the Swallow-Tailed Hawk, I know of none more social and gregarious. It migrates in numbers, both in spring and fall. Eight or ten follow the windings of our shores in loose flocks, as they flap and sail along, or cross one another in their gyrations. They nest, rear their young, and seek their food quite close together. Not only do these Fish-Hawks of mild disposition live in perfect harmony together; they even allow other birds of a very different character to build nests of material like their own, a circumstance which brings them close together. I have never seen an Osprey chase any other bird. So pacific and timorous is it that rather than encounter a foe only a little more powerful than itself, it will abandon its prey to it. The Bald Eagle is its greatest enemy, next to man. It never forces its young from the nest, as some other Hawks do, but, on the contrary, it feeds them even after they have begun to help feed themselves.

Notwithstanding all this, a false idea prevails among fishermen and coastal farmers that the Osprey's nest is the best scarecrow possible. It is true that no other Hawk will prey on their poultry while there is an Osprey about. But this circumstance arises simply from the fact that at the time when the Osprey arrives, myriads of water fowl normally leave the shores and salt marshes, just as they resort to our estuaries when winter approaches.

The Osprey also differs importantly from all other birds of prey in that it never attempts to take its prey in the air, although its rapid flight suggests that it could. I have spent weeks on the Gulf of Mexico where these birds abound, and have seen them sailing and plunging into the water. Shoals of flying-fishes were leaping from the sea to evade the pursuing dolphins. Yet the Osprey never attempted to pursue them while they were above the surface. It would, however, plunge after one, or after a bonita fish, after they went below the surface.

The bird's flight is as graceful and majestic as the Eagle's. By merely inclining its wings and tail it circles widely to an immense height; dives at times with partly closed wings and tail; then resumes its sailing as if the plunges were for amusement only. Its wings are extended at right angles to the body; this makes it easy to distinguish from other Hawks. If on the lookout for food, it flaps easily above the water at no great height, with an apparent listlessness; but in reality it is keenly observing all below. It will spy a fish, check its flight with a sudden shake of its wings and tail, poise a moment, and plunge headlong. If it fails to catch the fish, it continues its flight. It may disappear beneath the water for an instant when it dives, and cause a surge and mass of foam on the surface of the sea. If it emerges with a fish, it mounts a few yards in the air, shakes the water from its plumage, squeezes the fish with its talons, and flies with it to the nest to feed its young or to a tree to feast in peace. It does not, like other Hawks, remain on its perch until hunger again urges it forth, but usually sails and circles at a great height over the neighboring waters.

The Osprey is much attached to the tree to which it carries its prey, and it will not abandon it unless often disturbed there. It shows the same attachment for the tree where it nests, and returns to it year after year.

This bird arrives on our southern coasts early in February, and travels eastward as the spring season advances. Fishermen of the Middle districts hail its appearance with joy, because it is the harbinger of various kinds of fish on the Atlantic coast and in numerous rivers. About the first week of April or thereabouts it arrives there, to remain until the earliest frost in autumn. I have sometimes seen them during the winter in the muddy lakes near New Orleans; but they were emaciated and probably unable to follow their natural inclinations and fly on southward.

The females reach the breeding grounds eight or ten days after the males. The love season then commences. Their courtship differs from that of other Hawks. The males play about in the air among themselves, chase each other in sport, or sail beside or behind the female of their choice—to cries of joy and exultation. They alight on a tree holding last year's nest and doubtless congratulate each other on finding their home again. Caresses are mutual. Together they repair the winter's damage to their home with drifted seaweeds, which they take up from the beach in a mass with their talons. Within two weeks the nest is ready for the female to deposit her three or four yellowish white, densely red-brown spotted eggs.*

The nest is usually built in a tree near the water, but it may also be found in the depths of a wood a mile or more away . . . perhaps, in the latter instance, because frequent disturbance has driven the birds inland. It is sometimes fully four feet across, and composed of sufficient sticks, seaweed, grass tufts and the like to make its depth equal to its diameter. Though the Osprey may place its nest in the forks of an oak or pine with equal pleasure, I have noticed that the tree is likely to be quite large and, often, decayed. I have seen the Fish Crow and the Purple Grackle raise their families in nests which they dared to build among the outer sticks of the nest of the Osprey.

The male assists with incubation. One bird feeds another, but also goes in quest of food for itself at times. The male flies very high above the spot, ascending in a direct line, flapping his wings continually, holding his white breast to the breeze, and now and then cackling. At its utmost elevation—sometimes invisible to the human eye—the Osprey shrieks, and dives smoothly on half-extended wings towards his nest. But before he reaches it, he spreads his wings and tail and glides in a curve towards his beloved female. She partially raises herself from her eggs, emits a low cry, and resumes her former position as her delighted partner flies off to the sea to seek a favorite fish for her.

The parents become more and more attached to their growing young, feeding them abundantly—often after they have left the nest, which apparently the young do with reluctance. I have seen young Ospreys as large as their parents filling the nest; they are easily distinguished through good glasses by the white edge of their upper plumage. So much fish is borne to the nest that some of it falls to the ground and collects there. Only one brood is raised each season.

* Normal: three.

Fish Hawk or Osprey ♂ nat.
Faucon Pecheur de la Caroline Le Buffon
Falco Haliaetus

drawn from Nature by J. J. Audubon

The Osprey seldom alights on the ground; it walks with difficulty and in an extremely awkward manner. The only occasion is the collecting of materials for the nest in spring.

When I first moved to Louisville in Kentucky, in 1808, there were several pairs that nested opposite the Falls of the Ohio on the Indiana banks. The ground belonged to the venerable General Clark [of the Lewis and Clark Expedition]. Several times he invited me to visit the spot. But with the increase of population, these birds are seldom seen nowadays on the Ohio.

I have seen them sailing over the lakes near the Mississippi River in winter, and feeding on fish (killed by the Wood Ibis) which they themselves cannot discover in the muddy waters. The Ibises wade in immense flocks, trample the bottom of the lake and turn it into filthy puddles, in which the fish breathe with difficulty and rise to the surface to be destroyed. There is food not only for the Ibis, but the Vulture, Eagle, and Osprey. But I have not seen the Osprey feed on any other prey but this and what he takes by plunging into the water.

I have heard it said that the Osprey is sometimes drawn under the water and drowned when attempting to seize a fish too strong for it, and that some have been found sticking their talons in the backs of sturgeons and other large fry. I am unable to corroborate these reports. The largest fish which I have seen this bird take out of the water was a weakfish such as I have drawn in my portrait of the Osprey. It weighed about five pounds or more. The bird carried it into the air with difficulty, and dropped it on hearing the report of a shot fired at it.

Sparrow=Hawk

No bird can be more easily raised and kept than this beautiful Hawk. I once found a young male that had dropped from the nest before it was able to fly. Its cries for food attracted my notice, and I discovered it lying near a log. It was large, and covered with soft white down, through which the young feathers protruded. Its little blue bill and its eyes—still gray—made it look not unlike an Owl. I took it home and named it Nero.

I provided the young Hawk with small birds. Though it was not yet able to tear their flesh, it would scramble for them fiercely. In a few weeks it grew very beautiful, but so voracious that I turned it out to see how well it would shift for itself. This experiment gratified both of us. Soon it hunted for grasshoppers and other insects; on my way from my walks in the country I now and then threw a dead bird high in the air as I passed Nero. He never failed to see it from his perch, and he would sometimes launch towards it with such speed as to catch it before it reached the ground.

Before long the little fellow attracted the attention of his brothers, brought up close by. Accompanied by their parents they chased him at first, and forced him to flee behind one of the window shutters where he usually spent the night. But soon they became gentler towards him, as if forgiving his desertion of the nest.

My bird was fastidious in the choice of food. He would not touch a Woodpecker, no matter how fresh; as he grew older he refused all birds with the least taint.

To the last he continued kind to me, and never failed to return at night to his favorite roost behind the shutter. His courage often amused my family . . . he would sail off from his perch, fall on the back of a tame Duck which would set up a loud quacking and waddle off with him sticking to its feathers. But, as is often the case with spirited adventurers, the Hawk's audacity cost him his life. A hen and her brood chanced to attract his attention, and he flew to seize one of the chickens. The hen's maternal affection inspired in her a courage greater than Nero's, and the severe conflict which took place ended his adventures.

We have few more beautiful Hawks in the United States than this active little species which is found in many places—fields, orchards, barnyards, and kitchen gardens, but seldom deep in the forest. As it commits no depredations on poultry in its wild state, few men disturb it.

You will see it standing, beautifully erect, on the highest fence post, or on the broken top of a tree, or on a grain stack or barn corner, patiently and silently awaiting the appearance of a mole, a field mouse, a cricket, a grasshopper, or the like. It may leave its stand and fly low and swiftly to another spot, rise rapidly towards it and settle there so firmly that only a gentle vibration of its beautiful tail mars its immobility. But the instant its keen eye sees a target, the Hawk darts to it, takes it in its talons, and returns to its stand to eat it piece by piece. This done, the little hunter rises in the air, describes a few circles, moves in a direct line steadily by means of a tremulous motion of its wings, and plummets towards the earth but then checks its flight as if disappointed, reascends and proceeds. Some unlucky Finch may be the next to catch his eye. That is how the little marauder spends the winter months.

In spring he seeks a mate who at first flies from place to place while he pursues her. At length she yields to her dear tormentor's importuning, and they sail side by side, loudly screaming their unmusical love notes. With tremulous wings they search for and find a place to deposit their eggs—a deserted Woodpecker's hole. Joyfully the pair gambol through the air, chase away intruders, and settle down. The birds sit alternately during incubation, each feeding the other or standing watch. Six or seven round, beautifully spotted eggs are laid, and from them emerge the young, all downy white. Eventually their parents entice them from the nest. Some of the stronger ones launch at once into the air. The weaker ones now and then fall to the ground. All are well provided for by the parents until the young can shift for themselves. Together they search for crickets and such young birds as fall an easy prey. The family continues to hunt together in the same field, each bird choosing its own stand . . . a treetop or the head of a tall weed such as the great mullein. They may drop to the ground, then fly off in a body, separate again and resume their former stands. The strength of the young ones increases and their flight improves this way.

Autumn returns. The cricket is mute. The mouse retreats to her winter quarters. Clouds hide the sun, and hoarfrosts cover the ground. The long nights begin. Feathered choristers of the woods throng towards more congenial climes. In their rear rushes their enemy, the Sparrow-Hawk.

During the love season alone, when it may sail for half an hour, is the flight of this bird protracted. It can chase another bird with a good deal of speed, but never with that of the Sharp-Shinned Hawk or other species. If it teases an Eagle or a Turkey Buzzard, it quickly tires; and if another, stronger Hawk pursues it the Sparrow-Hawk soon withdraws into a thicket. It may sound its cry from its perch, but it does so mostly when on the wing, particularly before and after the birth of its young. It imitates the weaker cries of the young after they leave the nest to follow it.

It prefers the hole of a Woodpecker, but will content itself with an abandoned Crow's nest on occasion. So prolific is it that I do not recollect ever having found fewer than five eggs or young ones in the nest . . . as I have said, there may be seven.* The nearly globular eggs are a deep buff color, blotched all over with dark brown and black. The Sparrow-Hawk sometimes raises two broods in a season in the South, where it is a year-round resident. But in the more northern regions it seldom if ever raises more than one. I have even thought—though I am not quite certain—that they may lay more eggs in the South with each mating.

So much attached are they to their stand that they will return to it by choice for months in succession.

Although the greater number of these Hawks remove to the South as winter approaches, some remain in the state of New York during the severest mid-winter weather. These keep in the neighborhood of barns, where they may catch a rat or a mouse. I heard of one which caught a Sparrow and flew off with it, only to be seen by a Red-Tailed Hawk and forced to drop its live prey. This contented the Red-Tailed Hawk and also enabled the Sparrow to escape.

My pet Sparrow-Hawk, Nero, you may see in *The Birds of America.*

* Normal: four or five.

True Hawks

BROAD-WINGED HAWK

ONE fine May morning when Nature seemed to be enchanted at the sight of her own great works, when the pearly dew-drops were yet hanging at the point of each leaf, or lay nursed in the blossoms, gently rocked, as it were, by the soft breeze of early summer, I took my gun, and accompanied by my excellent brother-in-law, William G. Bakewell, who was at that time a youth, walked towards some lovely groves, where many songsters attracted our attention by their joyous melodies.

The woods were all alive with the richest variety. Divided in choice, we kept going on without shooting at anything, so great was our admiration of every bird that presented itself to our view. As we crossed a narrow skirt of wood, my young companion spied a nest on a tree of moderate height, and as my eye reached it we both perceived that the parent bird was sitting in it. Some little consultation took place, as neither of us could determine whether it was a Crow's or a Hawk's nest. We resolved that my young friend should climb the tree and bring down one of the eggs. On reaching the nest he said that the bird, which still remained there, quiet, was a Hawk and unable to fly. I desired him to cover it with a handkerchief, try to secure it, and bring it down together with the eggs.

All this was accomplished without the least difficulty. I looked at the bird with indescribable pleasure as I saw it was new to me. Then I felt vexed that it was not of a more spirited nature; it had defended neither its eggs nor itself. It lay quietly in the handkerchief, and I carried it home to my father-in-law's, showed it to the family, and went to my room, where I instantly began drawing it. The drawing which I then made is at this moment before me, and is dated "Fatland Ford, Pennsylvania, May 27, 1812."

I put the bird on a stick made fast to my table. It merely moved its feet to grasp the stick, and stood erect, but raised its feathers and drew its neck in upon its shoulders. I passed my hand over it to smooth the feathers by gentle pressure. It moved not. The plumage remained as I wished it. Its eye, directed towards mine, appeared truly sorrowful. I measured its bill with the compass, began my outlines, continued measuring part after part as I went on, and finished the drawing without the bird ever once moving. My wife sat at my side, reading to me at intervals, but our conversation had frequent reference to the singularity of the incident.

The drawing being finished, I raised the window, laid hold of the poor bird, and launched it into the air, where it sailed off out of my sight, without uttering a single cry or deviating from its course.

The drawing from which the plate was taken for *The Birds of America* was subsequently made, as I had to wait until I procured a male to render it complete.

The nest of the Broad-Winged Hawk is about the size of that of the Common Crow, and usually placed on fairly large branches near the stem or trunk of the tree. It is made of dry sticks and briers, which are its external material, beneath which are numerous small roots. Large feathers of the common fowl and other birds line it. The four or five eggs are dull grayish white, blotched with brown.* They are laid as early as the beginning of March in low places, but not until two weeks later in the mountainous parts of districts, where the bird often breeds. It feeds on wood-frogs, small snakes, and several small quadrupeds, and generally holds its prey with both claws while feeding. I must here remark that birds of prey never cover their victims by extending their wings over them, unless another bird tries to share or to carry off the fruit of their exertions. The Broad-Winged Hawk tends to attack birds of weak nature and seldom chases other birds of prey, though it is often teased by the small Sparrow-Hawk, the King-Bird, and the Martin.

* Two or three.

DUCK HAWK

THE French and Spaniards of Louisiana call all Hawks "Mangeurs de Poulets," or "Chicken Eaters." Farmers in various parts of the Union call them Hen Hawks, Chicken Hawks, Pigeon Hawks and the like, depending on their size. This way of naming rapacious birds is natural enough, but denotes little knowledge of their characteristics. There is no better illustration of such inaccuracy on the part of the ignorant than the case of this Hawk [Audubon named it Great-Footed Hawk, or Peregrine Falcon], a pair of which may be seen enjoying themselves over a brace of Ducks of different species in *The Birds of America*. Look at these two pirates, eating their *déjeuné à la fourchette*, as it were, and congratulating each other on its goodness. One might think them real epicures, but they are, in fact, true gluttons. The male has a Green-Winged Teal, his mate a Gadwall. Their appetites equal their daring; they well deserve the name of "pirates" which I have bestowed on them.

Within my own memory this Hawk was a scarce species in America. It is quite impossible for me to account for their increase, particularly in view of our more numerous plantations and the gunners who are ready to destroy Hawks at every opportunity.

Besides water fowl and Pigeons, it follows Blackbirds; I have seen it follow flocks of the latter and of Pigeons, and cause terror in their ranks which performed aerial evolutions to escape the grasp of its dreaded talons. For several days I watched one which had taken a particular fancy to some tame Pigeons. To obtain them it would even go so far as to enter their house through one of the holes, seize a bird, come out instantly through another hole, and so terrify the rest as to make me fear they might abandon the place. Fortunately, I shot the depredator.

Once while I was descending the Mississippi on a journey of four months' duration for the express purpose of observing and procuring various species of birds, I now and then saw this Hawk feeding on dead fish that had drifted to the shores and sandbars. My companion and I counted more than fifty of them, among which was the female painted for *The Birds of America,* shot on December 26, 1820. The ovary contained numerous eggs, two of which were as large as peas.

The Hawk will alight on the highest branch of a tree near marshes favored by the Snipe, move its head as if counting every little space below, and, if he spies a Snipe, will dart like an arrow, rustle his wings loudly, seize the bird and fly with it to the woods. It is a cleanly bird as to feeding, first plucking the feathers of its prey at points and eating it in pieces. It will fly off with the Snipe if an enemy approaches.

This Hawk is heavy, compact, and at maturity extremely muscular. The plumage differs greatly, according to age, and among individuals—from deep chocolate brown to light gray. The grasp is so firm that it will cling to the branch until life has departed, should it be hit while perched.

Except for pairing during the mating season, this is a solitary bird. The breeding season is so very early that it might be said to be in winter. I have seen the male caressing the female in the first days of December.

I never saw one attack a quadruped, though I have seen them perched within sight of squirrels.

Once, as I neared the coast of England in the month of July, two of these Hawks came aboard. I examined them with care and found no difference between them and those I had shot in America. They are at present scarce in England. Some of them roost in the cupola of St. Paul's Cathedral and in the towers of Westminster Abbey, and probably breed there. I have seen them depart from these places at dawn, and return in the evening.

In Kentucky I have known them to roost in the hollows of trees. One came to its sycamore a little before sunset, alighted on the branches, and soon flew into the hole to spend the night. I saw it fly out at dawn. I have also known them to roost for the night in the crevices of high cliffs along the Green River in Kentucky. When I was crossing the Homochitto River in Mississippi one winter, I saw these Hawks in greater numbers than ever before.

COOPER'S HAWK

AUDUBON INADVERTENTLY CLAIMED THIS BIRD AND
NAMED IT THE STANLEY HAWK.—ED.

On December 5, 1809, I drew the male of this species in its mature coloring in Louisville, Kentucky. But the figure is as stiff as those usually seen in books on natural history. The pair that I had engraved and colored for *The Birds of America* are a male, probably two years old, and an adult female. I did not have the good fortune to obtain an old male in the course of my rambles.

The Hawk's flight is rapid, even, and protracted, and at a short height above ground or forest. It glides silently, and with a swiftness that excels even that of the Passenger Pigeon—in a straight course unless pursuing its prey. If harassed, it will circle in the air five or six times, and again plunge downwards and continue its journey. It will bravely attack birds far larger than itself. One November morning I was watching some Parakeets near Bayou Sara, in Louisiana. I heard a cock crow not far from me, near a farmhouse. The next moment the Hawk flew past me so close that I could have touched it with the barrel of my gun, had I been prepared. Its wings struck with extraordinary rapidity; its tail appeared to be closed. Then I heard the hens cackle and the cock's war cry, and in the next second saw the Hawk rise lightly a few yards in the air, before plunging to the ground like lightning. It grappled with the cock, tumbled over and over, and paid no attention to me as I approached. I watched until the Hawk had given the brave cock a fatal squeeze, then I ran to take the marauder, but he had been keeping a hawk's eye on me and he disengaged himself to rise in the air with full confidence. I pulled the trigger and he dropped to the ground. He was a young male such as you see pursuing a Bluebird in *The Birds of America*.

Some years later, near Niagara Falls, I saw a female attack a brood of chickens, whose mother flew at it with such force as to throw it fairly on its back. The hen so assailed the Hawk with feet and bill as to enable me to run up and seize it.

So rapidly must this species travel from one extremity of the country to another in order to reach their breeding places that I have seen them copulate in Louisiana in February; but I have found their nest with eggs in which the chicks were far advanced in Connecticut on April 20. The nest, often found in forks of an oak branch, could easily be mistaken for that of the Common Crow. Its crooked sticks are lightly lined with grass and a few feathers. The three or four almost globular eggs—large for the size of the bird—are dull white, strongly granulated, and rough to the touch.

RED-TAILED HAWK

THE Red-Tailed Hawk performs partial migrations southward in severe winters, but it is more abundant in the South at all seasons.

To the mournful, repeated monosyllable *kae*, he will sail across a large plantation, on a level with the forest tree-tops which surround the place, and never once flap his wings. He moves his head sidwise to watch the ground below. His firm, protracted flight enables him to perform at a great height. I have seen him, when he spies an animal, check his sailing for an instant as if to mark the spot, and alight at once on the nearest tree, before descending for the attack with wings close to his body.

He may fly silently and low over a meadow or cotton field and, uttering no cry, mark his prey as before, ascend in a beautiful curve to the top of the nearest tree, then dive. If he sees nothing while passing over, he alights, shakes his feathers (especially those of his tail), preens himself, rises again while crying as usual, and repeatedly circles the field to make sure, sometimes from an immense height. He then proceeds elsewhere . . . if not to a field, to the forest to look for squirrels. He visits farmyards to pay his regards to the poultry, and without much precaution he plunges upon any chicks, ducklings, and young Turkeys he may see there, afterwards sweeping one off to the nearest wood. Hunger may impel him to swoop down on an old fowl also.

The Red-Tailed Hawks begin building their nest early in February in Louisiana, usually within a forest, on the tallest, largest tree. For eight or ten days both birds carry dried sticks and other materials to the spot, the center of a triple-forked branch. The large flat nest of sticks is finished with slender twigs and coarse grasses or Spanish moss.

The female lays four or five eggs of a dull white color, blotched with brown and black; the shell is smooth and very hard.* The male takes his turn on the nest, but seldom does one bird feed the other during incubation. They give their young an abundance of food, especially gray squirrels which the parents hunt together; one plunges at the fleeing rodent while the other watches to prevent its escape. Small hares, tame Pigeons, and poultry are also their quarry.

The pair often become as shy towards each other as if they had never met, once their young are reared. They even chase and rob each other of their prey then, at every opportunity. I have seen one flying with remarkable rapidity and crying *kae*, or performing beautiful evolutions through the air, until one or the other would become fatigued, give way, and make for the earth, where a battle would be waged until one Hawk was overpowered and forced to make off. It was after I had witnessed such an encounter that I made my drawing for *The Birds of America*, where you see a male Red-Tailed Hawk to have the advantage over the female, although she holds the hare firmly in one of her talons even as she is driven towards the earth, with her breast upwards. I have seen them pounce on wood rats and meadow mice, but never without first alighting on a tree before the act. I have also seen them pounce on a soft-shelled tortoise as that creature scrambled to the water and safety. They also attack bull-frogs and eat them.

In winter the Red-Tailed Hawk perches for hours at a time when the sun is shining and the weather calm, its breast turned to the sun, and its plumage glittering. It returns to roost so late in the evening, after a flight, that I have often heard its cry after sunset, mingling with the jovial notes of the Chuck-Will's-Widow and the ludicrous laugh of the Barred Owl. In Louisiana it roosts in the magnolias, and also in the tall cypresses of swamps, secure through the night amid the mosses of the branches.

The Red-Tailed Hawks are large, compact, muscular, and extremely wary. In seizing their prey, they extend their talons outward and beyond their heads, as I have depicted them in *The Birds of America*.

* Normal: two or three.

RED-SHOULDERED HAWK

The Red-Shouldered Hawk is one of the noisiest of its genus, especially in spring when its *ka-hee, ka-hee* sounds discordantly from on high as it sails in rapid circles. Its ordinary flight is even and protracted. Deep woods seem to be its chosen haunt, except in early spring; then it shows itself in open grounds near small lakes where it seizes Red-Winged Blackbirds and wounded Ducks. It may devour a whole squirrel at one meal . . . and so gorge itself as to fly with difficulty and to mar the beauty of its own form for the time being.

The male is particularly noisy at mating time. His cries are shrill as he circles, zigzags, and chases all other Hawks. Tall trees near woods are preferred for the circular nest, which is placed in the forks of a large branch and, in Louisiana, formed of dry sticks and Spanish moss and lined with grass and fibrous roots. The four, or occasionally five, eggs are broadly oval-shaped, granulated, pale blue, and faintly blotched with brownish red at the smaller end.* Should a man approach the nest, the female will fly off, but the male, who feeds her and also assists with incubation, sets up a hue and cry and plunges towards the assailant. The mutual attachment of the pair continues throughout life. They hunt together the whole year. Although they build a new nest each year, they frequent the same woods for that purpose. I knew the pair that I represented in *The Birds of America* for three years, and saw each of their three nests, all within a few hundred yards of the first. There is only one brood in the season.

The young keep to the nest until fully fledged, and for several weeks after they have started to fly, their parents feed them. Then, in about a month, they begin to shift for themselves, and hunt separately until spring and pairing time. The young have the rusty-red color of breast and shoulder feathers before they leave the nest. The shade gradually deepens as autumn approaches, and by the first spring they look like the old birds. There is little difference in size between the sexes; the female is merely a little stouter.

This Hawk seldom attacks poultry, but often pounces on Partridges, Doves, Wild Pigeons, and Red-Winged Blackbirds, as well as very young rabbits on occasion.

* Normal: two or three.

Eagles

WASHINGTON SEA-EAGLE

THIS BIRD, AN IMMATURE BALD EAGLE, WAS TAKEN FOR A NEW SPECIES
BY AUDUBON, WHO NAMED IT 'BIRD OF WASHINGTON'.—ED.

IT WAS in the month of February, 1814, that I obtained the first sight
of this noble bird, and never shall I forget the delight it gave me. Not
even Herschel, when he discovered the planet which bears his name,
could have experienced more rapturous feelings.

We were on a trading voyage, ascending the Upper Mississippi. The
keen wintry blasts whistled around us, and the cold from which I was suffering had to a great degree extinguished the deep interest which, at
other seasons, this magnificent river has been wont to awake in me.
I lay stretched beside our patroon. The safety of the cargo was forgotten,
and all that called my attention was the multitude of Ducks of different
species, accompanied by vast flocks of Swans which from time to time
passed us.

My patroon, a Canadian, had been engaged for many years in the
fur trade. He was a man of much intelligence; perceiving that these
birds had engaged my curiosity he seemed anxious to find something new
to divert me. An Eagle flew over us. "How fortunate!" he exclaimed.
"This is what I could have wished. Look, sir!—the Great Eagle, and
the only one I have seen since I left the lakes."

I was on my feet instantly. Having observed it attentively, I concluded, as I lost it in the distance, that it was a species quite new to
me. Convinced that the bird was unknown to naturalists, I felt particularly anxious to learn its habits.

My next meeting with this Eagle was in Kentucky, near the Green River junction with the Ohio. I was engaged in collecting cray-fish on the flats. There the river is bordered by high cliffs that follow its windings. I observed on the nearly perpendicular rocks a quantity of white ordure which I attributed to Owls, but one of my companions who lived within a mile and a half of the place told me it was from the nest of the Brown Eagle, meaning the White-Headed Eagle* in its immature state. I assured him this could not be, and remarked that neither the old nor the young birds of that species ever build in such places, but always in trees. He said that if I felt particularly anxious to know what nest it was, I might soon satisfy myself, as the old birds would come and feed their young with fish.

In high expectation I seated myself about a hundred yards from the foot of the rock. Never did time pass more slowly. I could not help betraying the most impatient curiosity. Two long hours had elapsed before the old bird made his appearance, which was announced to us by the loud hissing of the two young ones that crawled to the extremity of the hole to receive a fine fish. I had a perfect view of this noble bird as he held himself to the edge of the rock, like the Swallow, his tail spread and his wings partly so. I trembled, lest a word should escape from my companions, who entered into my feelings and gazed with me, although little interested.

In a few minutes the other parent joined her mate. We knew this to be the mother bird from the difference in size, the female of rapacious birds being larger. She also had brought a fish, but, being more cautious than her mate, she glanced around with quick and piercing eye and instantly perceived that her abode had been discovered. She dropped her prey, communicated the alarm to the male with a loud shriek, and, hovering with him over our heads, kept up a growling cry to intimidate us. This watchful solicitude I have ever found peculiar to the female:— *must I be understood to speak only of birds?*

The young having concealed themselves, we went and picked up the fish which the mother had let fall, a white perch weighing about five and a half pounds. We had plainly seen her bearing it in the manner of the Fish-Hawk or Osprey.

This day's sport being at an end, we journeyed homewards, agreeing

* Also the Bald Eagle.

to return the next morning. But, rainy and tempestuous weather setting in, we deferred the expedition. On the third day following, we passed the entire day without either seeing or hearing an Eagle, the sagacious birds no doubt having anticipated an invasion and removed their young to new quarters.

Two years of fruitless excursions went by from the day of the discovery of the nest to the one when my wishes were gratified. On returning to the house of Dr. Rankin, about a mile from the little village of Henderson, I saw an Eagle rise from a small enclosure not a hundred yards before me, and light upon a low tree branching over the road. I prepared my double-barrelled gun which I constantly carry, and went slowly and cautiously towards him. Quite fearlessly he awaited my approach, looking upon me with undaunted eye. I fired and he fell. With what delight did I survey the magnificent bird! Had the finest salmon ever pleased him as he did me? Never. I ran and presented him to my friend Dr. Rankin with a pride which they alone can feel who have devoted themselves from their earliest childhood to such pursuits, and who have derived from them their first pleasures. To others I must seem to "prattle out of fashion."

The name which I have chosen for this new species of Eagle, the "Bird of Washington," may be considered by some as preposterous and unfit. But as it is indisputably the noblest bird of its genus that has yet been discovered in the United States, I trust I shall be allowed to honor it with the name of one yet nobler, who was the savior of his country, and whose name will ever be dear to it. To those who may be curious to know my reasons, I can only say that as the New World gave me birth and liberty, the great man who insured its independence is next to my heart. He had a nobility of mind and a generosity of soul such as are seldom possessed. He was brave, so is the Eagle. Like it, too, he was the terror of his foes, and his fame, from pole to pole, resembles the majestic soarings of the mightiest of the feathered tribe. If America has reason to be proud of her Washington, so has she to be proud of her great Eagle.

BALD EAGLE

THIS noble bird is well known throughout the world, emblazoned as it is on our national standard which waves in the breeze in every clime . . . emblematic of freedom. May that peaceful freedom last forever! Yet it much grieves me that this bird should have been selected for the emblem of my country. I agree with the great Benjamin Franklin who said in one of his letters:

I wish the Bald Eagle had not been chosen as the representative of our country. He is a bird of bad moral character; he does not get his living honestly; you may have seen him perched on some dead tree, where, too lazy to fish for himself, he watches the labor of the Fishing-hawk. And when that diligent bird has at length taken a fish and is bearing it to his nest for the support of his mate and young ones, the Bald Eagle pursues him and takes it from him. With all this injustice, he is never in good case, but, like those among men who live by sharping and robbing, he is generally poor, and often very busy. Besides, he is a rank coward: the little King-bird, not bigger than a Sparrow, attacks him boldly, and drives him out of the district. He is, therefore, by no means a proper emblem for the brave and honest Cincinnati of America, who have driven all the King-birds from our country, though exactly fit for that order of knights which the French call *Chevaliers d'Industrie*.

The great strength, daring, and cool courage of this Eagle, plus his unequalled power of flight, render him highly conspicuous among his brethren. Had he a generous disposition towards others he might be looked up to as a model of nobility. His ferocious, overbearing, and tyrannical temper is, nevertheless, best suited to his state, and was wisely given him by the Creator to enable him to perform his offices.

Imagine yourself floating gently down the Mississippi at the approach of winter, amid millions of water fowl approaching on whistling wings from the north to seek a milder climate. The Eagle perches erectly on top of the tallest tree beside the broad stream, while with glistening, stern eye he surveys the vast expanse. He listens attentively to every sound, now and then glancing down to earth, lest the light tread of the fawn pass unheard. His mate is perched on the opposite bank, and, should all be tranquil and silent, she warns him by a cry to continue patient. At this he partly opens his broad wings, inclines a bit downwards, and answers in tones not unlike the laugh of a maniac. Then he resumes his erect attitude and silence returns.

Ducks—the Teal, the Wigeon, the Mallard and others—pass in great rapidity, following the course of the current. The Eagle heeds them not. They are then beneath his notice. But the next moment, when the wild, trumpet-like sound of a yet distant but approaching Swan is heard, the female Eagle comes shrieking across the stream. The male suddenly shakes all of his body before beginning to arrange his plumage with a few touches of his bill. The snow-white bird is now in sight, her long neck stretched forward, her eye watchful as that of her enemy. With seeming difficulty her large wings support her weight, flapping incessantly. So irksome do her exertions appear that her very legs are spread beneath her tail to aid her flight. But she approaches, and the Eagle marks her for his prey. As she passes the dreaded pair, the male starts from his perch with an awful scream that brings more terror to the ear of the Swan than the report of a large duck-gun.

Witness the Eagle's powers as he glides like a falling star and comes upon his timorous quarry like a flash of lightning. The Swan, in agony and despair, seeks by various manoeuvres to elude the grasp of his cruel talons, mounts, doubles—would willingly plunge into the stream were she not prevented. The Eagle, long possessed of the knowledge of such a possible stratagem for escape, attempts to strike her from beneath with his talons, to keep her in the air. The Swan, much weakened and with strength failing at the sight of the courage and swiftness of her antagonist, soon gives up hope. She gasps as the ferocious Eagle strikes the under-side of one of her wings with his talons and forces her to fall in a slanting direction on the shore. See the cruel spirit of this dreaded enemy of the feathered race. He exults over his prey, presses his powerful feet downward, and, all the while shrieking, drives his sharp claws deeper than ever into the heart of the dying Swan. The female Eagle watches her mate's every movement. If she did not assist him in the capture, it was not from want of will but merely from the assurance that the power and courage of her lord were quite sufficient for the deed. She sails to the spot, and together they feast.

Sometimes when these Eagles sail in search of prey, they take water fowl that have alighted on the stream—a Goose, Duck or a Swan. Aware that these birds may dive at their approach and elude them, the

Eagles ascend in opposite directions over the lake or water. Then, from a certain height one swiftly glides towards the prey, while the other approaches the spot where the attacked water fowl is likely to come to the surface after diving, and forces it to dive again. The first Eagle poises itself where its mate was and in turn forces its quarry to plunge again. These alternating glides and often repeated rushes fatigue the water bird, which swims deeply for shore in the hope of taking refuge among the rank weeds. But to no avail, for the Eagles follow it, and the moment it reaches the shore one of them pounces and kills it in an instant. Then the spoil is divided.

The White-Headed Eagle follows a different course during spring and summer, one less suited to a bird apparently so well able to supply itself without interfering with other plunderers. No sooner does the Fish-Hawk appear along our Atlantic shores or our large rivers than the Eagle follows it and robs it of its catch. He perches on a high place above the water to watch every motion of the Osprey on the wing. When the latter rises with a fish in its grasp, the Eagle rushes in pursuit, above the Hawk, with threatening motions which induce the bird to drop its prey. Instantly, the Eagle plunges with calculated swiftness to retrieve the fish. He carries off the prize to feed it to his young. Now and then he takes fish himself in the shallows of small creeks. I saw this occur in the Perkiomen Creek near my Pennsylvania plantation "Mill Grove," where the Eagles were catching red-fins by wading briskly through the water, and striking the fishes with their bills. I also saw a pair scrambling over the ice of a pond to get at some fish below but without success. This Eagle also greedily devours small livestock, poultry and carcasses of every description, driving off the Vultures and Carrion Crows or dogs and keeping them at bay until it is satiated. It frequently chases Vultures to force them to disgorge food which it devours. Near Natchez I watched Vultures at the carcass of a horse, until a White-Headed Eagle chanced along and caused them to take wing. The Eagle marked the Vulture which had not dropped its trailing portion as it flew off. The Vulture, seeing the Eagle, tried unsuccessfully to disgorge the long piece. The Eagle seized the dangling morsel and dragged the Vulture along by it for twenty or thirty yards, much against its will, until both fell to the ground. The Eagle struck the Vulture and killed it.

I have heard of several attempts of this bird to destroy children, but have never witnessed this myself, although I have little doubt of its having sufficient daring.

The flight of the Eagle, which I have observed with the naked eye or a good glass, is strong, uniform, and protracted at pleasure, with easy flappings, wings extended at right angles to the body, legs now and then hanging their full length. While sailing, the bird can ascend in circular sweeps, without a single flap or any apparent motion of wings or tail, until it disappears. Or it may sail off at only a few hundred feet in the air in a direct, rapid line. With its wings partly closed it may glide downward, then suddenly check its descent and resume its former steady flight. If it descends rapidly from an immense height, the motion makes a loud rustling sound like a violent gust of wind passing through branches. The eye can scarcely follow these often wholly unexpected falls.

This Eagle can raise any floating object not heavier than itself from the water, such as Ducks shot by the hunter. Its audacity is remarkable. While descending the Upper Mississippi I saw one of them pursue a Green-Winged Teal. It came so near to our boat that I could perceive the gleam of its eye. The Teal, about fifteen yards or so from us, was saved from the grasp of its enemy when one of our party winged the Eagle. It was taken aboard and kept on deck by a rope for the time being. After two days, it began to eat pieces of catfish. But as it became a disagreeable, dangerous associate, trying ever to strike with its talons, it was disposed of.

These birds exhibit much cowardice when surprised or unexpectedly approached. They at once rise and fly off in very low, zigzag lines, uttering a hiss which is unlike their usual disagreeable imitation of a laugh. They are especially cautious before men with guns, though lacking the power to smell gun-powder, as the Crow and Raven are absurdly said to do. Their sight, as perfect as that of any bird probably, is much affected by a fall of snow; they may then be approached without difficulty. When wounded the Eagle tries to escape by long quick leaps; if on water, where it has fallen, it will often reach shore with strokes of its expanded wings, provided the distance is not more than twenty or thirty yards. It can live without food for a long period—up to twenty days, I have been told. For defense these birds throw themselves backward, before furiously striking with their talons; their bills are open, their eyes full and vigilant.

Some persons have ventured to say that Eagles live a hundred years. I can only say that I once found a female which must have been very old. Tail and wings were rust-colored and so worn out that I imagined the bird had lost the power of moulting. Legs and feet were covered with large warts; claws and bill were much blunted; and the body was poor and very tough. It could scarcely fly more than a hundred yards at a time, and this with a heavy unsteadiness such as I never saw in any other Eagle. Yet the eye was sparkling and full of animation.

This Eagle is seldom seen alone. The first mating seems to continue until one of the pair dies. They hunt for the support of each other and seldom feed apart. Their love season begins earlier than that of any land bird I know—generally in December. They then fly about with a great bustle, circling and cackling before alighting on the dead branches of a tree where they are preparing a new nest or repairing their old one. There they caress each other. Incubation begins early in January. The nest, sometimes of great size, is usually on a very tall tree which, though not dead, is destitute of branches to a considerable height. The nest is composed of three- to five-foot-long sticks; pieces of turf; rank weeds; and, in the south, Spanish moss in abundance. It is five to six feet in diameter and sometimes the same depth owing to the accumulation of materials over a number of years. If built in a naked tree, it can be sighted from a long distance. Two to four eggs—more commonly three—are dull white and sometimes granulated.* Incubation lasts for more than three weeks; I have not been able to ascertain its precise duration, as I have observed the female sit for a few days in the nest before laying her first egg. I assured myself of this by climbing to the nest every day to look, while she was temporarily absent—a rather perilous undertaking when the bird is sitting.

I have seen the young when they are no larger than middle-sized pullets, covered with soft cottony down, their bill and legs disproportionately large. Their first plumage is grayish, mixed with varying brown; before the parents drive them off the nest they are fully fledged. I once caught three young ones by having the tree cut down, but as they could fly and scramble speedily, it was hard to overtake them, until finally, from fatigue, they resisted capture no longer. This happened on the shore of Lake Pontchartrain in April. The parents did not see fit to come within gunshot while the axe was at work. Their devotion to

* Two eggs.

the young is intense while they are nesting; to approach is dangerous. Though the eaglets are turned out when they can provide for themselves, they return to the nest to roost, or sleep on a branch close by for several weeks after they are fledged.

The young birds begin to breed the following spring, but not always in pairs of the same age. I have several times seen a brown one mated with a full-colored bird whose head and tail were pure white. In one instance the brown one was the female. This species requires at least four years to attain the full beauty of its plumage in captivity. In two cases the white of the head did not appear till the sixth spring. I suppose that when the bird is at full liberty, at least a year is required for this perfection. The weight varies—in males from six to eight pounds, and in females from eight to twelve.

They become much attached to their district and seldom spend a night away from it. While asleep they emit a loud hissing sort of snore, audible a hundred yards away in calm weather. Yet, so light is their sleep that the crackle of a stick under the foot of an approaching person immediately wakes them.

Before steam navigation on our Western rivers, these Eagles were extremely abundant there, particularly in the lower parts of the Ohio, Mississippi, and adjacent streams. I have seen hundreds going down from the mouth of the Ohio to New Orleans. Now, however, their number is considerably diminished, the game on which they were in the habit of feeding having been forced to seek refuge deeper in the wilderness from the persecution of man.

It is only necessary to add that the name by which this bird is known in America, that of Bald Eagle, is erroneous, as its head is as densely feathered as that of any other species, although its whiteness may have suggested the idea of its being bare.

GOLDEN EAGLE

THE Golden Eagle, though a permanent resident of the United States, occurs there rarely except in the mountains or the plains beneath. I I have seen a few along the Hudson's shores, others on the upper Mississippi, some in the Alleghenies, a pair in Maine, and one sailing low over the mossy rocks of Labrador.

Its flight is powerful but not equal in speed to that of the Hawks, or the Bald Eagle. It cannot, like the latter, seize its prey on the wing, but is obliged to glide down before it falls with the swiftness of a meteor on the spot where its quarry is hiding. Its keenness of sight makes up for this defect and enables it to spy on its target from immense heights, where its gyrations—slow, wide circles—are beautiful to watch. It often continues to circle, with utmost ease, for hours at a time.

The nest of this noble species is always placed on an inaccessible shelf of some rugged precipice—never, to my knowledge, in a tree. Very large, flat, of a few dead sticks and brambles, it is so slight that the eggs might be said to be deposited on the naked rock. The two, or sometimes three, eggs are three and a half inches long, with a diameter at the broadest of two and a half inches. The thick, smooth, dull white shell has undefined patches of brown at the larger end. The eggs are deposited the end of February or early in March. I have never seen the newly hatched young, but know that they do not leave the nest until they are nearly able to provide for themselves. Then their parents drive them off their home, and, finally, from their hunting grounds. A pair bred on the rocky shores of the Hudson for eight successive years, in the same chasm of the rock.

Their notes are harsh and sharp, like the barking of a dog, especially at the breeding season, when they become extremely noisy and turbulent. They fly more swiftly then than at other times, alight oftener, and evince a fretfulness not so observable after their eggs are laid.

They can fast for days at a time, but eat voraciously at every opportunity—fawns, raccoons, hares, Wild Turkeys and other large birds. Only when hard pressed by hunger do they devour putrid flesh or alight on carrion. They disgorge the indigestible. Muscular, strong, hardy, they can endure extreme cold, and they seek food in the most tempestuous weather. A full-grown female weighs about twelve pounds, a male about two and a half pounds less. The attachment of the pair appears to continue for years. They seldom travel far from their place of residence. Not until the fourth year does this species acquire the full beauty of plumage. Our Indians like to ornament their persons and implements of war with the tail feathers; they kill or raise this Eagle for the purpose.

According to one of Dr. Rush's lectures on the effects of fear on man, a company of soldiers were stationed near the Hudson River highlands during the American Revolution. A Golden Eagle had placed her nest in a cleft of the rocks halfway between the summit and the river. One of the soldiers was lowered to the nest by a rope around his body. The Eagle attacked him, and in self-defense he made repeated passes at the bird with his knife. Accidentally, he cut the rope almost off. It began to ravel; his companions hastily drew him up just in time to save him from plunging to the bottom. Dr. Rush stated that the effect of fear was so powerful that the soldier's hair became quite gray within three days of his perilous experience.

In February, 1833, I purchased a very fine Golden Eagle from the proprietor of the natural history museum in Boston. It was a deep, bold and stern one, and I was determined to possess it. The Eagle had been caught a few days previously in a spring-trap set for foxes in the White Mountains of New Hampshire. One morning the trap was missing. At last it was discovered more than a mile away, and it held the Eagle only by one of its toes. To escape its captors it flew about through the woods with the trap for several hundred yards, but was at last taken after a struggle.

After covering it with a blanket to protect it from the gaze of people in its adversity, I took it at once to where I was staying. I put the cage where I could have a good look at the captive. I was half inclined to give him his freedom, that he might return to his native mountains. I thought how pleasing it would be to see him spread his broad wings and sail away towards the rocks of his wild haunts. But then someone seemed to whisper that I ought to do a portrait of the magnificent bird; I abandoned my more generous impulse of setting him at liberty, for the express purpose of showing you his likeness.

For a whole day I watched his movements. On the next I decided on the position in which I might best represent him in my picture. And on the third I thought about how to take away his life with the least pain to him. A worthy friend and physician of the family suggested a method which he thought would probably be the easiest for ourselves and the least painful for the bird. A pan of lighted charcoal was placed in a very small room where we put the cage. Windows and doors were fastened and blankets tucked over and beneath the cage. I waited, expecting to hear him fall from his perch at any moment.

But after listening for *hours*, I opened the door, raised the blankets, and peeped through a mass of suffocating fumes. There stood the Eagle on his perch, his bright unflinching eyes turned towards me—as lively and vigorous as ever! I replaced the blankets and resumed my station outside the door. Towards midnight, having heard no sound, I again took a peep at my victim. He was still uninjured. The air was unbearable to my son and myself; even that of the adjoining room began to be unpleasant. However, I persevered for ten hours in all, and finding that the charcoal fumes would not produce the desired effect, I retired to rest, wearied and disappointed.

Early next morning I tried the charcoal anew, with sulphur added. We were nearly driven from our home in a few hours by the stifling vapors, but the noble bird continued to stand erect and to gaze defiance at us whenever we approached. His fierce demeanor made a dose impossible. At last I resorted to a method always used as a last resort. I thrust a long pointed piece of steel through his heart. My proud prisoner instantly fell dead without ruffling a feather.

I sat up nearly the whole of another night to outline him, and worked so constantly at the drawing that it nearly cost me my life. I was suddenly seized with an illness that much alarmed my family and completely prostrated me for some days. But thanks to my heavenly Preserver and the unremitting care of my friends, I was soon restored to health and enabled to pursue my labors. The drawing of this Eagle took me fourteen days, and I had never before labored so incessantly excepting at that of the Wild Turkey.

Ruffed Grouse

THE names of Pheasant and Partridge were given to this species by our forefathers. The first name is usually heard in the Allegheny Mountains, and westward and to the east of this range. But in Connecticut the name Partridge prevails in my day.

The Ruffed Grouse keeps to the districts which it frequents, but makes partial sorties or migrations as autumn nears. These do not equal the peregrinations of the Wild Turkey, Prairie Chicken, or little Partridge. Nevertheless, they can be observed at those times when their districts afford less food than others, though they might not be noticed were the birds not obliged to fly across rivers of great breadth, there being numerous others in the customary haunts. But before crossing, these parties of eight or ten, or twelve or fifteen, linger in the woods close by for a week or two, as if fearful of flying over the water. At length they cross it easily; I never saw any drop into the stream. Within a few days they proceed onward to the depths of the forest, to remain there until spring. Then they return to the region that they left. The males lead the way and proceed singly; the females follow in parties of three or four. In October, 1820, I saw a large number migrate in this way from Ohio, Illinois and Indiana into Kentucky.

The Ruffed Grouse likes the craggy sides of mountains and hills, the rocky borders of rivers, and small streams where evergreens and small shrubs grow profusely. However, they move to lowlands at times—even to the thickest canebrakes, where occasionally they breed. I have heard their *drumming* fifteen miles from the nearest hills, in lower Illinois and southern Kentucky's Choctaw territory.

Ordinarily, its flight is straight, stiff, and rather low, with continuous wingbeats for more than half its length, followed by sailing and balancing, much like a vessel sailing before the wind. If harassed, it produces a whirring sound in flight. Its walk is peculiarly graceful, the step elevated, the head erect with its feathers raised as well as those velvety tufts of the neck, and its beautiful tail gently opening. It poises on one foot a few seconds, utters a soft *cluck*, and seems aware that it is deserving of notice.

I have shot many a fine cock by imitating the sound of its own wings striking against the body. I did so by beating a large inflated bullock's bladder with a stick to the tempo which the bird itself beats when it sounds its *drumming*. A male Grouse, inflamed with jealousy, would fly towards me. An equally successful stratagem for decoying the males of our little Partridge is an imitation of the female call-note in spring and summer. But I have never been able to entice the Prairie Chicken by imitating its *booming*. Early in April the Grouse begins to *drum* just after dawn, and again towards sunset. It repeats the sounds more frequently during the day as the mating season advances. The male accomplishes it by beating its sides with its wings with such rapidity as to cause a tremor in the air not unlike distant thunder. It does so while standing erect on a log, after raising its feathers like a Wild Turkey cock, drawing its head towards its elevated tail, letting its wings droop, and strutting about for a few moments. The female, which never *drums*, flies directly towards him, opens her wings before him, balances to right and left, and then receives his caresses. They resort to the same trunk throughout the season, if not disturbed. The males are promiscuous, though not so much so as the Prairie Chicken. They have many severe battles at the mating time; the females watch, but never interrupt.

In early May the female forms a nest of dried leaves and herbaceous plants on the ground in some woodland thicket, by a fallen tree, or under a low bush, or where leaves have been heaped by the wind. Her five to twelve eggs are a dull yellowish color. She never covers them when she leaves the nest, so that Ravens and Crows readily find and eat them. But if she is present, she defends them with obstinacy, striking the intruder with her wings and feet like a chicken hen.

The young run about and follow the mother from the moment they leave the egg. At six or seven days they can fly a few yards, small though they are. The mother leads the search for food, covers the young at night with her wings, and shows intense affection and devotion when danger threatens. She draws attention to herself by feigning lameness, tumbling and rolling about as if severely wounded, and usually saves them by her methods. The little ones squat at the least cluck of alarm from her, and lie close together.

By that time the males are separated from the females. They associate in parties until winter approaches; then males, females and young mingle together. In summer these birds dust themselves in the roads and pick up gravel. I have seen them copulating towards autumn, and unaccountably, as but one brood is raised in the season.

The diet of this species—tree buds, seeds, berries and the like—gives its delicious flavor.

The Ruffed Grouse has various enemies besides man. Several of the Hawks fall swiftly upon them from the treetops, or seize them after gliding rapidly in their wake through the woods. Various quadrupeds are also among their foes, though of these some only suck their eggs.

They roost on trees among the thickest foliage.

Prairie Chicken

SEASON after season I studied this Grouse when I lived in Kentucky twenty-five years ago. There, before sunrise or at close of day, I heard its curious *boomings*, witnessed its obstinate battles, watched the progress of its courtships, noted its nest and eggs, followed its young until, fully grown, they departed for their winter quarters. They were looked on with more abhorrence than the Crows are in most places, in those days. They were guilty of mischief to the buds of orchards during winter, and of picking up the grain of the fields in spring. I little imagined as I watched them in that period of my life that the observations I recorded would ever be read by any save my family, all of whom shared my admiration of the works of Nature.

These birds were so abundant and bold that they would enter farmyards and feed with the poultry, alight on the houses, and walk in the very streets of the village. The farmers' children or those of his Negro slaves were kept at driving them away with rattles from morning to night, and at catching them in pens and traps. But now, to escape the murderous white man, they have all but abandoned Kentucky, and everywhere are decreasing rapidly. A good friend of mine in New York City recently refused a hundred dollars for ten brace which he had shot in the Pocono Mountains of Pennsylvania.

As soon as the snow melts and the first grasses appear in spring, it breaks up its great winter flocks into parties of twenty to fifty or more. The love season begins. The birds choose a spot for courtship. Before dawn the males fly swiftly and singly from their grassy beds to meet, challenge and fight their rivals. They are now in full dress and enact their part with a pomposity not surpassed by any other bird. Twenty or so of them assemble by daybreak, strut, and look disdainful and angry as they pass each other. They spread their tails and incline them forward to meet their neck feathers now rising like a ruff or frill, while globular, orange-colored air pouches sound the singular *boom*. They hold their stiffened wings downward so as to rub and rustle them on the ground, as Grouse rapidly passes Grouse. Their fiery eyes evince the pugnacious workings of their minds . . . their cry fills the air . . . and at the very first answer from some coy female, the feathered warriors begin their battle. They strike each other, and rise in the air to pounce, like Game Cocks. Feathers fly and are tinged with blood. The weaker give way and take to the bushes. Some fight on, and maintain their ground until, exhausted, they withdraw proudly and slowly. Both vanquished and victorious search for the females, who believe each to have triumphed and who receive them with joy.

A male already mated may suddenly be attacked by a disappointed rival who has been attracted by the cacklings of the happy couple. While the quarrel ensues, the female squats next to and almost under the breast of her lord, who throws himself on his daring antagonist and chases him away. I attempted to represent this moment in my portrait of the Prairie Chicken in *The Birds of America*. Many of the young males have battles even in autumn. The females join in, not to fight, but, much like the Wild Turkey, to conciliate them. Such battles and *booming* or "tooting" may occur not only before sunrise but at any hour, except where man's interference in the daytime hours has taught them to be quiet.

The nesting time depends on latitude—between early April and May 25, with the average around the first of May. Though carelessly formed of dry leaves and grasses woven in a fairly neat manner, the nest is always carefully placed among the tall grasses of some large tuft, or on the open prairie, or at the foot of a small bush in the barrens. The eggs are from eight to twelve—seldom more—and require eighteen or nineteen days of incubation by the female. The moment the young emerge from their shells the mother bird leads them away from the nest; the male ceases to be seen with her. This species never raises more than one brood the season unless the eggs are destroyed, in which case the female at once calls for her mate and produces a second set of eggs, smaller in number than the first. Though the young are fairly large by

August, they do not have much strength of wing until mid-October, a time when their enemies, the Hawks, raccoons, weasels, pole-cats, and wild cats are very numerous.

While living in Henderson, Kentucky, I purchased sixty live young Prairie Chickens which were expressly caught for me. I cut their wing tips and turned them loose in my four acres of garden and orchard. Within a week they would allow me to approach. I fed them an abundance of corn and various vegetables. This was in September. During the winter they became so gentle as to feed from my wife's hand, and walked about like tame fowls among the domestic poultry. At night each one chose a heap where a cabbage had grown and there each invariably placed its breast to the wind as it roosted. In the spring they strutted, *tooted* and fought as in the wild state. Many laid eggs which hatched young. So brave were the males that they never flinched before a large Turkey cock, and now and then would stand before one for a pass or two before running.

They generally prefer to rest on the ground, except in very severe weather when I have known them to roost in tall trees. At the approach of winter in Kentucky, they frequented the tops of sumach bushes to feed on the seed. The weight of the flock bent the branches. I have counted more than fifty on a single apple tree; the buds were destroyed in a few hours. They eat grapes, berries, grasshoppers, mistletoe leaves and the like. I have seen flocks flying to and fro across the broad Mississippi and above the mouth of the Ohio, and alighting in the tallest trees as easily as any other bird. They watch one another, and if one of them spies a grasshopper all the rest either fly or run to it. They like to dust themselves in paths and fields. Their walk has none of the elegance of that of the Ruffed Grouse, but is more like that of the common hen, if somewhat more erect.

Should you come upon a mother and her brood she will ruffle her feathers and feign readiness to attack you, though she never does. She will try every art to decoy you away.

The young birds sit on the ground in a circle, but the adults usually roost singly on little rises of ground a few feet apart. Though this species can walk with complete ease on large branches of the trees, they use their wings to steady their balance on the small ones.

Their flight is strong, regular, tolerably swift, and can be carried to the distance of several miles. It is less rapid, and the whirring of wings is less marked than with the Ruffed Grouse or "Pheasant." After beating its wings for a distance, it sails for a hundred yards or so— wings downward—to watch any pursuers.

Only the male *booms*—by means of bladders at the neck which he inflates perfectly until they resemble a small orange in size and color. He lowers his head to the ground, opens his bill, and sends forth a roll of notes like the sound of a large muffled drum. This done, he draws himself erect, refills the deflated air pouches by inhalation, and resumes his *tootings*. All my attempts to decoy this species by imitating its curious sounds were unsuccessful, although I found it easy to decoy the Ruffed Grouse.

Like the Wild Turkey, the males of this species spend a few weeks apart from the females after incubation, to recover their strength. When the young are grown the flocks gradually reunite, and young and old of both sexes intermingle, and continue in company until spring and incubation. The young males exhibit the bladders for booming and the long neck feathers before the first winter; by spring they attain maturity, but like many other species they increase in size and beauty for several years.

Wild Turkey

WHILE at Henderson, on the Ohio in Kentucky, I had many wild
birds. I had a fine male Turkey that I had raised from its youth, having
caught it when it was two or three days old. It became so tame that it
would follow any person who called it, and it was the favorite of the
little village where I lived. Yet it would never roost with the tame
Turkeys, but always slept at night on the roof of the house, where it
remained until dawn.

When it was two years old, it began to fly to the woods. There it
would remain for most of the day, returning home only when night came
on. It kept this up until the following spring, when, several times, I
saw it fly from its roosting place in the top of a tall cottonwood tree on the
banks of the Ohio. There, after resting a while, it would sail to the
opposite shore, where the river was nearly half a mile wide, and return
towards night.

One morning I saw it fly off at a very early hour to the woods. I paid
little attention. Several days passed, but the bird did not return. I was
going towards some lakes near Green River to shoot when I saw a fine
large gobbler cross the path before me and move leisurely along. Turkeys
were in the best condition for eating at that season. I ordered Juno,
my dog, to chase it and flush it into the air. The dog hurried ahead, and,
as it drew near the bird, I saw with great surprise that the Turkey did
not run off. Juno was about to seize it, when suddenly she stopped and
turned her head towards me. I ran to them, and you can guess my
surprise when I saw that the creature was my own favorite bird, and
discovered that it had recognized the dog and would not fly from it,
although it would have run off from a strange dog at once.

A friend of mine who was looking for a deer he had wounded

happened to come along. He put my bird on his saddle in front of him and carried it home for me.

The following spring the Turkey was accidentally shot when it was taken for a wild one. It was brought back to me when the hunter saw the red ribbon it wore around its neck.

How shall we explain the way my Turkey knew my dog at sight in the woods, after seeeing it at home in the yard and grounds? Was it instinct? Reason? Memory? Or the act of an intelligent mind?

About the beginning of October the Wild Turkey begins to fly in flocks towards the rich bottom lands of the Ohio and Mississippi. The males or "gobblers" search for food in parties of ten to a hundred. The females fly one by one with their separate broods, which by then are nearly grown. Or else they fly with other families of seventy or eighty birds which all avoid the old cocks or gobblers. The gobblers often fight with their young and destroy them by repeated blows on the head. But old and young all travel in the same direction, unless their progress is interrupted by a river or a hunter's dog forces them to scatter.

When they come to a river they gather on a high point above it, and often remain there a whole day or two, as if to talk things over. The males are heard gobbling, calling, and making much ado. They strut about as if trying to make up their minds or get up their courage. Even the hens and young behave in a rather pompous way, spreading their tails, running around each other, "purring" loudly, and performing extravagant leaps. Finally, when the weather looks settled and all is quiet, the whole flock flies to the highest tree-tops, and at a signal— a single "cluck" from the leader—they fly for the opposite shore.

The old and fat birds get over the water easily, even if the river happens to be a mile wide. But the younger and less robust ones frequently fall in the water. However, they do not drown, as you might imagine. They draw their wings close, spread their tails for support, stretch their necks forward, and move their wings vigorously as they make for the shore. On nearing it they stop for a moment if the point they reach is too steep to climb, then float downstream to an easier landing place, where, with a violent effort, they scramble out of the water. It is strange that they should ramble about on land for a while, as if bewildered. In this state of uncertainty they fall an easy prey to the hunter.

As early as mid-February the Turkeys prepare to mate. The hens fly from the cocks, who pursue them gobbling. When a hen calls from her roost, all the gobblers who hear her return the sound, and fly at once in her direction. If the males are on the ground when she calls, they spread their tails upright, draw their heads back on their shoulders, depress their wings with a quivering motion, and strut pompously about, blowing out a series of puffs from their lungs. Now and then they stop to look and listen, whether or not they can yet see the hen who called. Often the gobblers begin quarreling. A desperate battle takes place, ending in bloodshed and even in the loss of many lives, the weaker candidate for the hen's favor falling under repeated blows on the head by the stronger.

I have often been much interested to watch two males in a fierce fight, moving backwards and forwards, their wings drooping, their tails partly raised, their feathers ruffled, and their heads covered with blood. If one loses his hold, his chance is over, because the other one, while still holding fast, hits him violently with his spurs and wings, and in a few minutes brings him to the ground. The moment he is dead the conqueror treads him under foot, but, strangely enough, not with hatred, but with all the motions with which he courts the female.

When the cock finds a mate she also struts and gobbles. She turns towards him as he continues to strut, suddenly opens her wings, and throws herself towards him. I believe they remain mated for that season, but the cock by no means confines his attentions to any one hen. I have seen a cock caress several, when he happened to be among them in one place. The hens follow their favorite cock and roost in his immediate neighborhood, if not on the tree which he frequents. But after the hens begin to lay, they separate from the males in order to save their eggs. He would break them all in his ardent attentions to the hen, who carefully avoids him except for a short period each day. But by now the cocks become clumsy and slovenly, if one may say so. They cease to fight with each other, give up gobbling or calling so frequently, and become so indifferent that the hens have to make all the advances. The latter *yelp* loudly and continually for the cocks, run up to them, caress them, and employ various means to rekindle their expiring ardor.

During clear nights, or when there is moonshine, Turkey cocks sometimes strut and gobble where they roost, letting their puff swell and lowering their tail and feathers. They may do this every few minutes, for hours on end, without leaving the spot, and sometimes with-

Henderson May 8th 1815 -

Willet

out so much as getting to their legs, and without strutting, especially towards the end of the love season. When mating time is passing, the males become greatly emaciated, and they cease to gobble. Their breast sponge becomes flat, and they separate from the hens, retiring to dense woods and cane thickets. Because they are by then unable to fly, they often permit a person to come within a few feet of them. But they can still run swiftly and for a great distance. A slow Turkey hound has led me miles before I could flush the same bird into the air. Such chases I did not undertake for the purpose of killing the bird, it being then unfit for eating and covered with ticks, but to learn its habits. The reason they retire to the dense thickets, away from the hens, is to recover their strength and flesh by less exercise and by purging themselves with a certain kind of grass. When they improve, the cocks come together again and recommence their rambles.

Let us return to the females. About mid-April, when the season is dry, the hens begin to look for a place to lay their eggs, one concealed as much as possible from the eye of the Crow. That bird often watches the Turkey going to her nest, waits until she leaves it, then removes the eggs and eats them. The nest is a scooped-out hollow on dry ground with a few withered leaves in it, beside a log; or it may be in the fallen top of a dry leafy tree, under a thicket of sumach or briers, or close to the edge of a canebrake. The eggs, of a dull cream color, sprinkled with red dots, may run to twenty in number, but ten to fifteen is more usual.* When she is laying her eggs, the hen always approaches her nest with extreme caution; she scarcely ever takes the same course to it. When she leaves it she covers it carefully with leaves, making it hard for her enemies to find it. Indeed few Turkeys' nests are found, unless the hen has been suddenly started from it, or a cunning fox or Crow has sucked the eggs and left the tell-tale shells scattered about.

The hens show a preference for islands when nesting and rearing their young. Such places are frequented less by hunters. Also, the masses of driftwood at the heads of these islands may protect the Turkeys in emergency. I have found that a single gun-shot will send them running to the piles of drifted wood where they conceal themselves. I have often walked over these masses, which may be ten to twenty feet in height, searching for game which I knew to be hiding there.

If an enemy comes within sight of a hen while she is laying or

* Normal: eleven or so.

sitting, she never moves unless she knows she has been discovered. She crouches lower until he has passed. I have often come within five or six paces of a nest of which I was well aware, assumed an air of carelessness and whistled or talked to myself. The female remained undisturbed. But when I have gone towards the nest cautiously, the hen has never allowed me to come within twenty paces without running off, her tail spread on one side. After twenty or thirty yards' distance, she has begun to walk again with her usual stately gait, uttering a cluck every now and then. The hens seldom abandon their nest when men discover it. But it is my belief that they never go near it again when a snake or animal has sucked any of the eggs. If one of them finds her eggs stolen or destroyed, she yelps for the male as if to breed again; but she generally rears only one brood a season. Sometimes, perhaps for safety, several hens deposit their eggs in the same nest, and rear their broods together. I once found three sitting on forty-two eggs. In such cases the common nest is always watched by one of the females, so that no Crow, Raven or pole-cat dares approach it. A mother will not leave her eggs when near hatching under any circumstances, while life remains. She will allow herself to be enclosed and imprisoned on the nest rather than abandon it.

I once saw a brood of Turkeys hatched. I was watching with the plan to secure them, parents and all. I concealed myself on the ground within a very few feet of them, and saw the hen half rise, look anxiously on the eggs, cluck with a sound peculiar to hens at such moments, carefully remove each half-empty shell, caress the young birds with her bill, and dry them. Already the young stood tottering, attempting to make their way out of the nest. Yes, I have seen this, and I have left both mother and young to better care than mine—to the care of their Creator. I have seen them all emerge from the shell, and, a few minutes after, tumble, roll, and push each other forward with astonishing and inscrutable instinct.

The mother, before leaving the nest with her brood in tow, shakes herself violently, picks and adjusts her breast feathers, and takes on quite a different look. She peers obliquely upwards and to the side, stretches her neck to look for Hawks or other enemies, spreads her wings a little as she walks, and softly clucks to her innocent offspring to keep them close to her. They move slowly along. As the hatching usually takes place in the afternoon, they frequently return to the nest to spend the first night there after their walk. But then they move to high, rolling ground; the mother dreads rainy weather, which is extremely dangerous to the young when they are still only covered by down of surprising delicacy. Turkeys are scarce in very rainy seasons, for the young seldom recover if completely wetted. To prevent the disastrous effects of rainy weather, the mother plucks the buds of the spice-wood bush, and like a skillful physician she feeds them to her young.

After about two weeks, the young birds which had previously rested on the ground leave it for some very large low branch, flying there at night. They separate in two nearly equal groups and take shelter under their kind and careful mother's deeply curved wings. During the day they leave the woods for the glades or prairies, in search of strawberries, dewberries, blackberries and grasshoppers, and enjoying the sunlight. They roll in deserted ants' nests, to clear the loose scales out of their feathers and to prevent ticks and other vermin, these insects being unable to bear the odor of earth where ants have been.

By August the young are able to protect themselves from attacks by wolves, foxes, lynxes and panthers, rising quickly on their powerful legs and reaching the highest tree-tops with ease. By this time the young cocks have a tuft on their breast, and they begin to gobble and strut. The young hens purr and leap like their elders. All the Turkeys, young and old, now gather and begin to migrate.

When a lynx discovers a flock of these birds he follows them for some distance until he decides what direction they are travelling. Then he circles them and moves ahead, lies in ambush until they come up, and springs on one with a single bound. When the Snowy Owl or the Virginia Owl attacks them, they often escape in a rather remarkable way. The Owl will approach and hover around a naked branch of roosting Turkeys, but, usually, they are reconnoitering; a single *cluck* from one Turkey announces the murderer's approach to the whole party. Instantly they stand and watch the Owl which, having selected a victim, swoops down like an arrow. But its prey stoops, lowers its head, spreads its tail over its back, and lets its attacker glide over the smooth plane that it has thus formed. Then it drops to the ground, none the worse, but for the loss of a few feathers.

Turkeys, which are generally extremely shy, instinctively move from a man, whether he be white or a redskin, the moment they observe him. They usually go along at a walk, partly opening one wing then another, then folding them over each other, as if their weight were too great. As if to amuse themselves, they will run a few steps, open both wings and fan their sides as chickens do, and often take two or three leaps in the air and shake themselves. While searching among the leaves for food—pecan nuts, winter grapes, herbs, corn, berries, insects, tadpoles, and small lizards—they keep their heads up, and are constantly on the lookout. I suspect the sense of touch in their feet enables them to detect food while scratching the earth. But this habit of scratching the dried leaves in the woods is pernicious to their safety, as it shows their enemies that birds are in the vicinity.

After a heavy snowfall, when the ground is crusted with frost, the Turkeys remain on their roosts for three or four days or more. This proves their ability to go without food for long periods. When near farms, however, they go boldly into stables and about corn stacks to find food. During a thaw or wet spell, they will travel a remarkably long way, and then it is useless for animals or hunters to try to keep up with them. They have a dangling, straggling way of running in such weather, but, awkward as it may seem, it enables them to outstrip any other animal. Often, even when on a good horse, I have had to give up after several hours of following them.

Good dogs will scent Turkeys at extraordinary distances—say, half a mile. Well trained, the hound sets off at full speed, and in silence, until he sees the birds; then he instantly barks and pushes his way as much as possible into the center of the flock. They are forced to take wing in all directions. Their scattering is a great advantage to the hunter, for should they all fly one way they would be harder to overtake. When one alights on a tree, it stands perfectly motionless and is sometimes very difficult to see. If it is standing erect, you must approach with great caution, or it will fly off and perhaps to such a distance that it would be vain for you to follow. When merely winged by a shot, it falls to the ground in a slanting direction. Then instead of losing time by tumbling and rolling over like other birds so often, it runs off so fast that unless the hunter has a swift dog he may as well say farewell to it.

Speaking of the shooting of Turkeys, I feel no hesitation in relating the following experience which happened to me. One afternoon late in autumn, while in search of game, at a time when the cocks are together and the hens by themselves also, I heard a hen clucking. Immediately finding her perched on a fence, I made for her, advancing slowly and cautiously. I heard the yelping notes of some gobblers and stopped, listening to decide which way the sound came from, and afterwards running to meet them. Before they came in view I hid myself by a fallen tree, cocked my gun, and waited with impatience. Their yelping continued in answer to the female, which, all the while, remained on the fence.

I looked over the edge of the log and saw about thirty fine cocks advancing rather cautiously towards the very spot where I lay concealed. They came so near that the light of their eyes could easily be perceived. Then I fired one barrel, and killed three. The rest, instead of flying off, began strutting around their dead companions, so that I might easily have had at least another had I not looked on shooting again as unnecessary murder. So, I showed myself, marched to the place where the dead birds were, and drove away the survivors.

In spring the hunter *calls* the Turkeys by sucking air through one of the second joints of Turkey wing bones in a certain way. The sound resembles the voice of the female, and it calls the male who will approach and be shot. But this requires some skill, the cock being quick to detect a false sound. I have known many of the very wary and cunning *half-civilized* birds to answer without moving a step, thus entirely defeating the scheme of the hunter who lies in wait for him, and who dares not move from his hiding place. Many are shot in spring, while roosting, when they answer the imitation of a Barred Owl's cry with a rolling gobble.

The commonest way to catch Turkeys is with a pen set in the woods. A cage made of saplings is placed on the ground with a trench beneath it. A trail of scattered grains of corn lures them to the pen which has more corn inside it. They enter, feast, and then try to force their way out through the top or sides. They never think to look down and escape through the hole below, where they entered. Along comes the hunter who seals the trench and has his captives. I have seen as many as eighteen in a pen at one time. Sometimes, if the hunter neglects to visit the pen where wolves or lynxes are numerous, he may not secure his prize. One morning, I had the pleasure of trapping a fine black wolf in one of my pens. On seeing me it squatted as if supposing I would pass by and not discover it. One winter I kept an account of the produce of a pen which I visited daily, and I found that seventy-six had been caught in it in about two months. Though I have heard of catching as many as eighteen at a time, I myself never found more than seven in a pen at once.

Wild Turkeys often mix with tame ones, or fight with them and drive them off from their food. The cocks sometimes mate with tame hens. This is pleasing to the farmer, who is well aware that the half-breed Turkey is much hardier than the tame ones, and consequently easier to raise.

The great size and beauty of the Wild Turkey, its value as delicate and highly prized food, and the circumstance of its being the origin of the domestic race, render it one of the most interesting of the birds indigenous to the United States of America. At the time when I moved to Kentucky in 1807, Turkeys were so abundant that one weighing twenty-five to thirty pounds brought a quarter of a dollar.

Whooping Crane

NOW THREATENED WITH EXTINCTION. ONE SMALL FLOCK STRUGGLES FOR
SURVIVAL IN ITS TEXAS AND CANADIAN GROUNDS. HERE AUDUBON USED
THE NAMES SANDHILL CRANE AND WHOOPING CRANE INTERCHANGEABLY.
HE MISTOOK THE FORMER—A GRAY BIRD OF A DIFFERENT SPECIES—FOR
AN IMMATURE WHOOPER.—ED.

BY LATE October the lumberjack prepares to set out on his long voyage.
The trapper seeks the retreats of the industrious beaver, and the red
Indian makes plans for his winter hunts. The Ducks and Geese are
already on the Western ponds. Here a Swan or two follows their train.
As the observer of Nature stands watching the signs of this season of
change, he hears from on high the notes of the swiftly travelling but
unseen Whooping Crane. Suddenly the misty atmosphere clears and he
can perceive the passing birds. Gradually they descend, dress their extended lines, and prepare to alight on the earth.

With outstretched necks, and with long bony legs reaching backward,
they move on wings white as snow but tipped with jet, until they reach
the great savannah. There they wheel in circling flight, slowly approach
the ground, and with wings half closed and feet outstretched they
alight. They run along for a few steps to break the force of their descent,
then they shake and arrange their feathers. Proudly they stalk over
the withering grasses. With the long measured steps of so many gallant
chiefs they step majestically along, heads erect and eyes glistening with
delight. For now the long journey has been accomplished. The Cranes
are well acquainted with their winter resort.

The Whooping Crane reaches the Western country about mid-

October or the beginning of November in flocks of twenty or thirty individuals, or twice or thrice that number. The young, followed by their parents, keep to themselves. They spread from Illinois over Kentucky and all the intermediate States until they reach the Carolinas, the Floridas, Louisiana and the lands bordering Mexico, where they winter. Seldom do they return northward until about mid-April or early May. They visit the edges of large ponds for the rank herbage; fields or savannahs; swampy woods; and extensive marshes. So long as the temperature is sufficiently high the interior and the seashore suit them equally well. In the Middle States these birds are very seldom seen; to the eastward they are unknown, because all their migrations are made far inland. They leave their northern retreats, but return to them to breed and spend the summer.

While migrating, the Whooping Cranes appear to travel both by night and day. I have seen them proceeding during daylight and heard them overhead in the darkness. Be the weather calm or tempestuous, it makes no difference to these birds whose power of flight inures them to the winds. I have watched them urging their way along during heavy gales, shifting from high to low in the air with remarkable dexterity. Sometimes the flock will arrange itself in the form of an acute-angled triangle. Sometimes they move in a long line; or again they mingle without order, or form an extended front. But in whatever manner they advance, each Crane sounds his long note over and over. While with us, they always move about in flocks.

Allow me to refer to my journals, from which I shall extract some observations as to this majestic bird, which I hope you will find not uninteresting.

Louisville, Kentucky, March, 1810.—I had the gratification of taking Alexander Wilson* to some ponds within a few miles of town, and of showing him many birds of this species, of which he had not previously seen any but stuffed specimens. I told him that the white birds were the adults, the gray ones the young. Wilson, in his article on the Whooping Crane, has alluded to this, but, as on other occasions, has not informed his readers whence the information came.

Henderson, November, 1810.—The Sand Hill Crane arrived at the Long Pond on the 28th of last month . . . two flocks of young, and one of adults. . . .

* Author of first study of North American birds: *American Ornithology*, 1808-1814.

Both old and young immediately set to digging through the mud . . . very assiduously, with their bills, and succeeded in uncovering the large roots of the great water lily which often run to a depth of two or three feet. Several Cranes in the same hole tug at the roots and other substances until they reach the object they desire to devour. While thus engaged, with their heads lowered, they cannot see you or take notice of what may be going on around the place. . . . They were perfectly silent. I lay concealed behind a large cypress tree within thirty paces of the flock, thus buried as they were in the huge holes they had been forming. . . . I could plainly see the color of their eyes, which is brown in the young and yellow in the adult. . . . In the course of a week these birds turned up the earth, and dug holes all over the dry parts of the ponds. As soon as heavy rains fill the pools, the Cranes abandon them and resort to other places.

Natchez, Novemeber, 1821.—The Sand Hill Cranes now resort to the fields where corn, peas and sweet potatoes have been planted, as well as to the cotton plantations. They feed on grains and peas, dig up the potatoes . . . ; and in the wet fields they seize on water insects, toads and frogs, but never, I believe, on fishes.

Bayou Sara, April 12, 1822.—The Sand Hill Cranes have left all the fields and removed to the swamps and inner lakes. I saw some catching young Bull-frogs, Water Lizards, and Water Snakes, as well as very small Alligators. One struck at a young Snapping Turtle which escaped. The Wood Ibises and these birds do not agree; the latter chase the former up to their bellies in the water.

April 16.—I saw nine beautiful adult birds apparently in perfect plumage. They were round a fallen log about twenty yards from the water, all very busily occupied in killing a band of young Alligators. . . . I shot at them without much effect . . . ; they all flew off. On going up to the log I found several Alligators, seven to eight inches in length, apparently dead . . . bruised as if by a powerful blow. This led me to think that they kill a number of animals before they feed on them, as the Wood Ibis is wont to do. This afternoon I saw four young Cranes tearing up the ground in search of Cray-fish. One caught a butterfly as it fluttered near, and instantly swallowed it.

This species feeds only in the daytime, and on what I have mentioned, as well as moles and meadow mice, and, I think, snakes of considerable length. I found a fifteen-inch garter-snake in one's stomach. Its wariness is such that it takes all the cunning of an Indian hunter to approach it, especially if it be an old bird. The acuteness of sight and hearing is quite wonderful. If they see a man a quarter of a mile away, they are sure to take wing. If you tread on a stick and break it, the whole flock will emit its croaking cries. They generally see you long before you discover them, and so long as they are aware that you have not noticed them, they remain silent. But the moment you disclose to them your sense of their presence, some of them sound an alarm. For my part, I would as soon undertake to catch a deer by running as to shoot a Sand Hill Crane that had observed me. Sometimes, towards spring, when they are ready to depart for their breeding grounds, the voice of one will startle and urge to flight all within a mile of the spot. Then all the birds around join in a great flock, gradually rise in a spiral, ascend to a vast height, and sail off in a straight course. They roost on the ground or on high trees—the latter before sunset; six or seven settle on the largest branches of lofty trees. For half an hour or so they stand erect to dress their plumage, before crouching low like the Wild Turkey. Others may spend the night on some grassy hillock near large marshes. This bird stands on one leg till daylight, the other being drawn under the body; the head is thrust beneath the broad shoulder feathers. As they return to their feeding grounds at an hour determined by the weather, they emit their cries in a low undertone. On cold, clear mornings they start out early. Their alarm cry resembles the syllables *kewrr, kewrr, kewrooh*. Strange and uncouth as they are, they have always delighted me.

I have never had the satisfaction of finding any of the breeding places of the Whooping Crane. But I know that many breed long before they attain full plumage. The extraordinary strength of the thighs, legs and feet tend greatly to make it more terrestrial than the Herons. Their large nostrils, which resemble those of the Vultures, are well adapted to keep the inner parts of the organ from the damp earth and other matter with which they come in contact while rooting in the mud. I am convinced that they do not attain full size or perfect plumage until the age of four or five.* During the breeding season the plumage is improved by greater brightness; the redness of the fleshy parts of the head also deepens.

One afternoon in winter, as I was descending the Mississippi on my way to Natchez, I saw several Cranes standing on a large sandbar.

* Under two years. The reader will profit by comparing these observations with a modern authority: Robert P. Allen, *The Whooping Crane* (National Audubon Society, 1952).

Excited, I wished to procure some, and accordingly departed from the flatboat in a canoe. I urged the men to watch for me, as the current was rapid. I paddled to shore and landed under cover of a huge stranded tree. Then I lay flat on the sand, pushing my gun before me as I crawled nearer the log. The birds were less than a hundred yards from me. Anxious to show the boatmen how good a marksman I was, I took, as I thought, excellent aim. But all the birds flew off with alarm, excepting one which leaped into the air and at once came down again with a drooping pinion. As I rose on my feet it saw me for the first time, cried out lustily, and ran off with the speed of an Ostrich. In haste I pursued it, my rifle unloaded, to a pile of driftwood. As I approached, panting and almost exhausted, it immediately rose to its full height, ruffled its feathers and shook them, and advanced towards me with open bill and angry eyes. I was exhausted with the fatigue of the chase, I guess, and felt unwilling to encounter my antagonist. Keeping my eye on him I moved backwards. The farther I withdrew, the more he advanced, until I turned my back to him and took to my heels far faster than I had pursued him. He followed, and I was glad to reach the river. I plunged in up to the neck. The boatmen answered to my calls as fast as they could. The Crane meanwhile, still angry—in the water up to his belly, and only a few yards distant—now and then made thrusts at me with his bill. There he stood until my rescuers, highly delighted with my situation, came up.

I shall give you an account of one that I kept alive. It was nearly full grown when it was presented to me by the commander of the war sloop *Erie*. As can be seen in my painting of this bird, its plumage was changing from grayish brown to white. It had been wounded in the wing on the Florida coast. The fractured limb, which had had to be amputated, was healed. During its three months' voyage north it had become gentle and a favorite with the sailors.

I placed the Crane in a yard in Boston along with a beautiful Snow Goose. It would allow me to caress it. I fed it corn and kitchen scraps as well as bread, cheese, and apples. It was fond also of searching for worms and grubs in the wood pile. With the patience of a cat it would watch for the mice that burrowed near the pile, and kill them with a single blow and swallow them entire—one after another. It would pick up the straws intended to keep its feet clean and arrange them like a nest round its body. It would stand on one foot in a graceful posture for hours at a time. During intense cold it retired to a covered passageway as night approached, but always reluctantly and not till all was quiet and nearly dark. Even when snow lay deep on the ground it came out at the earliest dawn. Now and then it would take a run, spread wide its only wing, and leap repeatedly in the air, crying loudly as if anxious to return to its wild haunts. At other times it would look upwards and cry out as if to some acquaintance passing high in the air, but revert to its ordinary note whenever its companion, the Snow Goose, uttered her signals. It seldom swallowed its food without first carrying it to the water to dip it several times, and it would walk yards to do so if necessary. Although the thermometer stood as low as ten degrees some severe winter mornings, the Whooping Crane fattened and looked extremely well.

So strong was its natural suspicion that I often saw it approach cabbage leaves with measured step and look at each leaf sideways. If it accidentally tossed a leaf in the air while trying to break it in pieces, the Crane would run off as if from some dreaded enemy.

American Avocet

In June, 1814, I was travelling on horseback from Henderson, Kentucky, to Vincennes, Indiana. As I approached a large shallow pond near the latter town, I was surprised to see several Avocets hovering over the edges and islets of the pond. Although it was late, and I was both fatigued and hungry, I could not resist trying to find the cause of their being so far from the sea.

Leaving my horse at liberty, I walked toward the pond. On being warned at once by the four birds, I felt confident that they had nests, and that their mates were either sitting or tending their young. The pond, which was about two hundred yards long and half as wide, was surrounded by tall bulrushes along its margin. Near its center were several islets, eight or ten yards in length and arranged in a line. On making the way through the rushes, I found the water only a few inches deep. But the mud reached above my knees as I carefully advanced towards the nearest island. The four birds kept up a constant noise, remained on the wing, and at times dived through the air close to me, showing their displeasure at my intrusion.

My desire to shoot them was restrained by my anxiety to study their habits as closely as possible. As soon as I had searched the different islets, and found three nests with eggs and a female with her brood, I returned to my horse. I proceeded to Vincennes, about two miles distant.

Next morning at sunrise I snugly concealed myself among the rushes, where I enjoyed a fair view of the whole pond. In about an hour the males ceased to fly over me reproachfully, and resumed their ordinary activities. I noticed that the Avocet, whether on the water or on the ground, kept its wings raised until it had fairly settled. It stood in the water for a few minutes, balancing its head and neck somewhat in the manner of the Tell-Tale Godwit. It stalked about searching for food, or swam for a yard or so, from one shallow to another, or waded up to its body with its wings partly raised. Sometimes, with its fellows, it entered the rushes and disappeared for several minutes. They kept apart, but crossed each other's path in hundreds of ways, all perfectly silent and without the least sign of enmity towards each other. But whenever a Sandpiper came near, they instantly chased it.

I sent forth a loud shrill whistle without stirring. They suddenly ceased their rambling, raised their bodies and necks, emitted two or three notes each, and remained several minutes on the alert, afterwards flying to their nests and then returning. I watched them for about an hour. When they searched for food, they moved their heads to and fro sideways, passing their bills through the soft mud. Where the water was deeper they immersed their heads entirely and a part of their necks. They swam on the surface in pursuit of aquatic insects, and were also expert at catching flying insects, which they ran after with partly opened wings. Then they all flew to the islets where the females were calling more loudly than usual. The different pairs seemed to congratulate each other, with various curious gestures. Presently those on the nests left their task to their mates and betook themselves to the water, washed, shook their wings and tails as if overheated, or else tormented by insects, and then began searching for food.

I now paused to eat my humble breakfast.

About eleven o'clock the heat had become so intense that the Avocets gave up their search. Each retired to a different part of the pond. After pluming themselves, they drew their heads close to their shoulders and remained perfectly still as if asleep. After about an hour, they shook themselves, took to wing, rose about thirty or forty yards in air, and flew off towards the Wabash.

I desired to see one of the sitting birds on its nest, so I left my hiding-place as slowly and silently as possible and went towards the nearest islet. I knew there was a nest there, having broken some weeds to mark the precise spot the evening before. These markers I found withered by the sun. No student of Nature ever was, or even can be, too particular while thus marking the exact location of a nest. Indeed I my-self have lost many by being less attentive than I was this time.

Although a person can only advance slowly when wading through mud and knee-deep water, it does not take much time to cover forty or fifty yards. I was soon on the small island where the Avocet was comfortably seated on her nest. Softly, and on all fours, I crawled towards the spot, panting with heat and anxiety. Soon I was within three feet of the unsuspecting creature, peeping at her through the tall grasses. Lovely bird, how innocent and unaware she was, and yet how near to her enemy, even though he was also an admirer of her race! There she sat on her eggs, her head almost mournfully sunk into her plumage. Her eyes, unresponsive even to the sight of her mate, were half closed as if she were dreaming of the future. Having seen all this, I was content.

Then, poor thing, she observed me. Off she scrambled—running, tumbling, and at last rising on the wing to clucking notes of grief and anxiety. None but a callous-hearted person could have heard her without sympathizing with her fears. She floundered hither and thither over the pool, now lying on the surface as if ready to die, now limping to induce me to pursue her and leave her eggs alone.

Not until that day was I aware that gregarious birds can also induce others to leave their eggs by emitting cries of alarm, that all may join in an attempt to save their colony. But so it was with the Avocets. The other two sitters immediately rose on the wing and flew directly at me. The one with the four younglings rushed to the water, waded quickly off, and was followed by her brood which, to my astonishment, paddled along as well as ducklings of the same size.

How far such cries as those of the alarmed Avocet may be heard by others of its kind, I cannot tell. But this I know. The ones which had gone towards the Wabash reappeared in a few minutes after I had disturbed the nesting bird. They hovered over me. But having, I thought, obtained all desirable knowledge of these birds, I shot down five. Among them, unfortunately, I found three females.

They nest among the tallest grasses, using the former year's growth for their materials. I did not find a twig of any kind in their construction. The inside of the nest, about two inches deep and five inches in diameter, is lined with fine prairie grass that is different from that of the islets. The bed of the nest is an inch and a half in thickness. The islets of the pond did not seem liable to flood. The eggs were four in number, like those of most waders, and placed with the small ends together. They measured two inches in length, one inch and three-eighths at their widest point, and were of a dull olive color.

Having made my notes and picked up the dead birds, I carefully waded through the rushes three times around the whole pond. But, being without my dog, I failed to discover the young brood or their mother.

I visited the place twice the following day, again waded round the pond, and searched all the islets, but without success. Not a single Avocet was to be seen. I am persuaded that the mother of the four younglings had moved elsewhere. Since that time my opportunities of meeting with the Avocet have been few. On November 7, 1819, while searching for rare birds near New Orleans, I shot one which I found by itself on the edge of a bayou, and which I measured and described. In May, 1829, I saw three at Great Egg Harbor, but found no nests. On April 16, 1837, my good friend Captain Napoleon Costé of the United States revenue cutter *Campbell,* on board which I then was, shot three on an immense sandbar about twelve miles from Dernière Island on the Gulf of Mexico. He brought them to me in perfect condition. They were larger, and perhaps handsomer, than any that I have seen. They belonged to a flock of five that had been feeding. The captain saw several large flocks there, and told me that their only note was a single whistle.

Great Black=Backed Gull

Hɪɢʜ in the thin keen air, far above the rugged crags of the desolate shores of Labrador, proudly sails the Tyrant Gull, floating along on almost motionless wings, like an Eagle in his calm and majestic flight. On widely spread pinions he moves in large circles, constantly eyeing the winged and uneasy multitudes below with harsh, loud cries.

Onward he sweeps, passing over each rocky bay. He visits the little islands, and shoots off towards the mossy heaths, perhaps attracted by the notes of the Grouse or some other birds. As he flies over each estuary, lake or pool, the breeding birds prepare to defend their unfledged broods, or to insure their escape from the powerful beak of their remorseless spoiler, the Great Black-Backed Gull. Even the shoals of the finny tribes sink deeper into the water as he approaches. The young birds become silent in their nests or seek for safety in the clefts of the rocks. The Guillemots and Gannets dread to look up, and the other Gulls, such as the Silvery member of the species, give way, unable to cope with the destroyer.

Far off among the roaring billows, he spies the carcass of some monster of the deep, and glides steadily towards it. Alighting on the huge whale, he throws his head upwards, opens his bill, and, louder and fiercer than ever, he sends his cries through the air. Leisurely he walks over the monster to make sure that all is safe, then feeds till he is crammed to the throat, afterwards resting in the feeble sheen of the northern sun. Like all gluttons, he loves variety, and away he flies to some island where thousands of young birds or eggs are to be found. Neither the cries of the parents nor all their attempts to drive him away can induce him to desist until he has again satisfied his ever craving appetite. However, the Great Gull, although tyrannical, is a coward. Meanly does he sneak off when he sees the Skua fly up, a bird which, though smaller than he is, evinces such fearlessness as to strike the ravenous and merciless Gull with terror.

Towards summer these wanderers abandon the waters of the ocean to tarry a while on the wild shores of Labrador. There it was that I studied their habits. One by one they arrive, the older birds first, and as they view from afar this land of their birth, they cry out with all the joy a traveller feels when he approaches his loved home. Sooner or later the males fall in with the females of their choice, proceed in pairs to some secluded sandbar, and fill the air with their furious laughs until the rocks echo and re-echo. Each male bows, moves around his mate, and no doubt discloses to her the ardor of his love. Matters are managed to the satisfaction of all parties; day after day, at low tide, they meet as if by mutual agreement. The waters again advance, and the Gulls all move off in search of food. At length the nesting time arrives, and pairs move off in small parties towards the desert isles. Before two weeks have elapsed, incubation has commenced.

The nest is usually placed on the bare rock of some low island, sometimes beneath a projecting shelf, sometimes in a wide fissure. In Labrador it is made of carefully arranged moss and weeds; it is about two feet wide and raised at the edges to a height of five or six inches. But it is seldom more than two inches thick in the center, where feathers, dry grass, and other materials are added. In no instance have I found more than three eggs. These are two and seven-eighths inches long, two and one-eighth inches wide, broadly ovate, rough but not granulated, and of a pale, earthy greenish color spotted with brownish black, dark umber, and dull purple. They afford good eating.

This Gull lays from the middle of May to mid-June, and it raises only one brood in the season. They never leave their eggs for any length of time until the young make their appearance. Both sexes incubate, the sitting bird being supplied with food by the other. During the first week they disgorge supplies into the bill of the young, but after that, food is dropped beside or before them.

When approached by a man, the young Gulls walk with considerable speed towards some hiding place, or to the nearest ledge, beneath which they squat. After five or six weeks they are old enough to take to the water in order to escape, and swim with great buoyancy. If caught, they cry in the same manner as their parents, who, incidentally, completely abandon them as soon as they can seek their own food.

On June 18, 1833, several small Gulls were caught and taken on the deck of the *Ripley* [the schooner chartered in Maine to seek birds in Labrador]. They walked with ease and picked up the food thrown to them. As soon as one was about to swallow its portion, another would run up, seize the morsel and tug at it, and, if stronger, carry it off and devour it. Five days later, two others, which were several weeks old and partly fledged, were brought on board. Their notes, though feeble, perfectly resembled those of their parents. They ate greedily everything offered them. When fatigued they sat with their tarsi or ankle joints stretched forward, as Herons do, in a ludicrous attitude. Before a month had passed they had become acquainted with the cook and several of the sailors, had grown quite fat, and behaved much like Vultures. They never drank water, but often dipped their bills then shook their heads violently. They were fed until they were nearly able to fly.

Now and then the sailors would throw the young Gulls overboard while we were in harbor. This seemed to gratify both them and the men, for they would swim about, wash themselves, dress their plumage, and then make for the sides and be taken on board again.

During a violent gale, one night, while we were at anchor in the harbor of Bras d'Or, our bark rolled heavily. One of our pets went over the side. It swam to shore, where, after a considerable search next day, it was found shivering by the lee of a rock. After it was reunited with its brothers on board, their extremely animated, mutual congratulations were pleasant to see. Before we left the coast, the Gulls would sometimes fly into the water to bathe of their own accord, but they could not return to the deck without assistance, although they tried to.

I became much attached to them. I thought it highly interesting to note that even though the mercury did not rise above 55° in the thermometer, they would lie panting on their sides on the deck. Their enmity for my son's pointer dog was quite remarkable. That animal was of a gentle and kindly disposition, and they would tease him, bite him, and fairly drive him from the deck into the cabin.

A few days after leaving St. George's Bay in Newfoundland, we were assailed by a violent gale, and obliged to "lie to." Next day one of the

Gulls was washed overboard. It tried to reach the vessel again, but in vain. The gale continued. The sailors told me the bird was swimming towards the shore, which was not so far off as we could have wished, and which it probably reached in safety. The other one was given to my friend Lieutenant Green of the United States Army, at Eastport in Maine. In one of his letters to me the following winter, he said that the young Gull was quite a pet in the garrison, and doing very well, but that no perceptible change had taken place in its plumage.

On referring to my journal again, I find that while we were at anchor at St. George's Bay, the sailors caught many small cod for these young Gulls, which swallowed two apiece daily. After this meal it was curious to see the outline of the eight- or ten-inch fish traced along the Gulls' necks, which they had to keep stretched out for a while. They gaped and were evidently suffering, but would not throw up the fish.

The flight of the Great Black-Backed Gull is firm, steady, rather swift, protracted, and also at times elegant. While travelling, it usually flies at a height of fifty or sixty yards, in a direct course with easy, regular flappings. In stormy weather it skims quite low over the surface of the waters or the land, meeting the gale but not yielding to it, and forcing its way against the strongest wind. In calm weather and sunshine it is fond of soaring to a great height and flying about at leisure and with considerable elegance for an hour or so, like Eagles, Vultures and Ravens. To escape a bird of its species or an enemy pursuing it, it rapidly bounds through the air, until it is safe again and can rise and slowly sail in circles. When a man encroaches on its domain, it keeps above him at a safe distance, not sailing so much as moving to either side of him with continuous flappings. To secure fish, its more usual prey, it sweeps downwards with velocity, glides over the spot, and picks up its prey with its bill. If the fish be small, the Gull swallows it on the wing, but if large, it either alights on the water or flies to the nearest shore to devour it.

Until the breeding season it is comparatively silent, but it becomes very noisy then and until the young are well fledged. Its common notes when surprised or interrupted sound like *cack, cack, cack*. While courting, the notes are softer and longer, resembling *cawah*, which it repeats as it sails in circles near the nest and its mate.

This Gull walks well, moves firmly, and with an air of importance. It swims lightly but slowly, and can be quickly overtaken by a boat. Although it cannot dive, it will enter the water along the shores if it sees a crab or lobster, and try to seize it. I saw one at Labrador plunge after a large crab in about two feet of water, then haul it ashore and devour it before my sight. I watched its movements with a glass, saw it eat all but shell and claws, and fly off to its young and disgorge food beside them. I have often seen them attack a brood of ducklings swimming beside their mother, who would have to take to wing while her young ones dived beneath the surface. Unless they happen to rise among the rushes, they were often caught by the Gull when they reappeared. The Eider Duck is the only one of the tribe that will risk her life for her brood on such occasions. She will rise from the water, as her brood disappears beneath it, and keep the Gull at bay, harassing it until her little ones are safe under some rock shelves or shelter. Then she flies off in another direction, leaving the enemy to digest his disappointment. But let the poor Duck be sitting on her eggs in the open, and the marauder will assail her, force her off, and suck the eggs in her very sight. Young Grouse are also the prey of this Gull, which chases them over the moss-covered rocks and devours them before their parents' eyes. It follows the shoals of fishes for hours at a time, usually with great success, seizing flounder on the coast of Labrador and trying to swallow them whole. Once in Boston I saw one of these Gulls take up an eel from a mud-bank one cold winter morning. As the fish was fifteen to eighteen inches long, the Gull rose with difficulty, managing only to gulp the head, then it flew to the shore. There a White-Headed Eagle made its appearance, and soon overtook the Gull, which reluctantly dropped the eel in mid-air as the Eagle glided up, seized it in its talons, and carried it off.

This Gull is so shy and vigilant that even at Labrador we succeeded in obtaining no more than about a dozen old birds, and that only by stratagem. The time to surprise them was during violent gales, when they flew close to the tops of the highest rocks, where we concealed ourselves for the purpose of trying to take them. When we approached the rocky islets where they bred, they left, cackled and barked loudly, and followed us, as we departed, for more than a mile.

The Great Gull must live an extraordinarily long time, as I have seen one that was kept a captive for more than thirty years.

I owe thanks to my esteemed and learned friend Dr. Patrick Neill of Edinburgh [the horticulturalist and printer, who printed *Ornithological*

Biography], for the following very interesting account of the habits of a partly domesticated Great Black-Backed Gull.

In the summer of 1818, a "big Scorie," or Gull, was brought to me by a fisher-boy who said it had been picked up at sea, near the mouth of the Firth of Forth. The bird was not yet fully fledged, but it was quite uninjured, and quickly learned to feed on potatoes and the like from the kitchen. Soon it became tamer than my Ducks, and often peeped in at the kitchen window in hopes of a bit of fat meat, which it relished highly. The Gull would follow my servant, Peggy Oliver, who had a remarkable talent for domesticating uncommon animals and for gardening. It would spread its wings wide and call for food.

After its second moult I was agreeably surprised to find that it assumed the dark plumage of the back, and the shape and color of the bill of its kind, for at first I had taken it for only a large specimen of the Lesser Black-backed Gull. I had a pair of the latter which never allowed the newcomer to associate with them.

The bird was so perfectly tame that we did not take the precaution of keeping the quills of one wing cut short to prevent flight. We did not like to disfigure it, especially since it was often praised as a remarkably large and noble looking Sea-maw. In the winter of 1821-22 it acquired a companion, a cock Heron which had been wounded and brought to Edinburgh alive. The Heron had been kept for some weeks in a cellar of the old college, until the janitor—a person remarkably attached to natural history—presented it to me. We succeeded in taming this Heron completely, and it still remains with me in this year of 1835, with the whole garden to range in, the trees to roost upon, and the lake beside the garden for its pleasure.

For some time in the spring of 1822, the Great Gull was missing. It had not, as we at first supposed, been stolen or killed, but had taken flight northwards over the village, probably bound for the sea, or so I thought. I gave up all expectation of ever hearing more of it. It was not without surprise, therefore, that I heard my servant calling out with great exultation, as I drew near home one day late in October that year, "Sir, Big Gull is come back!"

There he was, walking about in his old haunts in the garden in company with the Heron, which, I am firmly persuaded, he recognized as his old friend. In the evening he disappeared, and for several days he returned in the morning, so that Peggy Oliver thought it best to catch him. He evidently did not like confinement, so we let him have his liberty, although he ran much risk of being shot on the mill pond by young sportsmen from Edinburgh. After his brief captivity he was more cautious and shy than before; but still he made almost daily visits to the garden, picking up Herrings and other food laid down for him.

In the beginning of March, 1823, his visits ceased. We saw no more of him till late in the autumn. These winter visits of his to Canonmills, my home, and his summer excursions to the unknown breeding place, continued for years with great regularity. But I noticed that after the Gull lost his protectress in 1826—whose funeral was attended by the most distinguished naturalists of Edinburgh, and by your friend Dr. Thomas MacCulloch of Nova Scotia—he became more distant.

In my notebook I find this entry for October 26, 1829: "Old Peggy's Great Black-backed Gull arrived at the pond this morning, for the seventh or eighth winter that he has regularly returned. He had a Scorie with him, which was soon shot on the loch by some Cockney sportsman." The young bird, doubtless one of the Great Gull's offspring, had its wing shattered, but remained alive in the middle of the pond, occasionally screaming piteously for two or three days, till relieved by death. The old Gull immediately abandoned the place for that winter, as if reproaching us for our cruelty.

By the next autumn, however, he seemed to have forgotten the injury to his feelings, for my record reads: "October 30, 1830: The Great Black-backed Gull once more arrived in the garden."

The periods of arrival, residence with us, and departure were quite similar the following year. But in 1832, not only October but November and December passed without Big Gull's making his appearance. I of course despaired of seeing him again. However, he did finally arrive, and I wrote in my notebook: "Sunday, January 6, 1833: This day the Great Black-back returned to the mill pond, for, I think, the eleventh season. He used to reappear in October, and I concluded him dead or shot by this time. He recognized my voice, and hovered over my head. Early in March he disappeared as usual, and reappeared here on December 23, 1833, a fortnight earlier than the date of his arrival the preceding season, but six weeks later than the original reappearance. He left at the beginning of March, 1834, for the season, first hovering around and then alighting on the pond as in former years."

The latest entry is: "March 11, 1835. The Black-backed Gull was here yesterday, but has not been seen to-day; nor do I expect to see him till November."

This Gull often attracts the attention of people passing the village of Canonmills, by its sweeping along so low and by the wide expanse of its wings. It is well known to the boys of the village as "Neill's Gull," and more than once it has owed its safety to their informing passing sportsmen of its history.

When it first arrives in autumn, it always makes many circular sweeps around the pond and garden, at a considerable height, as if reconnoitering. Then it gradually lowers its flight and gently alights at about the center of the pond. Should the gardener mount the garden wall with a fish in his hand, the Gull will move towards the overhanging spray of one of the large willow trees so as to catch the fish if it is thrown to him. There can be no doubt as to the identity of the bird. He shows that he recognizes my voice when I call aloud, "Gull, Gull"; and whether he happens to be on the wing or afloat, he immediately approaches me.

A few pairs of the Great Black-backed Gull breed at the Bass Rock yearly. It seems probable that my pet was hatched there. If I may be allowed, I would suppose that he resorted to the same spot for the purpose of breeding after he attained maturity. But having lost his mate or encountered some other disaster, he must have extended his migration to some very distant breeding place, which would have caused his return to winter quarters with us six weeks later than formerly.

Terns

SOOTY TERN

In May, 1832, I observed the Sooty Terns while cruising in the Florida Keys on the revenue cutter *Marion*, which my party called the "Lady of the Green Mantle." The Captain referred to these birds as "Black and White Sea Swallows." His pilot told me that they resorted by the thousands for the season on a certain island, and laid their eggs on the sand under the bushes in nests about a foot apart. I expressed a wish to land there, but we sailed on through the strange, extremely dangerous channels to a small harbor before we dropped anchor.

As the chain grated I saw a cloudlike mass arise a few hundred yards off. In a few minutes my assistant and I were in a yawl. As we landed I felt as if the birds would raise me from the ground, so thick were they all around us, and so quick was the motion of their wings. Their cries were deafening. Most of the females, however, remained on the ground —the naked beach—which was covered with birds.

The next morning I learned that vast numbers of the Terns habitually left the island at 2 A.M., flew towards the sea, and returned about four, or a little before day. Except during gales, this proved regularly the case, a proof that this species sees as well during the night as by day, when they also go to sea in search of food for themselves and their young. In this they differ from the Noddy Tern, which darkness obliges to land on the yards of vessels to sleep until daylight—a fact that gave the Noddy its name.

The Sooty Terns rarely alight on the water, though the Noddy both alights and floats, owing to the difference in their tail feathers, those of the former being long. It differs materially from all the other species of

Terns. It never dives headlong and perpendicularly as the smaller species do, but passes over its prey in a curved line before it picks it up. This action calls to mind the plunge of the Night Hawk over its female. I have often watched the Sooty Tern follow and hover in the wake of a porpoise which was pursuing its prey. At the instant when the porpoise makes a sudden dash or dip towards the surface to frighten and drive the small fry upwards, the Tern as suddenly passes over the spot and picks up a small fish or two.

The flight is not so buoyant or decided as that of other species such as the Cayenne Tern, except while taking prey. The Noddy always nests on trees or bushes, where it alights with as much ease as a Crow or Thrush. But this Tern never forms a nest of any sort; it deposits its eggs in a slight cavity which it scoops in the sand under the trees.

Early next morning I was put ashore on the Bird Key. I sat on the shelly sand almost motionless for several hours, so that the birds alighted about me within but a few yards. I could see plainly with what pains and efforts the younger females deposited their eggs. They opened their bills, and their panting showed their distress; but after they expelled the egg they immediately walked off awkwardly to a place which had no bushy branches to strike them when they rose to fly. Some within twenty yards of me had already begun incubation. Now and then a male bird disgorged a small fish within their reach. After some odd exchanges of nods, doubtless signs of affection, the caterer flew off. Terns which had not begun laying their eggs scratched the sand with their feet, like common fowl, in search of food, occasionally sitting in the shallow basin they had shaped to their form. Not the least sign of a quarrel did I see. Indeed they all appeared to be like happy members of a single family. A few went through the process of courtship in my presence, as if to gratify my wishes. The males frequently threw their heads over their backs as some Gulls do. They swelled their throats, walked round the females, and uttered a soft puffing sound as they caressed them. Then the two walked round each other, and at last rose and flew off.

The Sooty Tern lays three smooth, pale cream eggs.* I did not ascertain whether the male and female take turns sitting on the eggs, because the birds frequently left their eggs for half an hour or longer, and because of the slight difference in size and color between the sexes. The

* One egg.

eggs usually measure two and one-eighth inches by one and one half, and repose in depressions scooped in sand near roots or stems of bushes, in shade, close together. Lightish umber tints and still lighter marks of purple are added to the cream color. It is said that as soon as the eggs are hatched, the young ramble pell-mell over the island to be fed by their parents.

Early in August the Sooty Terns retire southward for the winter. Before the departure the young are grayish brown above and dull white beneath, and have a very short tail.

It would appear that at some not very remote period the Noddy Tern tried to appropriate this key where I studied the Sooty Tern. I found several thousand empty nests of that bird on the tops of bushes. They may have attempted to breed here but have been forced to withdraw to that neighboring island where they breed by themselves, a few miles away. Other observers have noted such conflicts among different species of birds. I have seen several instances of it, particularly among the Herons. Invariably, whether rightly or wrongly, the stronger party never fails to dislodge the weaker and to keep possession of the disputed ground.

ROSEATE TERN

On April 28, 1832, I visited a beautiful rocky islet named Indian Key, off the Florida coast. I tried for several hours to sleep on the night before, but the realization that this part of the country had not yet been examined by any industrious student of Nature made me wakeful. The rain fell in torrents, and the sound of large drops on the shingles of the veranda where my hammock hung helped little. At four o'clock I roused my companions, and in a few minutes all were up and breakfast was preparing.

Before six the rain abated. We made our way to the boats and pushed off through a gentle shower to look for unknown birds. In an hour the sky cleared and the sun dried our clothes. We saw hosts of Terns on a sandbar as we approached it. Beautiful indeed are Terns of every kind, but the Roseate excels the rest—at least in the lovely hue of its breast. I had never seen the species before. As they rose and danced by hundreds in the air, I thought of them as Hummingbirds of the sea, so light and graceful were their movements. They flocked together and hovered over us, then with a sudden dash plunged angrily towards us. Even their wrath sounded musical. As I said, I had not seen even the skin of a Roseate Tern before. You may rest assured that I took precious care of those which I now procured. I determined to ransack every key and beach to find the Tern's breeding ground.

It spends the breeding season along the southern shores of the Floridas. At different times during the nearly three months I spent among the keys I saw flocks of twenty, thirty, or more pairs on small detached rocky islands, associating with Sandwich Terns. The two species appeared to agree well, and their nests were intermingled. The three eggs* of the Roseate Tern differ in size and markings, but average an inch and three-quarters in length and an inch and one-eighth in breadth. The longish oval shape is rather narrowed at the small end, and is dull buff or clay colored, with spots and tints of umber and light purple. The eggs were deposited on the bare rocks among the roots of grasses, and left to the heat of the sun in fair weather. The eggs of the Sandwich Tern were more attended to during the day than these, but towards night both species sat on their eggs. Although I did not see the newly hatched birds, I obtained quite a number of one-year-olds; these remained apart from the old birds but had all the same habits as their elders.

This is a noisy, restless bird at all times, with a sharp shrill cry that resembles the syllable *crāk*. Its flight is unsteady and flickering, like that of the Arctic or Lesser Terns, but more buoyant and graceful. The Roseate Terns would dash at us and make off again with astonishing quickness, making much use of their tails. While searching their prey they carry their bills downward—perpendicularly—and plunge like a shot with their wings nearly closed about their bodies, then at once ascend. Each such plunge may secure the Tern a fish. It feeds also on small mollusks which float near the surface by the name of "Sailor's Buttons." The Tern usually keeps to parties of ten to twenty; these follow the shores of the keys and sandbars backward and forward. They hover above shoals of small fish and dash headlong at them for minutes at a time.

This species returns here regularly each spring about April 10, and goes southward early in September.

* Two eggs.

The delicate and beautiful rosy tint of the breast soon fades after death. Those not skinned immediately did not retain it for a week; after a month it could only be seen by parting the feathers. The tint disappears in winter on the live Tern, as well as the glossy black of the head. The length of the outer tail-feathers varies considerably. However, I could note no decided difference of size or color in the sexes, although I thought the females somewhat smaller than the males.

Atlantic Puffin

I saw a good number of these sea Parrots in Georgia the winter of 1831-32, though they seldom extend their southward migrations so far. I suspect they do so only in very severe weather. Those which proceed north of the Bay of Fundy leave the United States about mid-April, along the coast.

On my Labrador voyage I observed Puffins every day. As we approached that inhospitable land, we saw a few around the vessel, now floating on the swelling wave, now disappearing under the bow, diving with the swiftness of thought, or rising and flying swift and low over the sea. After we drew near the coast they covered a half an acre or more of water. Aware that they had begun to breed, I started an investigation of their habits.

The first breeding place that my party and I visited was a small green island of a few acres, pleasing to the eye. The sea ran high on the exceedingly rugged shores, so that a safe landing proved difficult. But finally, borne on the summit of a great wave, we reached the first rocks, leaped out, held the row-boat, and made it fast. Some of the many Puffins flew past us alarmed, like arrows. Others stood erect before their burrows. Some more timid ones withdrew within their holes as we advanced. The soil was so light and so easily dug that many of the burrows were five or six feet long, though only a few inches below the surface. The whole island was perforated like a rabbit warren. Every hole had an entrance placed due south, a circumstance which allowed the birds to emerge in our sight almost all at once—a highly gratifying spectacle. This visit occurred on June 28, 1833.

On August 12, our Captain, four sailors, two of my party and I visited "Perroket Island," about two miles from the harbor of Bras d'Or, a place known to all the cod-fishers and celebrated as a breeding ground for Puffins. The water was literally covered with thousands of these birds as we rowed towards the island; but the number that flew over and around it seemed much greater; one might have imagined half the Puffins in the world had assembled there. For every burrow in the island we had previously visited, there seemed to be a hundred within these rocky shores, beyond which the ground rose in the form of a high amphitheatre. On every crag or stone stood a Puffin, at the entrance of each hole another; and the sea around and the air above were filled by them.

The burrows were all inhabited by young birds of different ages and sizes. Clouds of Puffins with four- or five-inch "lint" fishes from the shoals, held by the head, flew over us. Though they emitted a loud croaking noise they never dropped the fish.

I observed with concern the extraordinary affection shown these birds by one another. Whenever one fell dead or wounded on the water, its mate or a stranger at once alighted by its side, swam round it, and pushed it with its bill as if to urge it to fly or dive. Seldom would the rescuer leave it until aware of danger, when it plunged below the surface in an instant. Some ran to their holes and dived inside. Those caught alive in the hand bit severely and scratched with their claws till we were glad to let them escape.

The burrows communicated in various ways, so that the whole island was perforated as if by a multitude of subterranean labyrinths, over which one could not run without the risk of falling at almost every step. The voices of the young sounded beneath our feet like voices from the grave, and the stench was so disagreeable that we were soon glad to get away. During our visit, the birds never left the place, but busied themselves with fishing, diving into their burrows, or feeding the young that stood waiting at the entrances. The young birds fought continually. Those which we caught did also, and used their yet extremely small, slender bills with great courage and pertinacity. Their cries resembled the wailing of young whelps. The parents fed the smaller ones by regurgitation, or placed small fishes in their mouths. They dropped fish for the larger ones to pick up.

The network of burrows had a round place scooped out on one side of the avenue, in the form of an oven. In the single burrows this oven-like place was at the end, and it was larger than the corridor. All the passages were flattish above and rounded beneath as well as on the sides. In many instances we found two birds sitting on their one and only egg in the same hole; for unless the first is destroyed or removed, it lays but one. The time of incubation is probably from twenty-five to twenty-eight days. Both birds work in digging the hole by means of their bills and feet. They also sit alternately, though the female does so the more industriously; the male labors harder at the burrow. No nest is formed for the reception of the pure white egg, which soon becomes soiled by the earth. It generally measures two and a half inches by one and three-fourths, but varies in size according to the age of the bird, as well as in shape, some being rounder at the smaller end than others.

The flight of the Puffin is firm, usually direct, and often pretty well sustained. It can rise at once from the water or the land, although it may run upon both before taking wing. This depends much on necessity; if pushed, it flies at once from the ground, or else plunges beneath the water's surface. There it swims with partly opened wings at a shallow depth like the diving species. In this way it also catches its prey. Sometimes it will dive to the bottom, many fathoms deep, for shell-fish and the like.

During the love season the males chase each other in the air, on the water, or beneath the surface, and with so much speed as to resemble the ricochets of a cannon ball.

After having kept several for about a week, I threw them overboard in the harbor where we lay at anchor and where the water was beautifully clear. After they left my gloved hand they plunged through the air, entered the water and swam off by the use of their wings to a distance of perhaps a hundred yards. Then they came up, washed their plumage for a time, and again made a dive in search of food. While on board they ran about from dark towards dawn, briskly and erectly, grunting unpleasantly; their footsteps could be counted as they ran about incessantly during the night. On coming close to my feet they would watch me like Hawks; if I looked towards them they instantly made for some hiding place.

The down of the young is black, with a white patch on the belly. Their bills do not acquire much of their ultimate form for several weeks; nor do they assume their perfect shape for years. Among the hundreds that

I have examined I have found great differences in the size and shape of the bill. The sexes differ in no perceptible degree except that the males are somewhat the larger. When two years old they may be considered of full size. The bill continues to grow and to acquire furrows until it becomes as you see it in *The Birds of America*.

Passenger Pigeon

IN THIS BIOGRAPHY A BIRD NOW EXTINCT COMES TO LIFE, AND IN IT, ITS
EVENTUAL DISAPPEARANCE IS NEITHER PROPHESIED NOR FEARED—ED.

I SHALL begin my description of the Passenger Pigeon with an account
of its flight, because the most important facts connected with its habits
relate to its migrations. It migrates for food rather than with a view to
escaping the severity of the northern weather, or to seek a southern
climate for breeding. Consequently such flights do not take place at any
fixed period or season of the year. Indeed it sometimes happens that a
continuance of a supply of food in one district will keep these birds
away from any other place for years. I know, at least, to a certainty, that
in Kentucky they remained for several years constantly, and were
nowhere else to be found. They all suddenly disappeared one season
when the mast (or acorns, nuts and tree pods) was exhausted, and they
did not return for a long period. Similar facts have been observed in
other States.

Their great power of flight enables them to survey and pass over an
astonishing extent of country in a very short time, as proved by well-
known facts. Pigeons have been killed in the neighborhood of New
York with their crops full of rice, which they must have collected in the
fields of Georgia and Carolina. These districts are the nearest possible
for a supply of such food. Their power of digestion is so remarkable that
they can entirely assimilate food in twelve hours; therefore, they must
have travelled between three and four hundred miles in six hours, showing their speed to be at an average of about one mile a minute. A velocity

such as this would enable one of these birds to visit the European continent in less than three days, were it so inclined.

This great power of flight is seconded by as great a power of vision, which enables them to inspect the country below as they travel at that swift rate, and to discover their food with facility. Thus they obtain the object of their journey. I have also proved another point by my observation that they fly high and in an extended front when passing over sterile or poor country. This enables them to survey hundreds of acres at once. On the other hand, when the land is richly covered with food, or the trees abundantly hung with mast, they fly low in order to discover the part most plentifully supplied.

Their body is formed in an elongated oval, which they steer with a long, well-plumed tail and propel with well-set wings, the muscles of which are very large and powerful for the size of the bird. A bird seen gliding through the woods and close to the observer passes like a thought; and the eye tries in vain to see it again, but the bird is gone. It propels itself with extreme rapidity by repeated flapping of the wings, which it brings more or less close to its body, according to the degree of velocity required. Like the domestic Pigeon, it often flies in a circling manner during the love season, supporting itself with both wings elevated at an angle, and keeping them in that position until it is about to alight. Now and then during these circular flights, the tips of the primary quills of each wing are made to strike against each other, producing a smart rap which may be heard thirty or forty yards away. Before alighting, the Wild Pigeon, like the Carolina Parrot and a few other species of birds, breaks the force of its flight by repeated flapping, as if apprehensive of injury from too sudden contact with the branch or spot of ground where it intends to settle.

The multitudes of Wild Pigeons in our American woods are astonishing. Indeed, after having viewed them so often and under so many circumstances, I now feel inclined even to pause and reassure myself that what I am going to relate is fact. Yet I have seen it all, and in the company, too, of persons who like myself were struck with amazement.

In the autumn of 1813 I left my house at Henderson on the banks of the Ohio, on my way to Louisville ninety miles distant. In passing over the Kentucky barrens a few miles beyond Hardinsburg, I observed the Passenger Pigeons flying from northeast to southwest in greater numbers than I had ever seen them before, it seemed to me. Feeling an inclination to count the flocks that might pass within the reach of my eye in one hour, I dismounted, seated myself on an eminence, and began to mark a dot with my pencil for every flock that passed. In a short time, finding this task impracticable because the birds were pouring by in countless multitudes, I arose. But before I travelled on, I counted the dots that I had put down and found that one hundred and sixty flocks had been recorded in twenty-one minutes. I met still more, farther on. The air was literally filled with Pigeons, and the noon-day light was obscured as by an eclipse. The dung fell in spots not unlike melting flakes of snow; and the continuous buzz of wings tended to lull my senses.

While waiting for dinner at Young's Inn at the confluence of Salt River with the Ohio, I saw, at my leisure, immense legions still going by. Their front reached far beyond the Ohio on the west, and the beech-wood forests directly east of me. Not a single bird alighted, for not a nut or acorn was that year to be seen in the neighborhood. Consequently they were flying so high that different attempts to reach them with a capital rifle proved ineffectual; nor did the reports disturb them in the least. I cannot describe to you the extreme beauty of their aerial evolutions when a Hawk chanced to press upon the rear of a flock. At once, like a torrent, and with a noise like thunder, they rushed in a compact mass, pressing upon each other towards the center. In these almost solid masses they darted forward in undulating and angular lines, descended to the earth and swept close over it with inconceivable velocity. Then they mounted perpendicularly so as to resemble a vast column, and, when high, they were seen wheeling and twisting within their continued lines, which resembled the coils of a gigantic serpent.

Before sunset I reached Louisville, fifty-five miles from Hardinsburg. The Pigeons were still passing in undiminished numbers. They continued to do so for three days in succession. The people were all in arms, and the banks of the Ohio were crowded with men and boys incessantly shooting at the pilgrims, which flew lower as they passed the river. Multitudes were thus destroyed. For a week or more, the population fed on no other flesh than that of Pigeons, and talked of nothing but Pigeons.

Shot at L. Ohio. Decemb. 11. 1809.
12 francs à la juene fem stage!
April.. Wild Pigeon.
J. Audubon.
No 109.

Passenger Pigeon A.W.
Columba Migratoria

It is extremely interesting to see flock after flock performing exactly the same evolutions which a preceding flock has traced in the air. Thus should a Hawk charge on a group at a certain point, the angles, curves and undulations described by the birds in their efforts to escape the dreaded talons of the plunderer are undeviatingly followed by the next flock that comes up. Should the bystander happen to witness one of these affrays and be struck with the rapidity and elegance of the motions, and desire to see them repeated, his wishes will be gratified if he but remain in the same place until the next flock of Pigeons comes along.

As soon as the Pigeons discover a sufficiency of food to entice them to alight, they fly around in circles, reviewing the countryside below. During these evolutions the dense mass which they form presents a beautiful spectacle, as it changes its direction, turning from a glistening sheet of azure, as the backs of the birds come simultaneously into view, to a suddenly presented, rich deep purple. After that they pass lower, over the woods, and for a moment are lost among the foliage. Again they emerge and glide aloft. They may now alight, but the next moment take to wing as if suddenly alarmed, the flapping of their wings produc ing a noise like the roar of distant thunder, as they sweep through the forests to see if danger is near. However, hunger soon brings them to the ground. On alighting they industriously throw aside the withered leaves in quest of the fallen mast. The rear ranks continually rise, passing over the main body and alighting in front, and in such rapid succession that the whole flock seems still on the wing. The quantity of ground swept in this way is astonishing. So completely has it been cleared that the gleaner who might follow in the rear of the flock would find his labor completely lost. While feeding, their avidity is at times so great that, in attempting to swallow a large acorn or nut, they may be seen to gasp for a long while as if in the agonies of suffocation.

When the woods are filled with these Pigeons, they are killed in immense numbers, although no apparent diminution comes of it. About mid-day, after their repast is finished, they settle on the trees to enjoy rest and digest their food. On the ground and on the branches they walk with ease, frequently jerking their beautiful tails and moving their necks backward and forward in the most graceful manner. As the sun begins to sink beneath the horizon, they depart *en masse* for the roosting place which, not infrequently, is hundreds of miles away, a fact ascertained by persons who have kept track of their arrivals and departures.

Let us inspect their place of nightly rendezvous. One of these curious roosting places on the banks of the Green River in Kentucky I repeatedly visited. As always, it was in a part of the forest where the trees were huge and where there was little underbrush. I rode through it for more than forty miles, and on crossing it in different parts I found it rather more than three miles wide on average. My first view of it was at nearly two hours before sunset, about two weeks before the coming of the Pigeons. Few of these birds were then to be seen, but a great gathering of persons with horses and wagons, guns and ammunition had pitched camp on the edge of the forest.

Two farmers from the vicinity of Russellville, more than a hundred miles distant, had driven more than three hundred hogs to be fattened on the Pigeons they hoped to slaughter. Here and there, people were busy plucking and salting birds already killed, and they sat amid large piles of them. The dung lay several inches deep, covering the whole roosting place. I noticed that many trees two feet in diameter were broken off at no great distance from the ground; and the branches of many of the largest and tallest had given way. It was as if the forest had been swept by a tornado, proving to me that the number of birds must be immense beyond conception.

As the time of the arrival of the Passenger Pigeons approached, their foes anxiously prepared to receive them. Some persons were ready with iron pots containing sulphur, others with torches of pine knots; many had poles, and the rest, guns. The sun went down, yet not a Pigeon had arrived. However, everything was ready, and all eyes were fixed on the clear sky which could be glimpsed amid the tall tree-tops.

Suddenly a general cry burst forth, "Here they come!" The noise they made, even though still distant, reminded me of a hard gale at sea, passing through the rigging of a close-reefed vessel. As the birds arrived and passed over me, I felt a current of air that surprised me. Thousands of the Pigeons were soon knocked down by the pole-men, while more continued to pour in. The fires were lighted, then a magnificent, wonderful, and almost terrifying sight presented itself. The Pigeons, arriving by the thousands, alighted everywhere, one above another, until solid masses were formed on the branches all around.

Here and there the perches gave way with a crash under the weight, and fell to the ground, destroying hundreds of birds beneath, and forcing down the dense groups of them with which every stick was loaded. The scene was one of uproar and confusion. I found it quite useless to speak, or even to shout, to those persons nearest to me. Even the gun reports were seldom heard, and I was made aware of the firing only by seeing the shooters reloading.

No one dared venture nearer the devastation. Meanwhile, the hogs had been penned up. The picking up of the dead and wounded birds was put off till morning. The Pigeons were constantly coming, and it was past midnight before I noticed any decrease in the number of those arriving. The uproar continued the whole night. I was anxious to know how far away the sound could be heard, so I sent off a man used to roaming the forest, who returned in two hours with the information that he had heard it distinctly three miles from the roosting place.

Towards the approach of day, the noise somewhat subsided. Long before I could distinguish them plainly, the Pigeons began to move off in a direction quite different from the one in which they flew when they arrived the evening before. By sunrise all that were able to fly had disappeared. The howling of the wolves now reached our ears, and the foxes, lynxes, cougars, bears, raccoons, opossums and polecats were sneaking off. Eagles and Hawks, accompanied by a crowd of Vultures, took their place and enjoyed their share of the spoils.

Then the authors of all this devastation began to move among the dead, the dying, and the mangled, picking up the Pigeons and piling them in heaps. When each man had as many as he could possibly dispose of, the hogs were let loose to feed on the remainder.

Persons unacquainted with these birds might naturally conclude that such dreadful havoc would soon put an end to the species. But I have satisfied myself by long observation that nothing but the gradual diminution of our forests can accomplish their decrease. They not infrequently quadruple their number yearly, and always at least double it. In 1805 I saw schooners loaded with Pigeons caught up the Hudson River, coming into the wharf at New York where the birds sold for a cent apiece. I knew a man in Pennsylvania who caught and killed more than five hundred dozen in a clap-net in one day. Sometimes the net took twenty dozens or more at a single haul. In March, 1830, the Passenger

Pigeon was so abundant in the New York markets that piles of them met the eye in every direction. I have seen the Negroes grow weary of killing them as the birds alighted for weeks at a time to drink the water from the pipes at the saltworks of Shawnee Town, on the Tennessee-Kentucky border.

The places they choose for breeding are of interest; though, as I have said, the season varies. Food is most plentiful and most attainable, and water is always at a convenient distance. The tallest trees of the forest are those in which the Pigeons nest. To them countless pairs resort and prepare to fulfil one of the great laws of Nature. At this period the note of the Pigeon is a soft *coo—coo—coo—coo*, much shorter than that of the domestic variety. The common notes resemble *kee—kee—kee—kee*, the first of these being the loudest, and the others gradually diminishing in power. With his tail spread and his wings drooping, the male, whether on the ground or on the branches, follows the female with a pompous demeanor. His body is elevated, his throat swells, his eyes sparkle, as he continues his cooing. Now and then he rises on the wing and flies a few yards towards the fugitive and timorous female. Like the domestic Pigeon and others, they caress each other by billing, an action in which the bill of the one is placed transversely in that of the other. Both birds alternately disgorge the contents of their crops by repeated efforts. After these preliminaries, the Pigeons begin building their nest in peace and harmony, crossing a few dry twigs in the fork of some branches.

Sometimes fifty to a hundred nests may be seen in the same tree. Were I not anxious that you should not feel disposed to refer my account of the Wild Pigeons to the marvelous, however wonderful, I might estimate a much greater number than one hundred.

There are two, broadly elliptical, pure white eggs.* The male keeps the female supplied with food during incubation. Indeed the tenderness and affection shown by these birds towards their mates are striking in the highest degree. It is a remarkable fact that each brood hatched usually consists of a male and female.

Here again, the tyrant of creation, man, interferes, disturbing the harmony of this peaceful scene. As the young birds grow up, their enemies, armed with axes, reach the spot and seize and destroy all they

* Normal: one, according to modern texts.

can. The trees are felled, and are made to fall in such a way that the cutting of one causes the overthrow of another. Or the crash shakes the trees near by so much that the young Pigeons, or squabs, are violently tossed to the ground. In this way immense quantities are destroyed.

The young are fed by the parents as described above. In other words, the old bird puts its bill in the mouth of the young one crosswise, or with the back of the two parts of the bill opposite the young bird's open mouth and disgorges the contents of its crop as food. As soon as the young are able to shift for themselves, they leave their parents and continue apart until they reach maturity. By the end of six months they are capable of reproducing their species.

The flesh of the Wild Pigeon is of a dark color, but affords tolerable eating. That of young birds is much esteemed. The skin is covered with small white filmy scales. The feathers fall off at the least touch, like those of the Carolina Mourning Dove. Like other Pigeons, it immerses its head up to the eyes while drinking.

In March, 1830, I bought about three hundred and fifty of these birds in the New York market at four cents apiece, and carried most of them alive to England. I distributed them among several noblemen, giving some to the Zoological Society also. A curious change of habits has taken place in those which I presented to the Earl of Derby in 1830. That nobleman has assured me that ever since they began breeding in his aviaries near Liverpool they have laid only one egg. My noble friend has raised many and distributed them freely. It is therefore not surprising that some which have escaped confinement have been shot. But that the Passenger Pigeon should have a natural claim to be admitted into the British fauna appears to me very doubtful.

This bird wanders continually in search of food throughout all parts of North America, and is wonderfully abundant at times in particular districts.

$\mathcal{D}$oves

ZENAIDA DOVE

NOT RECORDED IN THE UNITED STATES SINCE
THE AUDUBONIAN PERIOD—ED.

YOUTHFUL impressions are frequently stronger than those of more advanced age, and are usually retained. My father often told me that my first childhood attempt at drawing was from a preserved specimen of a Dove. Many times he repeated to me that birds of this kind are usually remarkable for their gentle dispositions, and that their mutual affection and their devotion to their offspring were undoubtedly intended in part to teach other beings a lesson in connubial and parental attachment. Be that as it may, hypothesis or not, I have always been especially fond of Doves. Who can approach a sitting Dove and hear its notes of protest, without a sense of wrong-doing?

The cooing of the Zenaida Dove is a peculiar sound. A man who had been a pirate once assured me, in the Florida Keys, that the soft, melancholy cry awoke feelings of repentance in his heart. He lingered near the wells where he heard it, and each time that he left the spot his fears for the future increased; for he was one of a band of the most desperate villains that ever harassed navigation off the Florida coasts. So deeply moved was he by the notes of any bird—and especially those of a Dove—the only soothing sounds he ever heard during his career of horrors—that he finally decided to escape from his vessel, to abandon his rough companions, and return to his family. Now he lives in peace among his friends as an honest man.

This Dove is a transient visitor of the keys of East Florida. It appears near Indian Key about April 15, continues to increase in numbers until October, and then returns to the West Indies from whence it came. It lays its two pure white eggs about the first of May. The males reach the breeding grounds of the keys before the females. They coo and ramble about in search of mates more than a week before the latter appear. But in autumn, males, females and young set out in small parties together. They seldom fly higher than the tops of the mangroves, or any considerable distance at one time, once they choose an island for a breeding place. Although it alights on trees with ease, and walks well on branches, it spends most of the time on the ground, walking and running in search of food with lightness and celerity. It carries its tail higher than the Ground Dove, but like it this Dove roosts on the ground. Its wings have not the whistling sound of the Mourning Dove's; nor does the male sail over the female while she is sitting on her eggs, as does the latter species. When crossing the sea, or going from key to key, it flies near the water's surface. If startled on the ground, it flies a short distance and alights in thick grass or the center of the low bushes. So gentle are they, as a rule, that I have approached some so near that I could have touched them with my gun while they stood gazing intently at me . . . as if I were an object not at all to be dreaded.

They choose keys the interior of which are covered with grass and low shrubs, the borders having hedges of mangroves or other low trees. They are by no means so abundant as the White-Crowned Pigeon, which builds on any kind of tree.

The Zenaida Dove's nest on the ground is sometimes placed at the foot of a low bush, artlessly exposed. Other times more discrimination is shown, and it is placed between two or more tufts of grass, the tops of which the Dove bends in such a way as to conceal the nest completely. The sand is slightly scooped out, and slender dried blades of grass are matted in a circle imbedded in dry leaves and twigs. The structure is more compact than any other Pigeon nest I know. The female seldom leaves the nest during incubation, unless disturbed. The cooing resembles that of the Mourning Dove, and morning is the time when it is heard— not from the ground but from a low, large branch. These birds are concealed and silent at mid-day when the Florida heat is almost insufferable.

They feed on grass seeds, leaves of aromatic plants, and various berries, including one extremely poisonous to man. They add gravel or particles of shell to their food for digestion.

The young, when unfledged, are of a deep purplish gray color; their bills and legs are black; and not until spring do they attain their full plumage. The birds leave the keys about the beginning of October. The more richly colored male is larger than the female. Their feathers fall off at the slightest touch. Like all other Pigeons, they quiver their wings with much force when about to die.

The Zenaida Dove resorts to certain wells on the keys, said to have been dug by pirates long ago. There they and other birds may be seen both morning and evening. The loose sand which they toss up about these wells suits them well to dust in, and to clean their apparel.

MOURNING DOVE

In *The Birds of America* I tried to give you a faithful picture of two pairs of Turtle Doves as gentle as ever cooed their love in the green woods. I placed them on a branch of Stuartia, which has a profusion of white blossoms, emblematic of purity and chastity. The female of my painting sits on her eggs and receives food from the bill of her mate. She listens with delight to his assurances of devotion. Nothing is wanting to render the moment as happy as any couple could wish on such an occasion. But on the branch above them, a love scene is just commencing. Still coy and uncertain, the female seems doubtful of the truthfulness of her lover, and, virgin-like, she resolves to test his sincerity by delaying the gratification of his wishes. She has reached the end of the branch; her wings and tail are already opening, and she will fly off to some more sequestered spot. If her lover follows with the same ardent devotion, they will doubtless become as blessed as the pair seen beneath them.

The Mourning Dove announces the approach of spring, and makes us forget the chilling blasts of winter by the soft melancholy of her cooing. Her heart is already so warmed and swollen by the ardor of her passion that it feels as ready to expand as do the buds on the trees beneath the genial sunshine.

The flight of this bird is extremely rapid and of long duration. The whistling of its wings, as it starts from trees or the ground on being approached, can be heard at quite a distance. It will then make several curious windings through the air as if to prove its flying prowess, but seldom far above the trees, or into dense woods or forest. It prefers the margins, or flying about fences and fields. Yet, during spring, and particularly while the female is sitting on her eggs, the male rises as if about to ascend to a great height, flapping his wings. But all of a sudden he comes downwards again in a large circle, sailing smoothly with wings and tail expanded until he alights on the tree where the nest is, or on one close to it. He may repeat these manoeuvres frequently during the days of incubation, and occasionally during his courtship. The moment he alights he jerks his tail gracefully and balances his neck and head. This bird walks with ease and grace on the ground, fences, and branches of trees, often jerking his tail. It can run swiftly when searching where food is scarce. It seldom bathes, but drinks by swallowing water in long draughts, with its bill often immersed up to the eyes. Its migration is not so extensive as that of the Wild Pigeon, nor in such numbers . . . two hundred and fifty or three hundred Doves are considered a large flock.

They breed in all parts of the United States that I have visited. They rear either one or two broods in the season, depending on the temperature or climate. In Louisiana they lay eggs early in April or in March, and have two broods. They seldom begin to lay in Connecticut before mid-May and rarely have more than one brood. On the shores of Lake Superior they are still later. Their two white, somewhat translucent eggs measure one and one-eighth inches in length and five and a half eighths in breadth. The nest is built in any kind of tree—on horizontal branches or twigs—and is formed of a few dry sticks so loosely put together as to appear hardly sufficient to keep the eggs or young from falling.

The roosting places preferred by the Mourning Dove are among the long grasses of abandoned fields, or at the foot of dry cornstalks, or on the edge of a meadow, though occasionally these birds resort to the dead foliage of trees and to the branches of evergreens. They rise and fly at a man's approach, no matter how dark the night may be, a fact which proves their remarkable power of sight. Unlike the Wild Pigeon they do not roost in masses close together at night. But like the Pigeons they return to the same roosting grounds from considerable distances. A few of them may mingle with the Wild Pigeons, just as the latter sometimes do with the Doves.

The Mourning Dove is more of a gleaner than a reaper of the farmer's fields. It may pick up a few grains in seed time, as its most serious crime, but it prefers the fields from which the grain has been cut and harvested. A hardy bird, equal to the severest winters of our Middle States, it sometimes remains in the North the year round. In winter the Mourning Doves feed among the poultry in farmyards, where they join Sparrows, Grackles, and many other birds and appear very gentle among them. But if disturbed, they prove extremely shy.

Parakeet or Parrot

THIS BEAUTIFUL BIRD, THE ONLY PARROT OF EASTERN NORTH AMERICA, HAS NOT BEEN TAKEN SINCE 1904. AS IN THE CASE OF OTHER BIRDS THAT HAVE VANISHED FROM NORTH AMERICA IN HISTORIC TIMES, IT WAS BRUTALLY AND NEEDLESSLY PERSECUTED.—WILLIAM VOGT.

DOUBTLESS you will say, while looking at the figures of Parakeets I painted for *The Birds of America*, that I did not spare my labor. I never do, so anxious am I to promote your pleasure. These birds are shown feeding on the cockle-bur, which in some rich old fields grows so close that to make one's way through it is no pleasant task. The burs stick so thickly to the clothes as to prevent a person from walking with any kind of ease. The wool of sheep is also much injured by them, and the tails and manes of horses are so tangled that the hair has to be cut close off, taking from the natural beauty of these animals. To this day [*circa* 1830] no useful property has been discovered in the cockle-bur, although in time it may prove as valuable, either in medicine or chemistry, as many other plants that were long considered of no importance.

The Parrots in my picture are shown feeding on the seeds. The bird alights on the plant, plucks the bur from the stem with its bill, and takes it from the latter with one foot, in which it turns it over until the joint is so placed as to meet the attacks of its bill. Then it breaks open the bur, takes out the fruit, and lets the shell drop. Once a flock has discovered a field well filled with these plants, they will eat or pluck off all the seeds, and return to the place day after day until hardly any are left. The plant, a perennial, might be stamped out in this way were it not reproduced from the ground. Our farmers have too much to do in cultivating their crops to attend to pulling up the cockle-burs by the roots, the only effective way to get rid of them.

The Parrot does not satisfy himself with cockle-burs, but eats or destroys almost every kind of fruit, a fact which makes him an unwelcome visitor to the planter, farmer, and gardener. Flocks frequently cover a stack of grain in a field, covering it up entirely like a brilliantly colored carpet, pulling out the straws, and destroying twice as much of the grain as would satisfy their hunger. They assail the pear and apple trees when the fruit is yet small and far from ripe, merely for the sake of the seeds. After alighting on these trees in great numbers they pluck off the fruit as if for mischief, open it to the core, and, disappointed with the seeds which are still soft and milky, drop the apple or pear and pluck another. They pass from branch to branch until the trees, which were so promising before the Parrots came, are left completely stripped—like water-logged ships abandoned by their crew and floating on waves still turbulent after the tempest has ceased. They visit the mulberries, pecan-nuts, grapes, and even the seeds of the dogwood, before they are ripe, and commit on them all similar depredations. Only maize never attracts their notice.

These outrages meet with severe retaliation from the farmers, who destroy the Parakeets in vast numbers while they are plucking fruit or tearing the grain from the stack. The husbandmen then approach them with perfect ease and commit great slaughter among them. All the survivors rise, shriek, fly round about for a few minutes, and again alight on the very place of the most imminent danger. The gun is kept busy, with eight, ten, or even twenty being killed at each discharge. As if conscious of the death of their companions, the living birds sweep over the bodies, screaming as loudly as ever. Yet they return to the stack to be shot at until so few remain alive that the farmer does not consider it worth his while to spend more of his ammunition. I have seen several hundred destroyed in this manner in a few hours, and have procured a basketful with a few shots in order to make a choice of good specimens for drawing the figures by which this species is represented in my work, *The Birds of America*.

The flight of the Parakeet is rapid, straight and continuous through forests, or over fields and rivers, with the body inclined in a way that enables the observer to see its upper and under parts by turns. The flocks deviate from a direct course only when impediments occur, such as houses or tree trunks, from which they glance away in a very graceful manner only as far as is necessary. The party keeps up a general cry. Seldom is one of these birds on the wing for very long without uttering its cry. Instead of alighting at once on a spot affording a supply of food, the Parakeets take a good survey of the neighborhood, pass over it in circles of great breadth, first above the trees and then gradually lower, until they almost touch the ground. Then suddenly they rise again and all settle on the tree that bears the fruit they seek, and on which they expect to regale themselves.

They are quite at ease on trees or any kind of plant, moving sidewise, climbing or hanging in every imaginable posture, and assisting themselves very dextrously with their bills in all their motions. They usually alight extremely close together. I have seen branches of trees as completely covered by them as they could possibly be. They appear shy and distrustful if one approaches them before they begin their plundering, and often, at a single cry from one of them, all take wing. They may not return to the same place that day. If they are shot at as they go, the cries of one wounded individual are sufficient to bring back the whole flock, enabling the sportsman to kill as many as he pleases. If the bird falls dead, they fly around it and then fly off.

These birds walk slowly and awkwardly on the ground, as if their tails inconvenienced them. Only when they see the sportsman at a distance do they lose no time in trying to hide, or in scrambling up the trunk of the nearest tree with the aid of their bills. They do not even attempt to run off when he approaches them unseen.

They roost in hollow trees, and crowding in together, they will sometimes fill the holes of the larger Woodpeckers. At dusk a flock may be seen alighting against the trunk of a large sycamore or any other tree which has a roomy hollow. They all cling to the bark just below the entrance, then crawl in to pass the night. If the hole will not hold the whole flock, those left at the entrance hook onto the bark by their claws and the tip of the upper part of the bill or mandible by which they appear to be hanging. I have frequently seen them there by means of a glass, and am satisfied that the bill is not then the only support.

The Parakeet which has been wounded and seized opens its bill, turns its head to bite, and, if it succeeds, can wound severely. It is easily tamed, if frequently immersed in water. They will eat as soon as they are placed in confinement. Nature seems to have implanted in them a propensity to destroy, so that they cut pieces of wood into atoms, books, and in short everything that comes their way. They cannot talk, no matter how much care and attention are devoted to their education, and their screams are so disagreeable that they are at best very indifferent companions. The woods are the best place for them. There the richness of their plumage, their beautiful mode of flight, and even their screams lend charm to our darkest forests and most sequestered swamps.

They are surprisingly fond of sand, alighting in flocks along the gravelly banks of creeks and rivers, or in ravines of old plantation fields. They scratch with bill and claw, flutter and roll themselves in the sand, and pick up and swallow a certain amount of it. They also, for the same purpose, enter the holes dug by the Kingfisher. Their fondness for saline earth brings them to the different salt licks scattered through our woods.

Our Parakeets are very rapidly diminishing in number. In some districts where they were plentiful twenty-five years ago, there are scarcely any to be seen. Once they were obtainable as far up the tributaries of the Ohio as the Great Kanawha, the Scioto, the heads of the Miami, the mouth of the Maumee at its junction with Lake Erie, on the Illinois River, and sometimes as far northeast as the boundary line between Virginia and Maryland. At the present day, very few are to be found north of Cincinnati, nor are many to be seen until you reach the mouth of the Ohio, where they flock in considerable numbers. I should estimate that there are not half as many along the Mississippi as there were fifteen years ago.

Their flesh is tolerable food when they are young, which accounts for the shooting of many young ones. The skin of their body is usually much covered with the mealy substances from the roots of their feathers. The head, especially, is infested by numerous minute insects, all of which shift from the skin to the surface of the plumage immediately after the bird's death. Their nest, or the place where they deposit their eggs, is simply the bottom of such tree cavities as those where they spend the night, as a rule. Many females lay their eggs together. I am of the opinion that each lays two eggs, although I have not been able to assure myself of this absolutely.* The eggs are round and light greenish

* Two or three.

Juglans olivæformis

Nº 207

Henderson June 9ᵗʰ 1810 Carolina Parrot x. x. x.
for imitation of colors the latter Psittacus Carolinensis drawn by J. J. Audubon
line being naturally glossy and rich

white in color. At first the young are covered with soft down, like the young Owls. During the first season, all the plumage is green, but towards autumn a frontlet of carmine appears. The tail is comparatively short at that stage. Two years pass before the male or female is in full plumage. The only external differences between the sexes are that the male is rather larger and that it has more brilliant plumage.

In my drawing, the upper figure, a female similar to the male in color, represents a kind of occasional variety in the species, having fourteen tail feathers. The specimen from which the drawing was taken was shot at Bayou Sara, in Louisiana. The present, resident location of the Carolina Parrot is: South Carolina, Georgia, Florida, Alabama, Louisiana, and up the Mississippi to Kentucky.

EDITOR'S NOTE:

Audubon's scientific description, prepared by his ghost-writer assistant, William MacGillivray, Edinburgh ornithologist, includes the following particulars, of interest in the light of the Carolina Parakeet's extinction:

Adult Male: length 14 inches; extent of wings 22 inches. Bill along ridge $1\frac{1}{12}$ inches; gape from tip of lower mandible ½ inch; tarsus ⅝ inch; middle toe 1¼ inches. Bill short, bulging, very strong and hard, deeper than broad, convex above and below, with a cere at base. Upper mandible curved from base, convex at sides, the margin overlapping . . . and trigonal, acute tip much exceeding the under mandible which is very short, broadly convex on back, truncate at extremity. Nostrils basal, round, open, placed in the cere. Head very large. Neck robust. Body rather elongated. Feet short and robust; tarsus scaly all round; toes scutellate above, flat beneath, two behind and two before, the latter united at the base; claws curved, acute.

Plumage compact and imbricated on back; blended on head, neck and under parts. Orbital space bare. Wings long, second and third quills longest. Tail long, wedge-shaped, of twelve, narrow, tapering feathers. Bill white. Iris hazel. Bare orbital space whitish. Feet pale flesh-color, claws dusky. Fore part of head and cheeks bright scarlet, that color extending over and behind the eye; the rest of the head and the neck pure bright yellow; edge of wing bright yellow spotted with orange. General color of other parts emerald green, with light blue reflections, lighter beneath. Primary coverts deep bluish-green; secondaries, greenish-yellow. Quills bluish-green on outer web, brownish-red on inner; the primaries bright yellow at base of outer web. Two middle tail-feathers deep green, the rest of the same color externally, their inner webs brownish-red. Tibial feathers yellow, the lowest deep orange.

Adult Female: similar to male in color. Upper figure in plate a female, of occasional variety, with fourteen tail-feathers.

$\mathcal{O}wls$

BARRED OWL

How often, when snugly settled under the boughs of my temporary encampment, while preparing to roast a venison steak or a squirrel on a wooden spit, have I been saluted by the exulting outbursts of this nightly disturber of the peace in my lonely retreat! How often have I seen this nocturnal marauder alight within yards of me—exposing his whole body to the glare of my fire—and eye me in such a curious manner that, had it been reasonable to do so, I would gladly have invited him to join me in my repast, that I might come to know him better. His lively motions and their oddness have often made me think that his society would be at least as agreeable as that of many of the buffoons we meet with in the world. But such acquaintance being impossible, you must be contented with the imperfect information that I can give you as to the habits of this Sancho Panza of our woods.

Were you to visit the noble forests of lower Louisiana, the happy country—Feliciana Parish—about mid-October, at twilight, as the dews fall on every plant to revive the leaves, fruits or blossoms ere morning, your ear would suddenly be struck by the discordant, screaming *whah, whah, whah, whah-aa* of the Barred Owl. You might compare the strange and ludicrous sounds, uttered so loudly, with the affected bursts of laughter you may have heard from some of the fashionable members of our own species. At this hour every night-insect rises on buzzing wings. The firefly, among thousands of other species, appears to guide their motions through the somber atmosphere. Numerous reptiles and quadrupeds begin their nocturnal prowlings. The fair moon, empress

· 174 ·

of the night, rises peacefully, like a watchful guardian, moving slowly and majestically along.

It is a great mistake to conclude that Owls are extremely dull . . . as they appear to be in the glare of day. This is as incorrect as the statement of Buffon that Woodpeckers are miserable beings. To one who has lived long in the woods, persons with such ideas would seem to have lived only in their libraries.

The Barred Owl is found in all parts of the country that I have visited, and is a constant resident. It is almost impossible to travel eight or ten miles in the woods of Louisiana without seeing several, even in broad daylight. At the approach of night they are heard to cry out from all the woods around the plantations. Should the weather be lowering, and rain near, their cries are so multiplied by day—and more so at night—as they answer one another in strange tones, that one might imagine some extraordinary fête about to take place among them. Their gesticulations are very unusual when they are approached. From its generally erect position it lowers its head and inclines its body to watch the intruder, throws forward the lateral feathers of its head till they become like a broad ruff, looks down as if blind, and moves its head to and fro in such a peculiar way as to suggest that that part is dislocated from the body. Should it suspect treachery, it flies off a short distance, alighting with its back turned to the person but immediately turning round with a single jump to resume its scrutiny. It may thus be followed for quite a distance. This Owl will answer an imitation of its cry and is frequently decoyed by it.

The flight of the Barred Owl is smooth, light, noiseless, and, if need be, long. I have seen it depart from a grove in a prairie and fly more than two miles to a forest, pursuing a direct course in broad daylight. I have watched till it was lost in the distance.

Once, while I was descending the Ohio in November, I saw a Barred Owl, about sunset, driven from its tree and teased by several Crows. It gradually rose in the air like a Hawk to a height so great that my eye lost sight of it; now and then it described small circles and flew in zigzag lines as it disappeared. I noted down this uncommon occurrence at the time, and was anxious to see the Owl return to view, but it did not reappear. So very lightly do they fly that I have frequently discovered one passing over me—only a few yards distant—by first seeing its shadow on the moonlit ground. Not the faintest rustling of its wings could be heard.

Their power of sight by day seems to be rather of an equivocal nature. I once saw one alight on the back of a cow; then, when the cow moved, the Owl left so suddenly as to prove to me that it mistook the animal for some other kind of perch. Although this Owl destroys squirrels at twilight, I have seen it startled by the sudden approach of one of these animals on a branch beside it. That is why, in my picture of the Barred Owl, I have shown one gazing in amazement at a squirrel only a few inches from him.

The Barred Owl is a destroyer of poultry, particularly half-grown chickens. It preys on mice, young hares, rabbits, small birds, and, in Louisiana, a certain brown frog of the woods. I have heard that it catches fish, but cannot vouch for the truth of the report.

About mid-March they begin to lay their eggs in the hollows of trees on the dust of decomposed wood, or in the old nest of a Crow or Red-Tailed Hawk. The eggs—from four to six—are smooth, pure white, and globular.* So far as I have seen, they rear only one brood in a season. The young are downy at first; some of the down still mingles with the feathers some weeks after the bird is nearly fledged. The parents feed them for a long time as they stand perched and hissing, yet unable to emit a call. This noise can be heard for fifty or probably a hundred yards on a calm night, and it is by no means musical, but rather—to a person lost in a swamp—extremely dismal.

The plumage varies considerably among individuals, and the more so among the males, which are smaller than the females. During the severe winters of the North, those that remain there suffer very much. The greater number remove to the South.

The Barred Owl proves an excellent mouser in captivity.

The antipathy shown to Owls by every species of day bird is extreme. They are constantly followed and pursued, but the day birds seldom prove dangerous enemies to them, being more nearly a source of extreme annoyance.

Very often this Owl is sold in the New Orleans market to the Creoles, who make *gumbo* of it and who declare the flesh to be palatable.

* Two or three.

Yellow-Billed Cuckoo — F. W.
Cuculus Carolinensis
L. Coucou de la Caroline Buffon   drawn by J. J. Audubon

N° 106.

GREAT HORNED OWL

THE Great Horned Owl, one of the Nimrods of our feathered tribes of the forest, may be seen by the lone boatman on a beautiful, serene summer night of moonlight as it sails silently and rapidly on, intent on feeding. Its wings spread wide, it glides across the river, sails over one hill after the other, or suddenly sweeps downward, afterward rising in air like a shadow, now seen distinctly, now mingled with the somber woods.

Picture a boat that has floated along until it comes opposite the newly cleared patch of ground of some squatter farmer. The moon shines on the hut, its slight fence, newly planted orchard, and a lone tree spared by the axe to serve as a roosting place for a scanty stock of poultry given by some liberal neighbor. In the tree's branches a Turkey hen spreads her wings over her offspring. The Great Owl hovers above them, sensing his quarry and sailing in wide circles while planning his attack. Ordinarily the hen would be sound asleep, but so intent is she on the care of her young brood that she rises and purrs so loudly that she rouses the neighboring hens and their protector. The cacklings turn into clamor. The squatter hears the uproar, primes his rifle, gently pushes open his half-closed door, and peeps out cautiously to ascertain the cause of the disturbance to his sleep. He sees the murderous Owl alighting on a dead branch of the tree, takes aim, and brings the foe to the ground, leaving it to some prowling opossum or other carnivorous quadruped. Again, all is tranquillity.

The Great Horned Owl occurs in mountainous districts as well as in the low alluvial lands that border rivers; in the interior; and near the seashore. Extremely hardy, it stands the severest winters. Its flight is elevated, rapid, easy and graceful, in large circles like those of an Eagle, rising and descending by the inclination of the tail. Now and then it glides silently close to earth with incomparable velocity, and drops as if dead on the prey beneath it. At other times it suddenly alights on a fence stake or stump, shakes and arranges its feathers, and utters a shriek so horrid that the woods around echo its dismal sound which is like the barking of a cur dog; or again like the last gurglings of a murdered man; or, if within fifty yards, a *hoo, hoo hoo-e* in so peculiar an undertone that the uninitiated might take the Owl to be more than a mile away. While uttering these unmusical cries, it moves its body—more particularly its head—into positions which to a man appear grotesque. Between each cry it snaps its bill as if to amuse itself; or perhaps the action is meant to whet its mandibles, as the wild boar sharpens the edges of its tusks.

The food of this Owl consists chiefly of the larger gallinaceous species—Wild Turkeys, Pheasants, Ducks, and domestic poultry. Hares, young opossums, squirrels and dead fish are equally agreeable to it.

I have found it plentiful along the Ohio and Mississippi shores, where it roosts among young cottonwood and willow thickets, as well as in the more retired woody swamps. Far south it takes to the gloomy cypress whose broad arms are covered with dangling Spanish moss that sways in the breezes. I have seen it perched erect, its plumage closed, its tufted head-feathers partly lowered, and its head half turned and resting on one shoulder.

The bird is easily approached in bright sunshine. But in cloudy weather it rises on its feet at the least noise, erects its tuft, nods knowingly, and flies off in an instant to a distant, inaccessible spot. If disturbed on willows near a river, it wisely sails over the stream.

I once nearly lost my life by going towards one that I had shot on a willow bar . . . for, while running up to the spot, I suddenly found myself sunk in quicksand up to my arm pits. And in this condition I might have remained to perish had not my boatmen come up and extricated me by forming a bridge of their oars and some driftwood. During this operation I had to remain perfectly quiet, as any struggle would soon have caused me to sink in over my head.

I have related the preceding mishap—and it is only one among many—to show that every student of Nature must encounter some difficulties to obtain the objects of his research, although these difficulties are little thought of when he has succeeded. So much is this the case with me that, could I renew the lease of my life, I could not desire to spend it in any other pursuit than that which has at last enabled me to lay before you an account of the *habits* of our birds, as well as their portraits.

The Great Horned Owls pair early in February. The male's strange evolutions in the air, or his motions when he has alighted near his beloved, are impossible to describe. He bows and snaps his bill ludicrously. No sooner has the female assured herself that her beau's attentions are out of sincere affection than she joins in the motions of her future mate. Both might be called *dancing mad* at that moment . . . like most Owls on such occasions, they little dream that one day they may be *horn mad*.

Their bulky nest of crooked sticks, lined with coarse grasses and feathers, is usually fixed to a large horizontal branch, the whole measuring nearly three feet in diameter. The eggs—three to six—are globular and dull white.* Only one brood is raised in the season. The young remain in the nest until fully fledged, and afterwards follow the parents for some time, uttering a mournful sound for food. They acquire full plumage the first spring, and until then are lighter, with more dull buff in their coloring. I have also found their nests in hollow trees, and twice in rock fissures, with little preparation in the way of grasses and feathers.

This Owl lives retired and is seldom found near farms after the breeding season. But because every isolated farm is visited by these dangerous and powerful marauders, it may be called abundant. It commits great havoc, and I have known a plantation to be all but stripped of poultry by this daring foe during the winter. Often it masters half-grown Wild Turkeys. On seizing Ducks, Guinea Fowl or domestic poultry, it carries them off in its talons to the deep woods.

When wounded, it exhibits a vengeful tenacity of spirit hardly surpassed by that of the noblest Eagle. It disdains to scramble away like the Barred Owl, but faces its enemy with undaunted courage, protruding its powerful talons and snapping its bill while its large goggle eyes open and close, and its feathers swell till its natural size is nearly double. But my picture of the male and female of this species will, I hope, give you a more perfect idea of the size and form than words can do.

* Two or three.

LITTLE SCREECH OWL

THIS Owl I found to be rare in the South, where I met but two during my long residence in Louisiana. In the North, however, it is plentiful, particularly during autumnal and winter months.

In the three figures which I presented in *The Birds of America* you will note differences between young and full-grown birds, and the contrast in coloring at these stages.

The flight of the Little Screech Owl is smooth, rapid, silent and prolonged. It rises above forest tree-tops to pursue large beetles, or sails low over fields and through woods in search of small birds, field mice, moles, or wood rats. It alights plumply, bends its body, turns its head to look behind it, performs a curious nod, utters its notes, then shakes and plumes itself before resuming flight. Now and then it clicks its mandibles while on the wing, but it does so more frequently when perched near its mate or young. This sound I have taken for a sign of manifest courage, to let the hearer know that the Owl is not to be meddled with. Yet few birds are gentler when seized; it will suffer a person to touch its feathers and caress it, without biting or striking with its talons, except rarely. I carried one of the young birds which appears in *The Birds of America* in my coat pocket from Philadelphia to New York while I travelled by water and by land. It remained generally quiet, fed from my hand, and never attempted to escape. I lost it at sea during my voyage to England in 1831.

Its notes are tremulous and doleful, somewhat like the chattering teeth of an extremely cold person, although much louder. They may be heard at a distance of several hundred yards, and are taken by some people to be of ominous import. The little fellow is usually found about farms and gardens. It alights on a roof, fence or gate and utters its mournful ditty at intervals for hours at a time, as if in great suffering, although this is far from being the case, all bird song signifying content and happiness. In confinement it continues its notes with as much satisfaction as if at liberty. Its cry is heard during the latter part of winter especially, that being the season of love, when the male is particularly attentive to the fair one, around whom he flies and struts much like the Common Pigeon, with numerous bows and nods, most amusingly.

Red Owl A.W.
Strix Asio

N° 188.

drawn by J.J. Audubon

The nest of a few grasses and feathers is in the bottom of a hollow tree trunk, or at a height of no more than six or seven feet from the ground, or as high as from thirty to forty feet. The four or five eggs are globular and pure white. This species, if not disturbed, lays only one set of eggs a season. The young remain in the nest until they can fly, and they are covered with dull yellow-white down. By mid-August they are fully feathered, and appear as in my painting. But individuals vary in coloring. I have seen some of deep chocolate hue and others nearly black. The colors change as the mating time advances. By spring its dress is perfect.

After nearly thirty years of observation, I may say that the vision of Owls of every species which breeds in the Northern and Middle States is poorer during day, and on moonlight nights when the ground is covered with snow, than that of species that breed and live in more northern countries. The Snowy Owl, the Fork-Tailed Owl and the Hawk Owl show no material difference in their power of vision, be the sun or moon shining ever so brightly on the snow. I have approached the Great Horned Owl (and other species that breed in the United States) during glaring snows. Yet, on the same day, my attempts to approach the Snowy Owl or the Hawk Owl were ineffectual. Nevertheless, on examining the structure of the eyes of all these species, I have found little or no difference.

The Little Screech Owl spends the day either in a tree hollow or hole, or the thickest evergreen woods. It is often observed on Jersey pine branches, just as I have drawn it for *The Birds of America*.

SNOWY OWL

This beautiful bird is merely a winter visitor of the United States, where it is seldom seen before November, and from whence it retires as early as the beginning of February.

The Snowy Owl hunts by day as well as in the dusk and at night, and falls swiftly on its prey, which it generally devours on the spot. It will pursue and strike Ducks, Grouse, or Pigeons in somewhat the style of the Peregrine Falcon. Its firm, protracted flight is smooth and silent. It favors the neighborhood of rivers and small streams which have cataracts or shallow rapids, liking as it does to fish along the borders like a wild cat. There, too, it keeps an eye on traps set for muskrats which it hopes to devour. Within our borders its usual food consists of hares, squirrels, rats and fishes, as I know from examining them by dissection. I have found the stomach capable of much distension.

At daybreak one morning, when I lay hidden in a pile of drifted logs at the Falls of the Ohio near Louisville, I saw this Owl secure a fish as follows. It lay flat on a rock beside the stream, its head towards the fishing hole. One might have supposed the bird sound asleep; it would remain there in that position until a good chance came for it to catch a fish. I believe it never missed. As the fish rose to the surface and near the edge, the Owl would thrust out the foot nearest the water and with it seize its prey and draw it out. The Owl then took the fish off a short way to devour it. Afterward it returned to the same fishing hole; or else it flew to inspect likelier holes, chose one, flew off a little distance from it, and began to squat low and move slowly towards the edge. There it lay flat again, to watch for fish. Whenever the fish was fairly large, the Owl struck not one but both feet into it, and flew off with it some little distance. Twice I saw the bird carry its prey across the Indiana Falls opposite Louisville, and on into the woods as if to be out of harm's way. I never heard it utter a single note at such a time, even when two Snowy Owls joined in the repast, as often happened. At sunrise or shortly after, the Owls left the fishing holes and flew to the woods. I did not see them again until the next morning, when they repeated the same feats.

In Boston the winter of 1833 I had some superb specimens of the Snowy Owl brought to me. One, a live male, had only been touched on the wing. He stood erect, kept his feathers close, but would not allow me to approach him. His fine eyes watched my every move. If I pretended to walk round him he would turn his head as far as he could to watch, open his wings, and hop to a corner, again face me, and watch my approach. He came from one of the islands off Boston, where a hunter in my employ followed him from rock to rock and took him with difficulty. That winter I saw one sailing high over the bay of Boston along with a number of Gulls which appeared to dislike his company, though the Owl paid no attention to their attempts to chase him at a respectful distance. I once met one while walking near Louisville with a friend in the middle of the day . . . perched on a stump in a field. On seeing us it flew off, sailed round the field, again alighted on the stump, showed much apprehension, and opened its wings several times as if to fly off. But with some care I approached and shot it. It proved to be a fine old female, the plumage of which was almost pure white.

I know nothing of its place or mode of breeding, for although everyone to whom I spoke of this bird in Labrador knew it, my party and I saw none there. We were no more successful in our search for it in Newfoundland.

SAW-WHET OWL

I HAVE observed this little Owl breeding in Louisiana, in Kentucky, and in the East as far north as Maine where it is scarcer. It is rare in lower South Carolina, where my friend John Bachman never saw it.

I call it the Little Owl or Acadian Owl, but in Massachusetts it is known as the Saw-Whet on account of the strong resemblance of its love notes to the noise of the filing of a large saw. These notes, heard oftenest from deep within a forest, produce a peculiar effect on the wayfarer, who imagines that he is near a saw-mill. I myself was deceived more than once by the sound. One day I heard it from inside my grist-mill while I was walking by the place which, I found, happened to be locked. I stepped to the miller's house to ask if anyone was at work at the saws. But the miller informed me that the sounds I had heard were merely the notes of the Owl whose nest was in a hollow tree close by, where Wood Ducks had formerly bred for years in succession.

Attracted by the snoring notes of the young ones, I found a nest of the Saw-Whet near Natchez in the broken stump of a small decayed tree, not more than four feet from the ground. The snoring so misled me that had my dog not smelled at the hole, I might not have discovered the brood of five. This was in early June, and the little things, almost ready to fly, looked exceedingly neat and beautiful. Their parents I never saw, although I often visited the nest before they left it. Here, as in other instances, the eggs or young nested merely on rotten particles of wood.* Once the Owl and its family occupied an old Crow's nest, which did not appear to have undergone any repair.

The Saw-Whet has a strong, curious propensity for visiting cities.

* Five to six white eggs.

Some have been caught alive in the Philadelphia Museum, as well as in Baltimore. In Cincinnati I had one brought to me which had been taken from the edge of a cradle where a child lay asleep—to the no small astonishment of the mother!

Being nocturnal it shows great uneasiness if disturbed by day, and flies off with hurried uncertainty to throw itself into the first covert. Towards dusk it becomes full of animation, flies swiftly, glides over the low grounds like a little spectre, and pounces on small quadrupeds and birds with the quickness of thought. Its common cry at night resembles the dull sounds of a whistle more than that of most Owls. The Saw-Whet Owl does not migrate.

Chuck-Will's-Widow

ALTHOUGH our Goatsuckers have powerful wings, they are particularly attached to certain districts and localities. The species now to be considered, the Chuck-Will's-Widow, is seldom observed beyond the limits of the Choctaw Nation in Mississippi or the Carolinas, and may properly be looked upon as a Southern species. Louisiana, Florida, lower Alabama and Georgia are regions where I know it to abound; there it appears early in spring, coming over from Mexico and probably still warmer climates.

About mid-March the Louisiana forests echo with its well-known notes. No sooner has the sun disappeared, and the nocturnal insects begun to emerge from their burrows, than the sounds, *chuck-will's-widow*— clearly and strongly repeated six or seven times in as many seconds— strike the ear. The call evokes pleasure mingled with a certain melancholy and I have often found it soothing. At any rate the sounds of this interesting bird foretell a peaceful and calm night. They seldom call in cloudy weather, and never when it rains.

The deep ravines, shady swamps, and pine ridges are all resorted to by this Goatsucker, to whom they afford safety during the day and food under night. They roost in the hollows of decayed trees, standing or prostrate, and seldom emerge except during incubation. I have found them in such hollows with several species of bats, asleep on mouldering particles of wood. The bats were clinging to the sides of the cavities. Instead of trying to escape me by flying out, they retired backwards to the farthest corners, ruffling all their feathers, opening their mouths as wide as possible, and uttering a hissing murmur not unlike that of some snakes. When I took one up and brought it to the light, it opened and closed its eyes in rapid succession, as if the encounter with daylight were painful. It snapped its little bill as a Flycatcher does, and, when I put it on the ground, it shuffled along as if extremely anxious to escape. Had I allowed it, the bird would have managed to move on out of sight, with as much ease and dexterity as if the time were twilight.

I once cut two of the quills of one of the Chuck-Will's after taking it home with me, to discover whether, after I allowed it to escape, it would return to the log where I found it. A few days later I found it in the same place, a fact which persuades me that they, like many other birds, resort to the same spot to roost.

The flight of this bird is as light as that of its relative, the Whip-Poor-Will, if not more so. It is more graceful and elevated, and somewhat resembles that of the Hen-Harrier,* with easy flappings mingled with sailings and curving sweeps which are extremely pleasing to behold. At the approach of night it begins to sing clearly and loudly for about a quarter of an hour from a fence post, or a decayed tree branch deep in the woods—seldom on the ground. The sound seems to give it some trouble; it raises its head in quick succession at each note. This over, it launches into the air and sweeps over the cotton fields or sugar plantations, cutting all sorts of figures. It mounts, descends or sails with such ease and grace that one might call it the "Fairy of the Night." Should it pass close to you, you will hear a murmur similar to the one it makes if surprised by day. Suddenly it checks its course, inclines to right or left, seizes a beetle or a moth, resumes its flight over the field, passes and repasses hundreds of times over the same ground, and now and then alights on a post or tall plant to sing with increased vivacity. It may follow a road or path and alight to pick up a beetle emerging from the ground, then rise high in the air, to give chase to insects passing from one wood to another. Or it may cling to a tree trunk to take the insects on the bark; it may inspect the whole tree, its motions as light as those of a Hummingbird that flutters from flower to flower. In this way it spends most of the night.

Utmost harmony prevails among the birds of this species. Dozens can be seen flying together and chasing insects in all directions without enmity or envy.

A few days after the arrival of the male birds, the females appear, and

* "Chicken Hawk."

the love season begins at once. The male pays his addresses to the female with a degree of pomposity that is only equaled by that of the Pigeon. The female, coy and silent, perches lengthwise on a branch while the male flies around her, alights before her, and with drooping wings and spread tail advances quickly, his song greatly impetuous all the while. They leave the branch together to gambol through the air.

In a few days the female, who has chosen a retired place in some thicket, deposits two elliptical, dull olive, brown-speckled eggs. But she has formed no nest for them, other than a little space carelessly scratched among the dead leaves. The eggs are difficult to find, unless the bird chances to fly off at the seeker's approach. But if these dear fruits of happy love are touched or handled, you can return to the place and search for them in vain. The bird sees at once that they have been meddled with. Both parents remove them to some other part of the woods where only chance could help find them again. They also remove the young, when very small, in this way. This singular feat has occupied my thoughts quite as much as the equally unusual manner in which the Cowbird deposits her eggs in the nests of birds of other species to be hatched. I have spent much time trying to ascertain how the Chuck-Will's-Widow removes her eggs or young. With the assistance of an excellent dog I found, in one instance, that neither eggs nor young were within a hundred yards or more of the spot where I first discovered them. The Negroes, some of whom pay a good deal of attention to the habits of birds and quadrupeds, assured me that these birds push the eggs or young along the ground with their bills. Some farmers, without troubling themselves much about the matter, suggested that the remarkable move was performed by the birds' carrying the eggs under their wings. Because the account of the Negroes appeared to me the more likely of the two methods, I made up my mind to investigate the matter and make certain.

I found that when the male or female, each of which takes turns at incubation, discovers that the eggs have been touched, it ruffles its feathers in a state of extreme dejection. It murmurs a low cry that is scarcely audible to a man who lies concealed not more than eighteen or twenty yards away. I saw the other parent return to the nest and fly so low over the ground that its little feet almost touched it as it skimmed along. After a few low notes and some gesticulations, all indicative of great distress, it took an egg up into its large mouth. The other bird did the same. Both flew off together, skimming low over the ground until they disappeared among the trees and branches.

I have never been able to determine how far they carry their eggs, nor have I witnessed the removal of the young. I have seen, however, that if a person comes up to the nest while the bird is sitting, but refrains from touching the eggs, the bird will return to them and sit as before.

The food consists of all kinds of insects. Larger species of moths and beetles are favored. No doubt the long bristly feathers of the mandibles or jaws contribute to preventing the escape of these insects after any part of them has entered the mouth.

As soon as the young are hatched the parents become silent, and are not heard again until before their departure towards the end of summer. Their cry is much less frequently heard then than in spring. They leave the South all of a sudden, about mid-August, for still warmer latitudes.

The Chuck-Will's-Widow shows a strong antipathy towards all snakes, no matter how harmless. Although it cannot injure the snake in any way, it alights near it and tries to frighten it away by opening its prodigious mouth and emitting a strong hissing murmur. It was after witnessing such a scene that I had the idea of showing the beautiful harlequin [coral] snake gliding along a dead branch between a male and female Chuck-Will's-Widow in *The Birds of America*.

Whip=Poor=Will

THIS species of Nightjar, like its relative the Chuck-Will's-Widow, is seldom seen by day, unless accidentally disturbed while resting, when it will rise and fly off to whatever distance it considers necessary for a peaceful noon-day slumber. As it moves over the places it inhabits, such as thinly covered timberland, in pursuit of moths, beetles and other insects, its flight is low, light, swift, noiseless and protracted. Its sleep, by day, is on the ground, or on the lowest branches of small trees and bushes, or on fallen tree trunks in the woods. You may then come within a few feet of it; should you find it sleeping and not alarm it, it will let you pass quite near without taking flight, so sound is its sleep about mid-day. In rainy or dark weather it sleeps less and is more on the alert; its eyes remain open for hours at a time. Its body is always parallel with the branch or trunk where it sits; it is my belief that it never alights on a branch or rail crosswise.

No sooner has the sun disappeared beneath the horizon than this bird sets out in pursuit of insects, low over the bushes, to right or left, before alighting on the ground to seize its prey. Repeatedly, in different directions, it passes over the same field, and skims along the skirts of the woods. Occasionally it settles on fence posts or tree stumps, before it sallies again like a Flycatcher after insects, afterwards returning to the post. It may drop to the ground to pick up a beetle.

Like the Chuck-Will's-Widow it balances in the air before tree trunks, or against the sides of steep banks, to discover ants and other small insects lurking there. So light and noiseless is its flight that the noise of its wings is not heard as it passes within a few feet of a person. There is only a gentle undulation in the air. It utters a low murmur all the while, a sound which is the only aid to one's discovering it in the dark, within a few yards. I have often heard it when walking or riding through the Kentucky barrens at night.

Immediately after their springtime arrival, their notes are heard in the dusk and through the evening in all the thickets and along the edge of the woods. Clear and loud, they are to me more interesting than those of the Nightingale. I have probably acquired this taste by listening to the Whip-Poor-Will in places where Nature's beauty and solitude are grandest. You can think how grateful I have been for the cheering voice of this my only companion when, fatigued and hungry after a day of unremitting toil, I have pitched camp in the wilderness as darkness put a stop to my labors! I have often listened to the Nightingale, but never under such circumstances; therefore, its sweetest notes have never awakened the same feeling.

The Whip-Poor-Will continues its lively song for several hours after sunset. Then it remains silent until the first dawn of day, when its notes echo through every vale and along the mountain valleys until the rising sun scatters the darkness. I have often heard hundreds in a woodland chorus, each trying to outdo the others. The fact that this bird may be heard at a distance of several hundred yards will enable you to conceive of the pleasure felt by every lover of Nature who may hear it. A fancied resemblance of its notes to the syllables *whip-poor-will* has given rise to its name, but an accurate description of its song is impossible, not to mention the feelings it excites in the listener. Were I to suggest that they are, in fact, not strictly musical, you might be disappointed. Of its three notes, the first and last are emphatic and sonorous, the intermediate one less so. They are preceded by a low *cluck* which is only audible within a short distance.

The Whip-Poor-Will may be approached without much caution on clear, moonlit nights.

It deposits its eggs about mid-May, on the bare ground or on dry leaves in the most isolated thickets. The short elliptical, round, greenish-white, blue-gray and light-brown-spotted and blotched eggs are two in number. The young burst the shell in fourteen days from the start of incubation, and at first look like a mouldy, almost shapeless yellowish mass. By the time they are able to fly they are brown and buff colored, the brown being beautifully dotted and zigzagged with darker lines.

Caprimulgus vociferus
Whippoorwill female. N. A. W.

N.º 11.   May 7.ᵗʰ 1812 Penns.

They attain full plumage before they depart for the south with their parents. I think their nocturnal, southward migration must be very rapid, because I have never found any in Louisiana at that season, though they proceed slowly on their return in spring. Both birds sit on the eggs; and they feed the young for a long time after they are able to fly—either on the wing, in the manner of the common House Swallow, or while perched on fences, posts, or houses. The food consists at first of ants, partly digested beetles, and large moths disgorged by the parents; after a fortnight the parents present the food whole, and the young swallow it with ease. It is a remarkable fact that even the largest moths that it feeds on are always swallowed tail foremost. The wings and legs, when swallowed, are found closely laid together, as if partly glued by saliva or gastric juice. The art of deglutition must be considerably aided by the long bristly feathers of the upper mandibles, which no doubt force the wings of the insects close together before they enter the mouth.

In *The Birds of America* I have shown a male and two female Whip-Poor-Wills, as well as some of the insects on which they feed. They appear on a branch of the red oak, a tree abundant on the edge of the Kentucky barrens where the Whip-Poor-Will is plentiful.

Chimney Swift

OUR country has furnished thousands of places for this Swift to breed in safety, free from storms, snakes and quadrupeds. With judgment worth noting, it has abandoned the hollows of trees and taken possession of the chimneys, which give forth no smoke in summer. Thus it has acquired its name. I remember well the time when it resorted to excavated branches and trunks in lower Kentucky, Indiana and Illinois. Indeed so strong is its original habit that not a few still take to such places, not only to roost but to breed. Especially is this the case in the still truly wild parts of our land, where these birds appear as particular in their choice of a tree as do those others in selecting a city chimney. Huge sycamores— mere shells—seem to suit them best.

In either situation the nest consists of small dry twigs obtained in a singular way. The Swifts whirl in flocks round the tops of decaying or dead trees as if in pursuit of insects. They throw their bodies against a twig, grapple with their feet, and snap it off by a swift jerk, then fly with it to the nesting place. The Man-o'-War sometimes does the same, but instead of holding the twig with its claws it carries it in its bill.

The Swift fixes the first sticks on the wood, rock or chimney wall with saliva and arranges them in a semi-circle, crossing and interweaving them as the framework spreads outwards. It spreads saliva an inch or more around its edge to fasten it securely. The nest is generally placed on the east side of the chimney and from five to eight feet from the entrance. In a tree hollow, where the Swifts breed in communities of their own, it is placed high or low according to convenience. Now and then the very frail fabric gives way, either under pressure of parents and young within it, or during sudden bursts of heavy rain which dash the nest to the ground. Thus the pure white eggs—four to six—may fall. Should the young accidentally fall, even without the collapse of the nest (as sometimes happens), they scramble up again by means of their sharp claws, one foot after another like the young Wood Ducks, supporting themselves with their tails. Two broods are raised in the season.

Some days before the young are able to fly, they scramble up the walls to almost the mouth of the chimney, where the parents feed them. The same occurs when they are bred in a tree.

The Swift's flight is hurried, far, wide, high and with repeated flappings, except during courtship when it sails with fixed wings. Then both sexes glide through the air to their shrill, rattling twitter, and the female receives the male's caresses. In wet weather it flies close to the ground. It skims the water to drink and bathe. Before it descends into a chimney or hollow, its always rapid flight is suddenly interrupted as if by magic—down it goes in an instant, whirling, whirring with its wings, and thereby producing a sound in the chimney like distant thunder. They never alight on trees or on the ground, being unable to move on them except in a very awkward fashion if caught and placed there. I believe that the old birds sometimes fly at night, and I have reason to think that the young are fed at such times, because I have heard the elders' whirring and the acknowledging cries of the brood on calm, clear nights.

In cities, early in spring, before they have begun breeding, these birds choose a particular chimney for a roost. Both sexes resort to it in multitudes from about an hour before sunset until long after dark. Before they enter the opening, they fly round and over it many times, but finally go in one at a time, until the lateness of the hour leads several to drop in together. They cling to the wall with their claws and support themselves by their sharp tails until dawn. Then with a roaring sound they all fly forth almost at once. I took the trouble to count the number that entered one chimney before dark in St. Francisville, Louisiana. I sat at a window close by the spot and reckoned upwards of a thousand; but I missed a considerable number. The town then contained about a hundred houses—hardly a city—a fact which suggested to me that most of these birds were bound south, and had merely stopped there for the night.

Immediately after my arrival in Louisville, Kentucky, to live, a friend asked me if I had seen the trees in which the Swifts were supposed to spend the winter, but which, he said, they only entered for the purpose of breeding. There was one tree remarkable for the immense numbers that resorted to it—a sycamore sixty or seventy feet high and seven or eight feet in diameter at the base. It was hollow and nearly destitute of branches. The birds entered about forty feet up, where the stump of a broken hollowed branch made out from the main stem. About four o'clock in the afternoon on a July day, I went to examine the tree, but the Swifts were still flying over Louisville and the surrounding woods and none had returned. I came back again as the sun was going down behind the Silver Hills, that beautiful evening. Thousands of Swifts flew close above me. Three or four at a time were pitching into the hole like bees into a hive. With my head against the tree I listened to the roaring within as they settled. It was quite dark when I left, but I was convinced that many more would enter. I did not pretend to count them . . . the number was too great, and the birds rushed to the entrance so thick as to baffle the attempt. The violent thunderstorm that later passed suddenly over Louisville made me think that the hurry of the Swifts was caused by its approach. So anxious had I become to ascertain their number before the time of their departure that I thought of them almost the whole night.

Next morning I rose early enough to reach the tree long before daylight. All was silent within when I placed my head to the tree, which I did for about twenty minutes. Suddenly I thought the great sycamore was giving way and about to come down on me. Instinctively I sprang from it. I looked up and to my astonishment saw the Swifts pouring out in a black continued stream and the tree standing firm as ever. Again I ran back to my listening post; I can only compare the noise within to the sound of a large wheel revolving under a powerful mill stream. It was yet dusky, so that I could hardly see the hour on my watch, but I estimated the time they took to get out at more than thirty minutes. They dispersed instantly in every direction.

With a hunting associate I determined to examine the interior of the tree. We went there with a strong line and a rope. We threw the line across the broken branch near the Swifts' entrance after several attempts. We fastened the rope to the line, drew the rope up and pulled it over until it reached the ground again. Taking the longest cane we could find, I mounted the tree by the rope without accident, and seated

myself at ease on the broken branch. But my labor was fruitless . . .
I could see nothing through the hole, and my cane (though it was about
fifteen feet long) touched nothing on the sides of the tree that could
give me any information. I came down fatigued and disappointed.

Next day I hired a man to cut a hole at the base of the tree. Inside
I found a matted mass of exuviae, rotten feathers reduced to a mould,
with fragments of insects and quills. I had a passage cleared, or rather
bored through this mass for nearly six feet. This took some time; I knew
by experience that if the birds should notice the hole below they would
abandon the tree, so I had it carefully closed.

The Swifts came as usual that night, and I did not disturb them for
several days. At last I took a lantern and went with my companion
about nine in the evening, determined to have a full view of the interior
of the tree. We opened the hole with caution. I scrambled up the sides
of the mass of exuviae, and my friend followed. All was perfectly silent.
Slowly and gradually I brought the light of the lantern to shine on the
sides of the hole above us. We saw the Swifts clinging side by side,
covering the whole surface of the hollow. In no instance did I see one
above another. Satisfied with the sight, I closed the lantern. With as
much care as possible, we then caught and killed more than a hundred,
stowing them away in our pockets and bosoms. Then we slid down
into the open air. Not a bird had dropped its dung on us in the hollow.
Closing the entrance, we marched towards Louisville perfectly elated. We
found only six females among the one hundred and fifteen birds.

To calculate the number of Swifts that clung to the tree, I considered
the dimensions of the hollow. Of 375 square feet of surface, I estimated
that 9,000 roosted there. Each square foot would contain thirty-two birds.

I visited the tree again on the second of August. I concluded that
the number of Swifts that resorted to it had not increased. But I found
many more females and young than males. Day after day I watched
the tree. On August 13, not more than two or three hundred came there
to roost. By the eighteenth of August, not one did I see near it; only a few
scattered ones were passing, as if moving southward. In September I
entered the tree at night, but not a bird was inside. I went to it once
more in February when the weather was very cold. Perfectly satisfied that
all these Swifts had left our latitude, I finally closed the entrance and
left off visiting it.

May arrived. I saw these wanderers of the air daily augmenting in number as they returned to the sycamore to roost. About the beginning of July I took it into my head to try closing the aperture above with a bundle of straw. The result was curious enough. The birds returned at night as usual, assembled, passed and repassed with apparent uneasiness. Many flew off into the distance, whereupon I drew the string which I had tied to the straw and removed the bundle. Many entered the hole, and continued to do so until I could no longer see them from the ground.

I moved to Henderson and did not revisit the tree until five years later. I found the Swifts still resorting to it. The wood with which I had closed the entrance below had rotted, or been carried off, and the hole was again completely filled with exuviae and mould. Later, during a severe storm, this ancient tenement of the Swifts gave way and came to the ground.

General William Clark assured me that he saw this species on all of his route to the Pacific during the Lewis and Clark Expedition. There can be no doubt that it still breeds in trees and rocky caverns in those wilds.

The food of this bird consists entirely of insects. It disgorges pellets of indigestible parts. It is furnished with glands that supply the unctuous matter with which it fastens its nest.

Ruby-Throated Hummingbird

Where is the person who, on seeing this lovely little fragment of the rainbow moving on humming winglets through the air, suspended in it as if by magic, and flitting from one flower to another, would not pause and turn his mind toward the Almighty Creator? We discover the wonder of His hands at every step. His sublime creations are everywhere in His admirable system of Nature.

No sooner has the spring sun restored the vernal season, and caused millions of plants to open their leaves and blossoms to his genial beams, than the little Hummingbird is seen. It advances on fairy wings, carefully visits every opening flower cup, and like a curious florist it removes the injurious insects. Poised in the air, it peeps cautiously and with sparkling eye into the flower, while appearing to fan and cool it. It avoids injuring the flower's fragile texture, and makes a delightful murmuring sound to lull the insects to repose within. Then its long delicate bill enters the cup of the flower, and its double-tubed tongue touches one insect at a time with saliva before drawing it out and swallowing it instantly. All this is done in a moment. The bird sips so little of the honey of the flower, as it leaves it, that the theft is a blessing, we may suppose, for the flower is thus kindly relieved of her insect destroyers.

The prairies, fields, orchards and gardens, and even the deepest shades of the forest, are all visited in their turn by this little bird, which everywhere meets with pleasure and food. Its gorgeous throat excels all competition in beauty and brilliancy. The resplendent, changing green of its delicate upper body gleams as it throws itself through the air with inconceivable swiftness and vivacity—upwards, downwards, to right and left. With great care it notes the advance of the warm season, and it retreats with equal caution as autumn approaches.

I wish it were in my power to impart to you the delight I have felt while watching a pair of these most favorite little creatures displaying their feelings and love for each other. The male swells his plumage and throat, dances on the wing, and whirls around the delicate female. Quickly he dives towards a flower, and returns with a loaded bill for her. When his caresses are kindly received he seems full of ecstasy. His little wings fan her as they fan the flowers, and he transfers to her bill the insect and the honey that he sought to please her. After the blissful compact is sealed, the courage and care of the male are redoubled. He even dares to give chase to the Tyrant Flycatcher, and harries the Blue-bird and the Martin to their boxes. I have seen, but cannot describe, all these proofs of the sincerity, fidelity, and courage with which the male assures his mate he will care for her while she is sitting on the nest. In *The Birds of America* I have painted a nest and several of these pretty birds feeding, caressing each other, and sitting on slender trumpet flower stalks while preening themselves. I trust this will afford a faithful idea of their appearance and varied manners.

Glance into the nest of the Hummingbird, which you may find attached to the twig of a rosebush or weed, or on the branch of an oak, or immediately above the path, or near the garden walk. It is made of light gray lichen, most delicate, and seldom more than twenty feet from the ground. They are far from particular where they build. The eggs are but half an inch long. If they are hatched, you will see a pair of young, little larger than bumble-bees—naked, blind, and so feeble as scarcely to be able to raise their little bills to receive food from the parents. The parents, full of anxiety and fear because of your nearness, will pass and re-pass within a few inches of your face, and alight on a twig not more than a yard from your body. There they await the result of your unwelcome visit in a state of utmost alarm, and their pangs cannot fail to impress you as you see their fears for their cherished children. How pleased you will be, on leaving the spot, to see their hope return after they examine the nest and find their nurslings un-touched! Such a scene of sorrow and of joy ought to make us determined to contribute to the happiness of others, and to refrain from wantonly or maliciously giving pain.

The little ones will not have their full brilliance of color till their second spring, although the throat of the male has a strongly ruby tint before they leave us in autumn.

This Hummingbird particularly likes flowers that are greatly tubular in form, like those with which I painted it for *The Birds of America.* Their food consists principally of coleopterous insects. The nectar which they sip from flowers is less to support them than to allay their thirst.

I have seen many of these birds kept in partial confinement. When they were supplied with artificial flowers made to hold honey or sugar dissolved with water for them, they seldom lived many months. Others which were supplied with fresh flowers from the woods or garden twice a day, and kept in a room with windows covered only by mosquito netting through which minute insects could enter, lived twelve months. The room was kept artificially warm during the winter. Though the birds mated, they made no attempt to nest in the orange-tree plant that was placed there for them.

The Hummingbird does not shun mankind so much as other birds generally do. Frequently it approaches flowers in windows, or even flies inside rooms when the windows are kept open during the extreme heat of the day. It returns, if not interrupted, as long as the flowers remain fresh and unfaded.

They are quarrelsome and have frequent battles in the air, especially the male birds. If one should be feeding on a flower and be approached by another, both rise in the air immediately, and twitter and twirl in a spiral manner until out of sight. Once the conflict is over, the victor at once returns to the flower.

Comparison with the large sphinx moth may, except for the color, enable you to form some idea of their appearance when on the wing, and of their peculiar mode of flight as they move in a direct line from flower to flower. They utter a few sweet notes when perched on a twig, or sometimes when on the wing.

Belted Kingfisher

You must not suppose that the bird biographies which I try to write are long or short according to the size of my subject. If I give you a long history for a large bird, this is merely because it is perhaps more common and better known to me. The little Belted Kingfisher I have had less frequent opportunity to study than some species.

You may be sure that, notwithstanding its partly suitable name, I myself should prefer to have called it the *United States' Kingfisher*. My reason for this is that it is the only bird of its genus found on our inland streams. Another reason is that although males, from time immemorial, have had supremacy, in this case the term *belted* is applicable only to the female. The male is destitute of the belt or band by which she is distinguished. But names already given to birds must not, I am told, be meddled with if generally accepted, whether apt or not.

The inland migrations of the Belted Kingfisher along the windings of our noble rivers are widespread. It breeds in all parts of the Union which I have visited. Its rapid flight is prolonged and high in migration, and whenever necessary. When, for instance, a whole river freezes over in a region, this bird ceases to skim over the surface in search of food, but instead passes high above the tallest trees and takes every shortcut above the river to reach a milder climate. This also seems to happen when it apparently tires of the fish of one lake and moves in a direct line to another over forests, and often by a route twenty or thirty miles inland from the stream. By a series of five or six flaps followed by a direct glide without visible undulation, it pursues its way, either in long flights on high, or when flying close over the water.

The bird will pass over a small pond in its excursions, suddenly check

N.º 110

L'Alcion *ou* *remarquée* ₁ *d'Amérique* Buffon
King Fisher
Le M. *Ceinte* King Fisher 104° *Chat. de* N.º Ohio July 15, 1808.
N.º *Floeds* Alcion *drawn of E.E. Audubon.*

its flight, poise in air like a Sparrow-Hawk, and inspect the water for possible fishes. If it sees one, it will remain poised for a few seconds, dash and spiral headlong into the water, seize the fish, and fly with it to the nearest tree or stump, where it downs it in a moment.

It ranges creeks and rivers, and follows their course up to the very source of the small rivulets. It is not unusual to hear its hard, rapid, rattling note among the murmuring cascades of high mountains, where the bird is a sign to the angler that trout are abundant. The calm waters of mill ponds permit it to discover its prey with ease; it chooses the bank away from the mill run and digs a hole in the earth or sand and deposits its eggs there. I have opened several such holes in different soils and situations, and also watched the birds there. After deciding on the spot, male and female cling to the bank much like Woodpeckers. They set their long, stout bills to work, and as soon as the hole is four, five, or six feet in a horizontal direction—or no more than eighteen inches, or up to ten feet—one of the birds enters it. It scratches out the sand, earth or clay with its feet, and keeps on striking it with its bill to extend the depth. All the while, the other bird appears to cheer the laborer and encourage its renewed exertions. They return to the same hole year after year. At Chickasaw Bluffs, on the Mississippi River, I saw holes more than fifty feet below the surface, but most of them beyond reach of flood waters of springtime and autumn. The hole is just large enough to admit passage of one bird at a time. The far end is rounded and shaped like a common oven, to allow the pair or the whole brood to turn around in it with ease. The pure white eggs, usually six in number, are deposited on sticks and feathers.* Incubation takes sixteen days, and is performed by both parents, both of whom show utmost solicitude for their young. To induce a human intruder to swim or wade after her, she will drop on the water as if severely wounded, and flutter and flounder as if unable to rise. Meanwhile, the male perches near by on a bough, or even flies to the edge of the bank, jerks his tail, erects his crest, rattles his notes with angry vehemence, and then springs off, to pass and repass the enemy while crying his despair.

They will offer their growing young an entire fish. I have often seen the little ones follow the parent birds, alight on the same branch

* Normal: five to eight.

with them, flap their wings, and call with open bill for the food which their elders have taken from the water. Their petition is seldom denied.

Once I tried, on two successive evenings, to capture a Belted King-fisher. The hour was long after nightfall. I put a net bag across the hole, then left the place for home. Next morning I found that a passage had been scratched under the net for the bird to escape. That evening I saw it enter the same hole. This time I put a stick in to fill it, but again it worked its way out. After this I abandoned my attempt. The bird continued to reside in the same hole.

I was ready to put my pen aside, as to the Belted Kingfisher, when I happened to read in my journals that I had seen this bird plunge into the sea after small fry in a hook of New York Harbor. I am not aware, however, that this is a common occurrence.

Woodpeckers

IVORY-BILLED WOODPECKER

VIRTUALLY EXTINCT. UNDER AUDUBON SOCIETY PROTECTION IN
FLORIDA; OCCASIONALLY REPORTED SEEN IN SOUTH CAROLINA.—ED.

I HAVE always imagined that there is something very closely allied to
the style of the great Van Dyck's coloring in the plumage of the beautiful
Ivory-Billed Woodpecker. I see this in its dark glossy body and tail. I
see it, too, in the large, well-defined white markings of its wings, neck
and bill, relieved by the rich carmine of the pendent crest of the male
and the brilliant yellow of the eye. These have never failed to remind
me of some of the boldest and noblest productions of that inimitable
artist's pencil. So strongly, indeed, have these thoughts become fixed in
my mind, on gradually more intimate acquaintance with this Woodpecker, that whenever I have observed one of these birds flying from
tree to tree I have mentally exclaimed, "There goes a Van Dyck!"
This notion may seem strange, perhaps ludicrous, but I relate it as
a fact, whether or not it agrees with your own ideas after inspection of
the portrait of this splendid species of the Woodpecker tribe in *The Birds
of America.*

I have visited the favorite resort of the Ivory-Billed Woodpecker,
those deep morasses overshadowed by millions of gigantic, dark, moss-
covered cypresses which seem to admonish intruding man to pause and
reflect on the many difficulties ahead. If he persists in venturing farther
into these almost inaccessible recesses, he must follow for miles a
tangle of massive trunks of fallen, decaying trees, huge projecting
branches, and thousands of creeping and twining plants of numberless

species! Would I could describe the dangerous nature of the ground, its oozing, spongy mire covered with a beautiful but treacherous carpet of the richest mosses, flags and water lilies. No sooner does this carpet feel the foot than it yields and endangers the very life of the adventurer as he approaches what he takes for a clearing, but which proves to be merely a lake of black muddy water. His ear is assailed by the dismal croaking of innumerable frogs, or the hissing of serpents, or the bellowing of alligators! Would that I could give you an idea of the sultry, pestiferous atmosphere that nearly suffocates the intruder during the noon-day heat of the dog-days in those gloomy and horrible swamps!

I have heard the amateur naturalist express astonishment that half-a-crown was asked by the person who had perhaps followed the bird through miles of such swamps, and, after procuring it, prepared its skin in the best manner, and carried it to a market thousands of miles distant from the spot where he obtained it. I must say this has grieved me as much as when I have heard some idle fop complain of the Louvre Gallery in Paris, where he had paid nothing to enter, or when I have listened to the same fatuous idler lamenting the loss of his shilling as he sauntered through the Exhibition Rooms of the Royal Academy of London, or any equally valuable repository of art.

But to return to the biography of the famed Ivory-Billed Woodpecker, the flight of this bird is graceful in the extreme, although seldom prolonged to more than a few hundred yards at a time, unless when the bird has to cross a large river. This it does in deep undulations, opening its wings to their full extent and nearly closing them to renew the propelling impulse. The flight from one tree to another is performed by a single sweep, even though the distance be as much as a thousand yards. The bird appears as if merely swinging itself in an elegantly curved line from the top of one tree to the top of another, exhibiting all the beauty of its plumage. It never utters a sound on the wing except during the mating season. But at all other times, after it has alighted, its remarkable voice is heard—at almost every leap which it makes, while ascending the upper trunk of a tree, or in its highest branches. Its notes are clear, loud and yet rather plaintive, and are heard at a considerable distance, perhaps half a mile. They resemble the false high note of a clarinet, usually repeated three times in succession, *pait, pait, pait.* They are heard so frequently that they lead to its destruction, which is aimed at, not because the species is a destroyer of trees but more because of its beauty. Its rich scalp attached to its upper mandible forms an ornament for the war-dress of most of our Indians, or for the shot-pouch of our squatters and hunters, by all of whom the bird is shot merely for that purpose. I have seen entire belts of Indian chiefs closely ornamented with the tufts and bills of this species, and have observed that a great value is frequently put upon them. Travellers of all nations are also fond of possessing the upper part of the head and the bill of the male. I have often remarked that on a steamboat's reaching what we call a wooding-place [where it stops to take on wood for fuel] the *strangers* were very apt to pay a quarter of a dollar for two or three heads of this Woodpecker.

The Ivory-Bill nestles earlier in spring than any others of its tribe. I have seen it boring a hole for that purpose in the beginning of March. The hole is, I believe, always made in the trunk of a live tree, generally an ash or a hackberry, at a great height. The birds pay much regard to the tree's location and to the slanting of its trunk, preferring retirement and wishing to protect the opening from access to running water during beating rainstorms. To prevent the latter, the hole is generally dug immediately under the junction of a large branch with the trunk. It is first bored horizontally for a few inches, then directly downwards, and not in a spiral manner as some people have imagined. This cavity is more or less deep, according to the circumstances; sometimes not more than ten inches, at other times nearly three feet downward into the core of the tree. I have been led to think that these differences result from the more or less immediate necessity under which the female may be of depositing her eggs. Again, I have thought that the older the Woodpecker is, the deeper it makes its hole. The nests average about seven inches in diameter within, but the entrance, which is perfectly round, is only just large enough to admit the bird.

Both birds work most assiduously at this excavation. One waits outside to encourage the other while it is engaged in digging, taking its place when it is fatigued. I have approached trees while these Woodpeckers were thus busily employed, and by resting my head against the bark I could easily distinguish every blow given by the bird. In two instances I observed that when the Woodpeckers saw me at the foot of the tree in which they were digging their nest, they abandoned it forever. The first brood, generally six eggs, are deposited on a few chips at the bottom of the hole, and are of a pure white color.* About a fortnight before they venture to fly to any other tree, the young are seen creeping out of the hole. The second brood makes its appearance about the fifteenth of August. The Ivory-Bills raise no more than one brood each season in some places.

The young are at first the color of the female. Towards autumn their crests, which were wanting at first, nearly equal the mother's in size. This is particularly true of the first breed. The males have a slight line of red on the head by then, and do not attain their richness of plumage until spring, or their full size until the second year. Even then a difference may easily be seen between them and much older individuals.

Their food consists principally of beetles, larvae, and large grubs. I have seen this bird hang by its claws to the vines of ripe grapes, in the position so often assumed by a Titmouse, and reaching downwards help itself to a bunch of grapes with much apparent pleasure. It also feeds on persimmons and hackberries as soon as the fruit becomes quite mellow. It never attacks the corn, or the fruit of orchards, although it sometimes chips off the bark of the belted trees of the newly cleared plantations. It seldom comes near the ground, but prefers the tops of the tallest trees at all times. However, it will attack a half standing, broken shaft of a large dead and rotten tree in such a manner as nearly to demolish it in the course of a few days. I have seen the remains of some of these ancient monarchs of our forests so excavated, and in such a singular way, that the tottering fragments of the trunk appeared to be merely supported by the great pile of chips by which its base was surrounded. The strength of this Woodpecker is such that I have seen it detach pieces of bark seven or eight inches long with a single blow of its powerful bill. By beginning at the top branch of a dead tree, it will tear off the bark for twenty or thirty feet in a few hours, leaping downwards with its body in an upward position. All the while it tosses its head to right and left, or leans it against the bark to detect the spot where the grubs are concealed. Immediately afterward it renews its blows with fresh vigor, sounding its loud notes as if highly delighted.

* Normal: three.

. 206 .

November 28th 1812

N° 78

Ivory Bill Wood Pecker

This species generally moves in pairs after the young have left their parents. The female is always the most clamorous and the least shy. Their mutual attachment continues, I believe, throughout life. Except when digging a hole for nesting, these birds seldom if ever attack living trees for any other purpose than that of procuring food, in the process of which they destroy insects that would otherwise prove injurious to the trees.

I have frequently observed the male and female retire to rest for the night in the same hole where they had long before reared their young. This usually happens a short time before sunset.

The Ivory-Bill, when wounded and brought to the ground, immediately makes for the nearest tree, ascends it with great rapidity and perseverance, and squats and hides in the topmost branches. As it ascends it moves spirally round the tree, and utters its loud *pait, pait, pait,* at almost every hop, until it reaches a place where it feels itself safe. They sometimes cling to the bark with their claws so firmly as to remain cramped to the spot for several hours after death. To take them by the hand is a rather hazardous undertaking; they strike with great violence, and inflict very severe wounds with their bills and claws, which are extremely sharp and strong. On such occasions they utter a mournful and very piteous cry.

I have only to add that I found it very abundant along the finely wooded margins of that singular stream called "Buffalo Bayou" in Texas, where my expedition obtained several specimens.

PILEATED WOODPECKER

It would be difficult for me to say where I have not met with that hardy inhabitant of the forest, the Pileated Woodpecker. Even now, when several species of our birds are becoming rare, either to gratify the palate of the epicure or to adorn the cabinet of the naturalist, it is to be found everywhere in the wild woods, although scarce and shy in the peopled districts.

It remains pretty constantly in the place which it chooses after it leaves its parents. One can seldom approach it unless under cover of a tree or by accidentally surprising it. It moves from one tree to another in large, newly tilled fields girdled with forest, cackling out its laughter-like notes as if delighting to lead you a wild goose chase in its pursuit. When followed, it always alights on the tallest branches or tree trunks, moves to the farthest side, and peeps in silence as it watches your progress. So well does it seem to know the distance at which a shot can reach it that it seldom permits the hunter to come that near, warily flying off. Even in the wildest parts of eastern Florida, where I have followed it to assure myself that the birds I saw were of the same species as the one found in our distant Atlantic States, its vigilance was not in the least abated. I chased it for miles from one cabbage-tree to another without ever getting within shooting distance. At last I was forced to resort to a stratagem. I *seemed* to abandon the chase, took a circuitous route, concealed myself in the course of the Woodpecker, and waited until it came up. Then, it being now on the side of the trees next to me, I had no difficulty in bringing it down. I shall never forget how I spent several days in the Great Pine Forest of Pennsylvania, trying to obtain one to prove it identical with others seen elsewhere.

Their natural wildness never leaves them, even if they have been reared from the nest. My generous friend, the Reverend John Bachman of Charleston, gives an instance of this, and speaks also of their cruelty:

A pair of Pileated Woodpeckers had a nest in an old elm tree in a swamp one year. Early the next spring two Blue-birds took possession and there had young. Before the young were half grown the Woodpeckers returned to the place, and, despite the cries and repeated attacks of the Blue-birds, the Woodpeckers took the young—and not very gently, as you can imagine—and carried them off some distance. Next, the nest itself was disposed of by them. They cleaned and enlarged the hole, and there they raised a brood. The nest, it is true, was originally their own. The tree was large, but so situated that I could reach the nest from the branches of one beside it. The hole was about eighteen inches deep, and I could touch the bottom with my hand. The eggs, which were laid on fragments of chips expressly left by the birds, were six—large, white and translucent.*

Before the Woodpeckers began to sit, I robbed them of their eggs to see if they would lay a second time. They waited a few days as if undecided. Then suddenly I heard the female at work again in the tree. Once more she deepened the hole, made it broader at the bottom, and began to lay again. This time she laid five eggs; I allowed her to bring out her young and did not touch the eggs. Both male and female took turns at incubating, each

* Normal: four.

. 208 .

visiting the other at intervals, peeping into the hole to see that all was right and well there, and flying off afterwards in search of food.

When the young were grown enough to be safely taken out, and I could see them peeping out of the hole occasionally, I carried them home to study their habits in confinement, and attempted to raise them. I found it exceedingly difficult to entice them to open their bill to feed them. They were sullen and cross; three died in a few days, but the others were raised on Grasshoppers forced into their mouths. In a short time they began picking up the Grasshoppers thrown into their cage, and they also ate cornmeal, preferably dry. All their time was spent in trying to escape their prison, which they regularly demolished every two days, although it was made of tolerably thick pine boards. At last I had one constructed of oak at the back and sides, with oaken rails in front. This was too much for them; their only comfort was in passing their bills through the hard bars and holding them there.

In the morning, after drinking water freely, they invariably upset the large cup or saucer, turning it over. After this they attacked the trough of food and soon broke it to pieces. If I chanced to bring my hand near them, they made passes at it with their powerful bills with great force.

I kept them in this way until winter. They were at all times uncleanly and unsociable birds. I opened the door of my study one morning and one of them dashed off by me, alighting on an apple tree near the house. It climbed for some distance, and kept watching me from one side and then the other, as if wondering as to my intentions. I walked into my study. The other was hammering at my books. The Woodpeckers had broken a bar of the cage. Judging from the mischief they had done, they must have been at liberty for some hours. Tired of my pets, I opened the door; the one in the study, hearing its brother's voice, flew towards him to the same tree. They remained about half an hour, as if consulting. Then, taking to wing, they flew off southward, with much more ease than could have been expected from birds kept so long in captivity. The ground was covered with snow. I never saw any more of these two. No birds of this species have ever bred, since, in the hole where I found these birds, which I consider much wilder than the Ivory-Billed Woodpecker.

I was surprised in the Great Pine Forest of Pennsylvania to see how differently this bird worked on the bark of different trees while searching for its food. On the hemlock and spruce, whose bark is hard to detach, it hit the bark sideways in an oblique direction, and worked in close parallel lines, so that when a piece was loosed after a while, and broken off by a side stroke, the surface of the tree trunk looked as if grooved by a carpenter's gouge. In this way the Pileated Woodpecker often strips the entire trunk of the largest trees of that forest. But when it attacked other kinds of timber, it pelted at the bark in a straight-forward manner, detaching a large piece by a few strokes, and leaving the trunks smooth and uninjured by its bill.

When this bird is surprised, it is given to very astonishing fits of terror. In Louisiana I have several times crept up to one busily search-ing for food on a low rotten stump near the ground. I have come so near the tree as almost to touch it, have struck the stump with my cap as if to catch the bird; it has instantly lost all power and presence of mind, and fallen to the ground as if dead. If not captured it has quickly recovered, and flown off with more than its usual speed. If you surprise them while they are feeding on a tree, they will now and then attempt to save themselves by turning round the trunk or branches instead of flying off, unless two persons are present. But if there are two men, it well knows, it would seem, that flying away is not always a sure means of escape. If wounded, it will mount at once to the highest fork of the tree if it can, and squat there in silence. It is then very difficult to kill it. Sometimes, when it is shot dead, it clings so firmly to the bark that, like other Woodpeckers, it may remain hanging for hours. When winged and brought to the ground, it cries loudly as its enemy ap-proaches. It uses every means in its power to escape, often inflicting a severe wound if seized without caution.

The flight of the Pileated Woodpecker is powerful, and, on occasion, greatly prolonged, resembling the flight of the Ivory-Bill in all respects. Its notes are loud and clear. The rolling sound produced by the ham-mering of its bill may be heard a quarter of a mile away. It almost al-ways breeds in the interior of forests, on trees in deep swamps over the water. It seems to prefer the southern side of the tree, and retreats to its hole in winter and during rainy weather. Sometimes, though not often, its hole is bored perpendicularly, but usually like that of the Ivory-Bill, and to a depth of from twelve to eighteen inches, a breadth of two and a half to three inches, and at the bottom sometimes five or six. I believe it rears only one brood in a season. The young follow their parents for a long time after coming out, receive food from them, and remain with them until the return of spring. Old and young are fond of retiring at night to their holes, to which they return especially often in winter.

Many years of observation convince me that the bills of Woodpeckers of all sorts are longer when the birds are just fledged than at any future period of their life. Through use, the bills become not only shorter but also much harder, stronger and sharper. When it first leaves the nest, the bird's bill bends easily; six months later it resists the force of fingers; and at twelve months the bill has acquired its permanent, bony hardness. I have found the bill of a young bird seven-eighths of an inch longer than that of an adult. This difference I have shown in the picture in *The Birds of America*. The young birds search for larvae or fruits, as if aware that their bills are too tender to attack the bark of trees or the wood itself.

I found this Woodpecker more abundant in the Texas territory than anywhere else. On Galveston Island I saw one tapping against the roof of a house. This was the first and only instance of so much familiarity in a bird of this species that I have encountered.

So much attached is it to the tree in which it has a hole that during winter it is often seen with its head out, as if looking to the weather, the unfavorable state of which induces it to sink out of sight, and probably compose itself to rest. It may be found in the same neighborhood during the whole year. Like many others of this family, it usually spends the night in the same hole.

RED-COCKADED WOODPECKER

In quickness of motion the Red-Cockaded Woodpecker is more like the Common or Banded Three-Toed Woodpecker than any other with which I am acquainted. It glides upwards and sidewise along and beneath the trunks and branches, moving with astonishing alertness, emitting a short, shrill, clear note at every motion. While on the wing it also sounds this note, which can be heard at a considerable distance, at the commencement of each curve of its undulating flight. Often it issues a tremulous note on alighting—short, sharp and shrill. During the love season its cries resound through the pine woods.

Near Bayou Sara in Louisiana, I once slightly wounded two males, which I put into my hat in order to carry them home. The first, having been brought to the ground, was easily taken, but the case was different with the other. It hopped off at once towards the nearest tree, crying loudly all the while, and on reaching it ascended as if unhurt. However, I obtained it by accidentally knocking it off the bark with a clod of earth. It defended itself courageously, and pecked at my fingers with so much vigor that I was obliged to let it drop several times out of my hand. Confined in my hat, they remained still and sullen, and when I looked at them they both hid their heads as if ashamed of their situation. Whenever I chanced to fire my gun, it alarmed them, and they uttered a plaintive cry, differing from their usual note which they sound while at liberty.

One died before I reached home, probably from the great heat. The other, however, was well, and I put it in a cage. It examined every part of its prison until it found a spot through which it thought it might escape. There it began to work, and soon made the chips fly off. In a few minutes it made its way out, leaped on the floor while uttering its common *cluck*, hopped to the wall, and ascended it as if it had been the bark of one of its favorite trees. The room was unfinished and its bricks were bare. As the bird passed along them it peeped into the interstices and seized the spiders and other insects lurking in them. I kept this bird two days, but when I found that the poor thing could procure no food, I gave it its liberty. I was glad to find that its wounded wing was so far healed that it could fly thirty or forty yards at a time, so that it had a good chance of being able to reach its favorite pines again, with the scent of which it was strongly imbued.

On a high tree it appears to be entirely black in color. Even when close at hand, the red line over the eye is generally covered by the adjacent dark feathers. At least this was the case with the two mentioned above. It is fond of the company of small Woodpeckers and Pine Warblers. The nest is often bored in a decayed stump about thirty feet high, the wreck of a noble pine destroyed by the irresistible fury of a hurricane. I have found as many as six eggs, smooth and pure white; but usually there are four. In winter I have seen several of these birds enter a hole at dusk. In cold drizzly weather I have seen them do the same at various hours of day.

Say's Phoebe

KNOWN TO AUDUBON AS PEWEE, OR PEWIT FLYCATCHER

CONNECTED with the biography of this bird are so many incidents relative to my own life-story that, could I turn from my usual method of describing birds, this piece would contain less about the Pewee than about my own habits in my youthful days as an American woodsman.

While young I had a plantation that lay on the sloping declivities of the Perkiomen Creek in Pennsylvania. I was extremely fond of rambling along its rocky banks. For it would have been difficult to do so either without meeting with a sweet flower, spreading open its beauties to the sun, or observing the watchful Kingfisher perched on some projecting stone over the clear water of the stream. Now and then the Fish-Hawk itself, followed by the White-Headed Eagle,* would make his appearance, and by his graceful aerial motions raise my thoughts far above them into the heavens, silently leading me to the admiration of the sublime Creator of all.

These impressive and always delightful reveries often accompanied my steps to the entrance of a small cave scooped out of the solid rock by the hand of Nature. It was, I thought then, quite large enough for my study. My paper and pencils, and now and then a volume of Edgeworth's natural and fascinating *Tales*, or La Fontaine's *Fables*, afforded me ample pleasure. It was in that place that I first saw to advantage the force of parental affection in birds. There it was that I studied the habits of the Pewee, and there I was taught most forcibly that to destroy the nest of a bird, or to deprive it of its eggs or young, is an act of great cruelty.

The nest of this plain-colored Flycatcher was fastened to the rock

* Bald Eagle.

immediately over the arched entrance of this calm retreat. I had peeped into it. Although it was empty, it was still clean, as if the absent owner intended to revisit it with the return of spring. The buds were already much swelled, and some of the trees were ornamented with blossoms. Yet the ground was still partially covered with snow, and the air had the piercing chill of winter.

I chanced, one morning early, to go to my retreat. The sun's glowing rays gave a rich coloring to every object around me. As I entered the cave a rustling sound over my head attracted my attention, and on turning I saw two birds fly off and alight on a tree close by. The Pewees had arrived! I felt delighted, but, fearing that my sudden appearance might disturb the gentle pair, I walked off, while continuing to look at them. I concluded that they must have just come, for they seemed fatigued. Their plaintive note was not heard, their crests were not erect, and the vibration of the tail, usually so conspicuous, was wanting in power. Insects were still few in number at that date, leading me to think that the return of the birds was prompted more by their affection for the place than any other motive. No sooner had I gone a few steps than the Pewees, with one accord, glided down from their perches and entered the cave. I did not return to it any more that day, and as I saw no birds around it or in the neighborhood, I supposed that they must have spent the day within it. I concluded also that these birds must have reached this haven either during the night or at the dawn of that very morning. Hundreds of observations have since proved to me that the Pewee always migrates by night.

Early next morning I went to the cave, yet not early enough to surprise them in it. Long before I reached the spot, my ears were agreeably saluted by their well-known note, and I saw them darting about through the air, chasing insects over the water. They were full of gaiety, and frequently flew into and out of the cave, sometimes lighting on a favorite tree near it, while seeming engaged in the most interesting conversation. The light fluttering or tremulous motions of their wings, the jetting of their tail, the erection of their crest, and the neatness of their attitudes, all indicated that they were no longer fatigued, but on the contrary, refreshed and happy.

When I entered the cave, the male flew violently towards the opening with almost incredible swiftness, like the passing of a shadow.

Several days in succession I went to the spot and saw with pleasure that, as my visits increased in frequency, the birds became more familiarized with me. Before a week had elapsed, the Pewees and myself were quite on terms of intimacy. It was now the tenth day of April. Spring was early that year. No more snow was to be seen. Redwings and Grackles were about, here and there. The Pewees began working at their old nest. I decided to spend the greater part of each day in the cave in the enjoyable company of this friendly pair. My presence no longer alarmed them. They brought fresh materials, lined the nest anew, and made it warm by adding a few large soft feathers of the Common Goose which were strewn along the edge of the creek water. While both birds sat on the edge of the nest, there was a remarkable and curious twittering that is never to be heard on any other occasion. It was, I thought, the soft, tender expression of the pleasure they both appeared to anticipate in the future. Their mutual caresses, simple as they might have seemed to another onlooker, and the delicate manner used by the male to please his mate, riveted my eyes on these birds and excited sensations I can never forget.

One day the female spent the greater part of the time in her nest. She frequently changed her position. Her mate showed much uneasiness, would alight by her sometimes, sit by her side for a moment, suddenly fly out, then return with an insect which she would take from his bill with apparent gratification. About three o'clock in the afternoon I saw her uneasiness increase. The male bird looked unusually despondent, until, of a sudden, his mate rose on her feet, looked sidewise under her, flew out of the cave (followed by her consort), rose high in the air in circles and motions more curious to me than any I had seen before. The pair flew above the water, the female leading her mate throughout her meanderings.

Meanwhile I peeped into their nest, and saw their first egg, so white and so transparent—I believe that eggs soon lose this peculiar transparency after being laid—that the sight was more pleasant to me than if I had seen a diamond of the same size. The knowledge that, in such a frail covering, life already existed, and that before many weeks a weak, delicate and helpless yet perfect creature would burst the shell and immediately call for the most tender care and attention from anxious parents, filled my mind with the same wonder that I feel when I search the heavens for the meaning of all I see.

In six days six eggs were deposited. As they increased in number the bird remained a shorter time in the nest. She deposited the last egg in a few minutes, after once more alighting. I thought this might be a law of Nature, to keep the eggs fresh to the last. About an hour after laying the last egg she returned, settled in her nest, and, after arranging the eggs several times under her body, she spread her wings a little and began the arduous task of incubation.

Day after day passed by. I gave strict orders that no one should go near the cave, much less enter it, or indeed destroy any nest on the plantation.

Whenever I visited the Pewees, one or other of them was on the nest, while its mate was either searching for food, or perching in the vicinity, filling the air with its loudest notes. Often I reached my hand out near the sitting bird; so gentle had they both become, so well acquainted were we, that neither moved, even when my hand was quite close. Now and then the female would shrink back into the nest, or the male would snap at my fingers or leave the nest in great anger, fly round the cave a few times, letting out his querulous whining notes, then light again on the nest and resume his labors.

At this very time, a Pewee's nest was attached to one of the rafters of my mill, and there was another under a shed in the cattle yard. Each pair, it seemed, had laid out the limits of its own domain, and seldom trespassed on the grounds of its neighbor. The cave Pewees fed or spent their time so far above the mill on the creek that the mill Pewees never came in contact with them. The Pewees of the cattle yard confined themselves to the orchard. Yet I sometimes could hear the notes of the three distinctly, at the same moment. I then had an idea that all of these birds were descended from the same stock. I had ample proof that this supposition was correct, because the brood of young Pewees that were raised in the cave returned, the following spring, and established themselves farther up the creek and elsewhere in the neighborhood.

On some other occasion I will speak of the return of birds and their progeny to their birthplace, to convince you that every country owes the increase of new species of birds and quadrupeds to the habit of such returning, caused by the benefits of more open country lands under cultivation. But now, with your leave, I will return to the Pewees of the cave.

On the thirteenth day the little ones were hatched. One egg did not hatch, and on the second day after the birth of her brood the hen very deliberately pushed it out of the nest. In it I found the embryo of a bird partly dried up, with its vertebrae attached to the shell, a condition which probably caused its death. Never have I witnessed the attention of birds to their young so closely. Their entrance with insects was so frequently repeated that I thought I saw the little ones grow as I gazed upon them.

The old birds no longer looked on me as an enemy, and they would often come in close by me as if I were only a post. I now took it upon myself to handle the young frequently. Several times I took the whole family out and blew the exuviae of the feathers from the nest. I attached light threads to their legs; these they invariably removed, either with their bills or with the assistance of their parents. I renewed them, however, until I found the little fellows habituated to them. At last, when they were about to leave the nest, I fixed a light silver thread to the leg of each, loose enough not to hurt the part, yet so fastened that the bird could not remove it.*

After sixteen days the brood took to wing, and the old birds, dividing the time with caution, began to arrange the nest anew. A second set of eggs was laid, and by the beginning of August a new brood made its appearance.

The young birds took much to the woods, as if they felt more secure there than in the open fields. But before they departed they all appeared strong, and did not mind making long sorties into the open air, over the whole creek, and the fields around it. On October 8 not a Pewee could I find on the plantation. My little companions had all set off on their travels. For weeks afterward, however, I saw Pewees arriving from the North, and lingering a short time as if to rest before moving southward.

When the Pewees returned to Pennsylvania I had the satisfaction of observing them again, in and about the cave. There again in the very same nest two broods were raised. I found several Pewees' nests some distance up the creek, particularly under the bridge, and also came upon several in the adjoining meadows, attached to the inner parts of sheds erected for hay and grain. Several of these birds which I caught on the nest had the little banding ring on the leg, I was pleased to find.

* This was the first "banding" of young wild birds in America. The first Banding Society in the U. S. A. was founded a century later.

At this time [1805], I was obliged to go to France, where I remained nearly two years.*

On my return, early in August, I had the satisfaction of finding three young Pewees in the nest of the cave. But this was not the nest I had left in it. The old one had been torn away from the roof, and the one which I found there was above the place where the old one had stood. I noticed at once that one of the parent birds was as shy as possible, while the other allowed me to approach within a few yards. This was the male bird, and I felt sure that the old female had paid the debt of Nature. On inquiring of the miller's son, I found that he had killed the old Pewee and four young ones to make bait for catching fish. Then the male Pewee had brought another female to the cave!

As long as the plantation of "Mill Grove" belonged to me, there continued to be a Pewee's nest in my favorite retreat. But after I sold it, the cave was destroyed, as were nearly all the beautiful rocks along the shores of the creek, to build a new dam across the Perkiomen.

While travelling on horseback with a friend in Virginia, I was asked by him to go somewhat out of our way in order to visit the renowned Natural Bridge of that state. My companion, who had visited it before, wagered that he could lead me across the rock bridge before I was aware of it. This was early in April. I had read descriptions of this place and felt confident that the Pewee Flycatcher must be found there. I trotted ahead, intent on proving to myself that constant attention to one subject must sooner or later have its reward in one's knowledge of it.

I listened to the notes of the different birds, and at last distinguished the Pewee. I stopped my horse to judge the distance that the bird might be from me, and a moment later told my friend that the bridge was less than a hundred yards from us. It was impossible for us to see the bridge itself. My companion's surprise was great.

"How do you know this?" he asked. "For you are correct."

"Simply," I answered, "because I hear the notes of the Pewee, and know that a cave or a deep rocky creek must therefore be near."

We moved on. The Pewees rose from under the Natural Bridge of Virginia in numbers. I pointed to the spot and won the wager.

This rule I have almost always found to work both ways. The nature of the place where the observer may be, whether high or low, moist or

* Actually one year.

dry, sloping north or south, with whatever kind of vegetation or tall trees or low shrubs, will generally give a hint as to its inhabitants.

The flight of the Pewee is performed by a fluttering, light motion, frequently interrupted by sailings—slow when the bird is flying to some distant point, rapid when in pursuit of prey. Often it mounts straight up from its perch after an insect, swallowing it whole unless it happens to be large. It will pursue one for a considerable distance, seldom without success.

It alights with great firmness, immediately erects itself in the manner of Hawks, glances all around, shakes its wings with a tremulous motion, and vibrates its tail upwards as if by a spring. Its tufty crest is generally erect, and its whole appearance neat if not elegant. The Pewee has its particular stands from which it seldom rambles far—a fence stake near the road, the corner of the barn roof, or the highest dead twig of a tall tree. During the heat of the day it reposes in the shade of the woods. In the autumn it may choose a mullein stalk for its stand, or a rock jutting over a stream. Now and then it lights on the ground for an instant, but it does so principally in winter, or else in spring while collecting materials for its nest.

The nest resembles that of the Barn Swallow, consisting of mud, grasses and mosses in regular layers. It is lined with delicate root fibers, shreds of vine bark, wool, horse-hair, and sometimes a few feathers. It is from five to six inches across, with a depth of four to five inches. Both birds work at it alternately, bringing pellets of mud or damp earth to be mixed with moss on the outside. Sometimes the exterior is entirely mossy. The nest is firmly attached to a rock, a wall, the rafter of a house, or the like. In the Kentucky barrens, I have found nests fixed to those curious places called *sink-holes* as deep down as twenty feet below the surface of the ground. When the Pewees return in spring they strengthen their old nest by adding to the outside of it. This prevents it from falling, as it sometimes does when several years old. In Maine they may take possession of the nest of the Swallow. The eggs are from four to six, rather long, pure white, generally with a few reddish spots near the larger end.

I have found the Pewee abundant in Florida in winter, in full song and as lively as ever, also in Louisiana and the Carolina cotton fields. I have met with these birds on the Magdalen Islands, the coast of Labrador, and in Newfoundland.

$\mathcal{S}$wallows

PURPLE MARTIN

The Purple Martin appears in New Orleans early in February or a few days before, in northern Kentucky as early as mid-March, and around Philadelphia about the tenth of April. It reaches Boston about April 25, and its parties continue their migration much farther north as the spring continues to open.

It frequently rears three broods in Louisiana. On February 4, 1821, I walked for two miles on the banks of the Mississippi below New Orleans, constantly looking up at the prodigious flocks while passersby regarded me with astonishment. My thermometer stood at 68° Fahrenheit, that calm, drizzly day. These arriving Martins were moving over the vicinity in a mile-and-a-half-long mass, a quarter of a mile wide, and at a considerable height. Each bird performed circular sweeps as it seized food along the way. On February 9, not far from where the Battle of New Orleans was waged, I enjoyed another such sight, although I did not think the flock so large.

I saw them arrive at the Falls of the Ohio, near Louisville, Kentucky, in small detached parties of five or six birds when the thermometer was as low as 28°, and the next day at 45°, and again, in the same week, so low as to cause the death of all the Martins, or to render them incapable of flight. They are usually plentiful there by March 25.

All the Purple Martins return to the South about August 20. They assemble, in parties of fifty to a hundred and fifty, about city spires and steeples, or on the branches of a large dead tree on farmland. For several days the assembly continues. They make occasional westward sorties, uttering their cry in chorus, fly swiftly for several yards, then turn back abruptly, and with easy sailing return to the tree or steeple. This action seems to be for exercise, as well as to determine their course, and to rehearse their arrangement so as to counter the fatigues of the long journey ahead. While they are resting between these sorties, they dress and oil their feathers, clean their skin, and rid their bodies of the insects which infest them. But for a few who take cover, they remain on their roosts exposed to the night air. At length, on the dawn of a calm morning, they start with one accord, move due west or southwest, and join other parties as they proceed, until an enormous flock such as I have described is formed. Their progress south is much more rapid than their spring migration, and they now keep closer together. So powerful is their flight that when they meet the gust of a violent storm, they appear to slide along the edges of it, as if determined not to lose an inch of their gains. The front ranks face the storm with pertinacity—up—down—along the skirts of the opposing currents and into their undulating recesses. They are determined to force their way through. The rest follow close behind, all huddled together into a mass like one large black spot. Not a twitter can be heard. The instant that they pass the current they relax their efforts, refresh themselves, and twitter in united congratulation that they have won the contest.

Although their flight is graceful and easy, it cannot be compared with that of the Barn Swallow. But the Purple Martin is expert at bathing and drinking while on the wing, over a large lake or river. As it comes in contact with the water it dips in the hind part of the body with a sudden motion, then rises and shakes like a water spaniel. To drink, it sails close over the water with both wings raised high to form an acute angle. Then it lowers its head, dips its bill in quick succession, swallowing a little each time.

The Purple Martin alights with ease on trees, especially the willows, and keeps moving its wings and tail as it shifts about in search of leaves for its nest. Despite the shortness of its legs, it frequently alights on the ground to pick up insects, or to walk to the edge of a puddle to drink—with open wings—as if not feeling perfectly comfortable. It also opens its wings in this way while on trees.

Courageous and persevering, the bird will defend its rights against dogs and other quadrupeds hostile to it. These Martins attack and chase every kind of Hawk, Crow, or Vulture, a fact which endears them to the farmer. They often follow and tease Eagles. I shall relate to you a certain occurrence, to give you an idea of their tenacity.

I had a large, roomy house built and fixed on a pole near my home, in an enclosure where for some years several pairs of Martins had reared their young. After that, one winter, I also put up several small boxes as an invitation to Bluebirds. The Martins arrived in the spring, and, imagining these smaller apartments preferable to their mansion, they took possession of them after driving the Bluebirds out. I watched the battles, and saw that one of the Bluebirds had as much courage as his antagonist. But the Martin's more powerful blows forced the Bluebird to give up his house, in which the nest was nearly finished. The Martin showed his head at the entrance, when the Bluebird continued to annoy him, and merely retorted with gloating insults. I saw fit to interfere, mounted the tree to which the Bluebird's house was fastened, caught the Martin, and clipped his tail with scissors in the hope that this would induce him to move to his own quarters. No such thing. No sooner had I launched him into the air than he rushed back at once into the box. Again I caught him, clipped each wing tip, but not so much that he could not fly for food, and once more set him at liberty. However, the desired effect was not produced. The pertinacious Martin kept the box despite my wishes that he should give it up. Angrily I seized him and disposed of him.

At the house of a friend in Lousiana, some Martins took possession of various holes in the cornices. There they reared their young for several years, until the insects which they attracted to the house led the owner to take steps. Carpenters cleaned the cornices and closed the holes. The Martins were in despair, and began to bring twigs and the like to build nests wherever they could find holes in the building. Not until they were chased off repeatedly did they resign themselves to some Woodpeckers' holes on dead trees of the plantation. The next spring, a house was built for them, according to the practice which has become general, the Purple Martin being a privileged pilgrim, the harbinger of spring.

Its note may not be melodious, but it is pleasing, especially in the early morning, and when the male twitters to his love. The farmer rises from his bed as he hears its notes, which are among the first. The Indian is also fond of the Martin's company, and hangs up a calabash on some twig near his camp; and in this cradle the bird keeps watch for Vultures which would otherwise harm the deer skins and venison meat which the Indian is drying. The Negro slave of the South also neatly scoops out a calabash and hangs it close to his hut. At the sound of the horn that calls him to labor, he cannot help thinking how happy he would be were he free to gambol day after day, like that bird. Almost every country tavern has a Martin box on the upper part of its signboard . . . the handsomer the box, the better the inn proves to be, I have noticed.

All our cities have houses for the Purple Martin, and not even lads bent on mischief often disturb this favorite who sweeps along the streets, seizes flies, peeps into human homes, hangs to eaves, or mounts high above the city. He plays with the string of a child's kite, snapping at it as he passes with unerring precision. Or he sweeps along roofs, or he chases Grimalkin the cat—enemy of his brood.

He repairs the old nest or builds a new one of dry sticks, willow twigs, grasses, leaves, feathers and whatever rags he can find. In the Middle districts he waits about ten days after his return there before he builds. There are four to six pure white eggs. Two broods are reared in a season, except in Louisiana where there are sometimes three. The first comes forth late in May, the second about the middle of July. The male takes part in the incubation. An extremely attentive mate, he twitters on the box and flies past the hole, to low, emphatic, and prolonged notes less musical than his common *pews*. The food consists entirely of insects, including large beetles. They seldom seize the honey-bee.

BARN SWALLOW

The Barn Swallow makes its first appearance at New Orleans between mid-February and the first of March, and apparently in pairs rather than flocks, or else in small parties. They return to the places where they nested before, or where they were reared. Their migratory progress depends much on the weather. So hardy does the species seem to be that I have seen it near Eastport, Maine, in company with the Cliff Swallow as early as May 7, in 1833—when masses of ice still hung from every cliff. Its return is welcomed by all, for it seldom appears before the final melting of the snows, and is looked upon as the harbinger of summer. Man teaches his offspring to cherish this Swallow, which never commits any depredations on his property and which everybody loves for that reason also.

The returning pair examine last year's tenement, choose a place to build a new nest, perhaps, or repair the old one. The nest they attach to the side of a beam or rafter in a barn or shed, or under a bridge, or even in an old well, or in a sink-hole like those found in the Kentucky barrens. I have seen seven or eight nests within a few inches of each other . . . and in some large barns I have counted forty, fifty or more. Both birds bring pellets of mud or moist earth in their bills and place it against the wood, wall, or rock. They place these pellets in regular layers which they mix (especially the lower layers) with long slender grasses which often dangle from the nest. The first layers are short; each successive layer increases in length as the birds work upwards, until the final length of the inverted cone is about eight inches and the greatest diameter six. The nest, which weighs over two pounds, is fully an inch thick at the top. I have often noted the expansion of the upper layer in repaired or enlarged nests. But there is considerable variation in the size of the nests, depending on the space of time the birds have to build them before they begin to deposit their eggs. I have seen some of a late period which were destitute of grasses and which required seven days to build—with labor from dawn to sunset, but with several hours of rest in mid-day. Inside the shell of mud is a bed several inches thick, of slender grasses arranged in a circle, with soft feathers arranged on top of them. I have never heard of a Barn Swallow's nesting in a chimney; the stronger Chimney Swift may prevent it.

The eggs—four to six—are rather small, elongated, semi-translucent, and white, sparingly spotted with reddish brown. Incubation takes thirteen days, and both sexes sit, though the female performs the principal part of the task. Each feeds the other, and at night they rest beside each other in the nest. In South Carolina they build early in April, in Kentucky about the first of May. This species seldom raises more than two broods in the South and the Middle districts . . . never, I believe, more than one in Maine and farther north. After the young reach a good size, the devoted parents roost near by. When the little ones are fully fledged, their elders entice them to fly, and, soon after their first lessons, to follow to fields, roads or rivers. They alight, not far apart, on low walls, posts and rails, or withering twigs or branches, near a place where the parents can find food for them. As they improve in flying, the parents often feed them on the wing; both rise obliquely in the air, come close together, and the food is quickly delivered. They separate and continue their gambols. In the evening the family retires to the nest, where it usually resides until time for migration.

For about a fortnight, between mid-August and early September, young and old fraternize more closely in the loose flocks which are continually increasing. They alight on tall trees, churches, barns, and courthouses to remove insects or to plume and dress themselves for hours, to an almost incessant chirping. Occasionally they make short sallies, then return to the same spot where the flock had gathered. But by September 10, great flocks have set out for the South; others arrive from the North. Dawn is usually the hour of their departure, high above the trees and towns; but I have seen them flying on a fine, clear, quiet evening also. They alight close together at suitable places, and for a while twitter loudly, as if in invitation to other approaching flocks or stragglers to join them.

The flight of the Barn Swallow probably surpasses that of any other species of the feathered tribes except the Hummingbird. In fine weather they perform their circuits at a high elevation, with truly admirable lightness and ease, playing over river, field or city with equal grace. In wet weather they move more swiftly and in tortuous meanderings, pass and re-pass, now low, now along walls. On the ground they are by no means awkward, but they appear hampered. It aids its very short steps with its wings, and prefers flying. When it alights on a twig, it shows a peculiar, tremulous motion of wings and tail. Its food is entirely insectivorous, the crustaceous parts of which it disgorges in pellets.

In *The Birds of America* I have shown a pair of Barn Swallows in their most perfect spring plumage, with a nest from the rafter of a barn in New Jersey, in which there was at least a score of them.

CLIFF SWALLOW

In the spring of 1815 I saw a few of these Swallows for the first time, at Henderson, Kentucky, on the banks of the Ohio. It was an exceedingly cold morning, and nearly all of them were killed by the severity of the weather. I wrote a description at the time and named them *Hirundo republicana* because of their mode of association while nesting and rearing young.

For years I despaired of meeting others, but in 1819 my hopes were revived by the curator of the Western Museum in Cincinnati, who said that a strange species had made its appearance near there and built nests in clusters against walls. I immediately crossed the Ohio to New Port, Kentucky, and no sooner had we landed than the chirruping of my long-lost strangers greeted me. Many were busily engaged in repairing the damage done to their nests by storms of the preceding winter. The United States Army commander of the garrison allowed us to examine the walls where the birds were building. He told us that four years earlier he had seen a few nesting under the eaves and cornice; they had worked rapidly and peaceably, and had departed as soon as the young were able to travel. They had returned there each springtime since in increased numbers, usually about April 10. April 20 was the time of my visit. They had finished about fifty nests, and more were in progress.

About daybreak they flew to the river bank near by to fetch the muddy sand there. They worked assiduously till near noon, as if aware that the heat of the sun was necessary to dry and harden their moist tenements. Then they ceased labor for a few hours and amused themselves by performing aerial evolutions, courting and caressing their mates with much affection, and snapping at insects on the wing. Meanwhile they often examined their nests to see if they were drying; as soon as these seemed firm enough, they resumed their labors.

Until the females began to sit, they all roosted in the hollow limbs of sycamore trees on the banks of the Licking River. But when incubation started the males alone resorted to the trees. A second party arrived, and, hard pressed for time, betook themselves to the holes in the wall where bricks had been left out for the scaffolding. They fitted these with projecting necks that were similar to the nests already completed. They deposited their eggs on a few bits of straw, and all caution was necessary for us to examine them, as the slightest touch would cause the frail nest to crumble. I procured some by means of a tablespoon. Each nest contained four white, dusky-spotted eggs. Only one brood is raised each mating season.

The energy with which they defend their nests is truly astonishing.

I had taken care to visit them at sunset, and supposed they would all have been on the sycamores. But only one female was sitting; she gave the alarm and at once called out the whole tribe. They snapped at my hat, body and legs, passed between me and the nests within an inch of my face, twittering their rage and sorrow. As I withdrew they continued their attacks for some distance. The note which they uttered may be perfectly imitated by rubbing a cork dampened with spirits against the neck of a bottle.

A third party arrived a few days later and began to build. In a week they had finished. Thirty nests hung clustered like so many gourds, each with a neck two inches long.

On July 27 the young were able to follow their parents. Each had a white frontlet, and they were scarcely distinguishable from their elders as to plumage.

On August 1, they all assembled near their nests, rose about 399 feet in air, and at 10 A.M. departed in a loose flock, due north. They returned about dusk. They continued these excursions until the third day, no doubt to exercise their migratory powers. Then, uttering a farewell cry, they took the same course at 10 A.M. again, and finally disappeared.

I was extremely anxious to settle the long-debated question respecting the migration or supposed torpidity of Swallows. After years of observation and reflection I remarked that, among all migratory birds of whatever species, those that remove farthest from us depart sooner than those which retire only within the confines of the United States. I further remarked that those that remain later return earlier in the spring. These observations were confirmed by my discovery of numerous Warblers, Thrushes, and the like in full feather, and so on, as I advanced towards the Southwest at the approach of winter. I also found that the Swallow which the French of lower Louisiana call the Little White-Bellied Martin (Wilson's *Hirundo viridis*) remains at New Orleans later than others of the species.

Blue Jay

In my painted portrait of the Blue Jay you will see three individuals of this beautiful species—rogues and thieves who are enjoying the fruits of their knavery and sucking eggs pilfered from the nest of some innocent Dove or harmless Partridge! Who could imagine that a form so gracefully and resplendently garbed by Nature should harbor so much mischief . . . that selfishness, duplicity, and malice should be the moral accompaniments of such physical perfection? Yet so it is, and how like beings of a much higher order are these gay deceivers, about whom I could write you a whole chapter were not my task of a different nature.

The Blue Jay can subsist in both cold and warm climates. Everywhere it manifests the same mischievous disposition. It imitates the cry of the Sparrow-Hawk so perfectly that the little birds hurry into coverts to avoid what they believe to be that marauder. It robs every nest it can find, sucks eggs like the Crow, and will devour young birds. A Jay in an aviary in Charleston destroyed all the other species caged with it; first rats were supposed to be the culprits; then mice were accused; but the Jay that had been raised in the aviary was the villain.

In the winter of 1830 I purchased twenty-five of these birds in Louisville to ship to Liverpool via New Orleans, with a view to turning them out in the English woods. I placed them in a large cage for the purpose, and was surprised to see how cowardly each newcomer was as I added a few live Jays at a time. But after a day or two they were as gay and frolicsome as if in the woods, each newcomer quite unwilling to allow the others to walk over him and trample him as they did in the beginning. When the cage was filled it was amusing to listen to their hammering, all perched side by side, and each pecking at a grain of corn like so many blacksmiths paid by the piece. They drank often, ate nuts, grapes, dried fruits, and especially fresh beef. They roosted peacefully together and were pleasing pets. If one chanced to cry an alarm, all would leap and fly with as much concern and ado as if their worst enemy were in their midst. They bore the passage to Europe pretty well. Most of them reached Liverpool in good health; but a few days later a disease caused by insects on their bodies caused some to die every day. Remedies proved vain. Only one individual reached London, but it soon died.

Our party observed no Blue Jays in Newfoundland or Labrador during our stay there. It became more and more rare as soon as we began to sight the Canada Jay during our voyage. But they are plentiful in the United States, and often a nuisance to the farmers.

The Blue Jay is expert at discovering a fox, raccoon or any quadruped hostile to birds, and will follow them, screaming, as if to enlist the help of every other Jay or Crow. It behaves in this way towards Owls also, and even towards Hawks on occasion.

In Louisiana I have seen it breeding near planters' houses, high in trees growing in the avenues, or in yards; it may occupy an old or abandoned nest of the Crow or Cuckoo. In the South, from Louisiana to Maryland, it breeds twice a year, but east of Maryland seldom more than once. Though it occurs in all places from the seashore to the mountains, it seems more abundant in the latter. Its nest is made of twigs or other coarse materials, and lined with fibrous roots. The four or five eggs are dull olive, spotted with brown.

Truly omnivorous, the Blue Jay feeds on all sorts of flesh, seeds and insects. Like most boasters, he is more tyrannical than brave, dreads the strong, domineers over the feeble, and flies from equals. Often he is a downright coward and lets the challenging Cardinal Grosbeak beat him off the ground. The Red Thrush, Mockingbird and many others, although inferior in strength, never allow him to approach their nests with impunity. The Jay, to be even with them, creeps silently towards their eggs and young and devours these at every opportunity. I have seen one go its rounds from one nest to another daily, to suck the eggs, and with as much regularity and composure as a physician calling on his patients. I have also seen its sad disappointment on returning to its home and finding its mate in the jaws of a snake, its nest upset and its eggs all gone. I have more than once thought on such occasions that, like all

. 229 .

culprits, it evinced strong remorse when brought to a sense of its enormities.

The Blue Jay feeds with special diligence during migration, which takes place during the day only. A person travelling or hunting by night may disturb the rest of a Jay, which in terror sounds an alarm that all its travelling companions will answer. Their multiplied cries make the woods resound far and near. They usually alight at fairly frequent intervals during migration, for like true rangers they ransack and inspect the woods, fields, orchards, and even the gardens. The more they are chased, the noisier they become, unless a Hawk suddenly happens along. Then they are instantly struck dumb; as if ever conscious of deserving punishment, they either remain motionless for a while, or sneak off silently into the densest thickets, where they remain hidden as long as their dangerous enemy is near. Their movements on the wing are exceedingly graceful. As they pass from one tree to another, their expanded wings and tail—so beautiful in tint and form—never fail to delight the observer.

Raven

To others I leave the task of repeating the fables and unedifying matter accumulated down the ages respecting the Raven and other remarkable species. Instead I shall relate what I have learned during years of laborious but gratifying observation. I shall confine myself to the particulars gathered in the course of a life spent chiefly in studying the birds of my country. There have I sought to search out things hidden since the creation of this wondrous world, or seen only by the naked Indian. Who is the stranger to my own dear country that can adequately conceive of the extent of its primeval woods, the glory of its solemn forests that for centuries have waved before breeze and tempest, of its vast Atlantic bays, of its thousands of streams, vast lakes and magnificent rivers? There is the diversity of our Western plains, our sandy Southern shores with their reedy swamps; protecting cliffs; rapid Mexican Gulf currents; rushing tides of the Bay of Fundy; majestic mountains; and thundering cataracts. Would I might delineate it all, but now let me resume my task which (and with reverence would I say it) seems to have been imposed upon me by Him who called me into existence.

In the United States the Raven is a migratory bird in some measure, in that it retires south during severe winters, but returns northward at the first signs of milder weather. Mountains, steep banks of rivers, rocky shores of lakes, and cliffs of quiet islands are the places to watch them.

Notwithstanding all the Raven's care, his nest is invaded wherever it is found. Its usefulness is forgotten, its faults are multiplied by imagination, and because ignorance, prejudice, and destructiveness have figured in man's mind to this bird's detriment from time immemorial, it is shot at. Some say they destroy the Raven because he is black, others because he has allegedly killed a sheep or lamb, and others because they find his croaking unpleasant and ominous! For my part, I admire the Raven, because I see much in him to excite our wonder. True, he may hasten the death of a weakly lamb, or eat the eggs of other birds, or steal young fowls and eggs from the farmer. But consider how many sheep, lambs and fowls are saved by his destruction of grubs, worms and insects, mice, moles and rats, weasels, young opossums and skunks! With the perseverance of a cat, he watches the burrows of foxes and pounces on the cubs. Our farmers know full well that he warns them of the wolf's prowlings around their yards and that he never intrudes on cornfields except to their benefit. But they also know his power; interfere as you may with tales of pity or of truth, they reply that the bird is a Raven, and, as La Fontaine most truly said, "Might triumphs!"

The powerful, even flight is capable of great prolongation at certain periods. In fine weather the Raven will sail at an immense height for hours at a time. Although hardly swift, it can nonetheless contend with various kinds of Hawks, and even with Eagles if attacked by them. It can chart its course through thickest fogs of the North, and traverse immense tracts of land or water, flying without rest.

Small animals of every kind, eggs, dead fish, carrion, shell-fish, insects, worms, nuts, berries and other fruits are the food of this omnivorous bird. I have never seen one attack a large living animal as the Turkey Buzzard and Carrion Crow are prone to do. But I have known it to follow men hunting without dogs, and to feed on the scraps. It will carry off salted fish placed in a spring to freshen. It often rises with a shell-fish to break it by letting it fall on a rock. Its sight is exceedingly acute; but its smell, if it possesses that sense, is weak, a fact which makes it resemble our Vulture.

Its breeding season varies according to latitude, from early January to early June. I have found young Ravens on the banks of the Lehigh and Susquehanna rivers on the first of May; about ten days later on the majestic Hudson; about June the first, off the Bay of Fundy on Grand Manan; and as late as mid-July in Labrador. The nest of sticks, coarse weeds, wood, and animal hair is always built among the most inaccessible rocks. Its four to six oval eggs are two inches long at the least and are light greenish blue dappled with light purple and yellowish brown blotches which nearly cover the larger end. Incubation is nineteen or twenty days, and, unless the eggs or young are removed or destroyed, one brood a year is raised. The old birds return to the same nest year after year; and should one partner be destroyed, the other will lead a new one to the same abode. The young keep to the nest for many weeks before they can fly. Should one parent be killed after they are hatched, the survivor usually finds a mate to help feed them.

Although I have found eggs which measure rather more than two inches in length and one and three-eighths in breadth, others measure one and seven-eighths by one and four-twelfths. They also differ considerably in the tint of their ground color and in their markings.

The Raven is of a social disposition. Flocks of forty, fifty, or more may be seen together after the breeding season. It becomes attached to its owner if treated gently in captivity, and will follow him about with its stately walk like a familiar and confiding friend. It can imitate the human voice and is sometimes taught to speak a few words very distinctly. Vigilant, industrious, and, when the safety of their young or nest is at stake, courageous, they drive away Hawks and Eagles; but in no case do they venture to attack man, whom they avoid with utmost wariness and cunning.

On the Labrador coast, at Little Mecattina Harbor, in July 1833, I saw a Raven's nest under a shelf of rugged and fearful rocks. The young were nearly fledged, and now and then called loudly to their parents as if to ask why our vessel had come there. One of them tried to fly away and fell in the water. We caught it and I trimmed one wing and let it loose on deck along with some other birds that I was observing. The mother kept sailing high over the schooner; the young captive seemed to understand her repeated notes, for it walked carefully to the bowsprit, opened its wings and tried to fly, but instead fell into the water and was drowned. In a few days the whole family left the place and we saw no more of them.

I once found a nest at a narrow point of the Lehigh River in Pennsylvania, in a deep fissure of rocks about twenty feet above the water—a most secure situation. The nest, in fact, hung over the stream, so that it was impossible to reach it either from above or below. Many years ago I saw another just beneath the soaring arch of the Natural Bridge in Virginia and situated on a small projecting stone barely a foot square. But the Raven appeared quite satisfied as to the security of her brood on that narrow bed. The Natural Bridge is placed on the rise of a hill, which appears to have been rent asunder by some convulsions of the earth. Tradition reports that General George Washington threw a dollar over the bridge from the creek below. I visited it on a fleet wild horse of the prairies, called Barro.

I have heard of the Raven's nesting not far from the eyrie of a Golden Eagle in the New York highlands.

In *The Birds of America* I have shown a very old male Raven on a branch of shell-bark hickory, not because the bird alights on any particular tree by preference, but because I thought you might be interested in seeing so fruitful a branch from our forests.

*W*rens

CAROLINA WREN

I FREQUENTLY heard the Carolina Wren singing from the roof of an abandoned flat-boat tied up to the shore a small distance below the city of New Orleans. When its song, a short ditty somewhat resembling *come-to-me, come-to-me,* was finished, the bird went on creeping from one board to another, thrust itself through an auger hole, entered the boat's side at one place and peeped out another, catching numerous spiders and other insects all the while. It possesses the power of creeping and of hopping in a nearly equal degree.

While I was at "Oakley," the plantation of my friend James Pirrie, near Bayou Sara, Louisiana, I discovered that one of these Carolina Wrens was in the habit of roosting in a Wood Thrush's nest. The nest, on a low horizontal branch, was filled with fallen autumn leaves. The bird thrust his body beneath the leaves, and, I have no doubt, found the place very comfortable.

BEWICK'S WREN

THE Wren I named for England's great woodcut artist, Thomas Bewick, I shot on October 19, 1821, about five miles from St. Francisville, Louisiana. It was standing in the position in which you see it in *The Birds of America* (or as nearly as I could represent it with my pencil), and upon the fallen trunk of a tree not far from a fence. My drawing of Bewick's Wren was made on the spot. Another was shot a few days after, by my young friend and painting pupil Joseph R. Mason, who assisted me in my Mississippi River country explorations.

Eight or nine years later, in November, 1829, I had the pleasure of meeting another Bewick's Wren about fifteen miles from St. Francisville. It was near the house which I was then visiting. For several days I observed its habits, as it moved along the bars of fences, occasionally hopping sidewise, or flying to a peach or apple tree close to the fence, and ascending to the top branches, as if about to sing but without uttering more than a low *twitter*. I honored this species with the name of Bewick, a person too well known for his admirable talents as an engraver on wood, and for his beautiful work on *The Birds of Britain*, to need any eulogy from me. I enjoyed the pleasure of a personal acquaintance with him, and found him at all times a most agreeable, kind, and benevolent friend.

HOUSE WREN

As for the House Wren, when passing from place to place during the love season, or while its mate is sitting on the nest, this sweet, sprightly, active, vigilant, and courageous little bird flutters slowly through the air, singing all the while. It delights to be near and about the gardens, orchards and habitations of man, and is often heard in the very center of cities, where many little boxes are put up against the walls of houses or on tree trunks, as in the country also. In these it nestles and rears its young. But it is satisfied with any crevice or hole in the walls, with a window sill, eaves, the stable, barn, or even a piece of timber under a porch roof. I knew of one to live in the pocket of an old broken-down carriage, and many in such an old hat as you see represented in the picture of this Wren in *The Birds of America*. The little creatures anxiously peep out or hang to the side of the hat, to meet their mother who has just arrived with a spider, while the male is on the lookout, ready to act should any intruder come near. The same nest is often reclaimed for several successive years, merely receiving a little mending from season to season.

The familiarity of the House Wren is extremely pleasing. In Pennsylvania a pair of these birds had formed a nest, and the female was sitting in a hole of the wall within a few inches of my drawing room. The male was continually singing within a few feet of my young wife and myself, while I was engaged in portraying other birds than Wrens. When the window was open, the Wren's company was extremely agreeable, as was its little song which continually reminded us of its happy life. It would now and then dive into the garden at the foot of the window, seek food for its mate, return and creep into the hole where it had its nest and be off again in a moment. Having gathered some flies and spiders, I now and then threw some of them towards him; he would seize them with great alacrity, eat some himself, and carry the rest to his mate. In this manner it became daily more acquainted with us, entered the room, and once or twice sang while there.

One morning I took it in to draw its portrait, and, suddenly closing the window, I easily caught it, held it in my hand, and finished its likeness, after which I restored it to liberty. This, however, made it more cautious, and it never again ventured within the window, although it sang and looked at us as it had done in the beginning. It is the one you see placed in the hat in *The Birds of America*.

The antipathy of the House Wren towards cats is extreme. Although it does not attack puss, it follows and scolds her until she is out of sight. It makes war on the Martin, the Bluebird and the House Swallow, the nest of any of which it does not hesitate to appropriate for itself when occasion offers. Its own nest of dry, crooked twigs is so closely woven as scarcely to allow any other bird to enter. Grasses are arranged around the outer surface, and the nest is warmly lined with feathers and other soft materials. There are five or six oval eggs of a pale reddish color, and two broods of young are raised in the season.* The eggs are five-eighths inch long and four and one-half eighths wide.

The male seems to delight in attempting to surpass other Wrens in vocal powers while the eggs are in the nest. He is often seen within sight of another male bird, straining his little throat and gently turning his body from side to side, as if pivoted on his upper joints. For a moment he thinks the musical powers of his rival superior to his own, and he darts towards him. A battle ensues, and when it is over he immediately resumes his song, whether he be the conqueror or not.

When the young first leave the nest, it is interesting to see them follow the parents among the currant bushes in the gardens, like so many mice. They hop from twig to twig, throwing the tail upwards.

* Six to eight white, heavily brown-dotted eggs. Nest: box, tree hole, or cavity.

They put their bodies in a hundred different positions, all learned by watching the parents, who scold them even without cause, but as if to prevent the approach of enemies, so anxious are they for the safety of their young ones.

My good old friend John Bachman of Charleston told me he had known the House Wren to fill up vacant parts of its nesting places when these are larger than necessary. He found one made of a clothes-line box more than a foot square, "which must have cost its tiny architect many days of hard labor." The variety and size of the things which were used to fill the box included a snake-skin several feet long, large twigs, pieces of India-rubber suspenders, oak leaves, feathers, shavings, hair, hay and so on. So anxious was the Wren to fill the space that the eggs were never hatched.

WINTER WREN

THE Winter Wren, still another of the species, has a song that excels that of any other bird of its size with which I am acquainted. It is truly musical, full of cadence, energetic and melodious. Its very length is surprising. Dull indeed must be the ear that thrills not on hearing it. The song, from the dark depths of a swamp, acts so powerfully on the mind as to inspire a feeling of wonder and delight. At such times it has usually impressed me with a sense of the goodness of the Almighty Creator, who has rendered every spot of earth in some way of use to the welfare of his creatures.

Once I was travelling through a gloomy part of a thickly tangled wood in the Great Pine Forest of Pennsylvania, not far from Mauch Chunk. I was intent on guarding myself from venomous snakes which I expected to encounter. The sweet song of this Wren came suddenly on my ear, and so cheeringly that I lost all fear of danger. I pressed forward through the rank briers and stiff laurels in pursuit of the bird, which, I hoped, was not far from its nest. But the Wren, as if bent on puzzling me, rambled here and there among the thickest bushes with uncommon cunning, now singing in one spot not far distant, and presently in another in a different direction.

Fatigued by much exertion, I at last saw it alight on the side of a large tree, close to the roots. It warbled a few notes which I thought exceeded any that it had sung before.

Suddenly another Wren appeared by its side, but this one darted off in a moment. The other disappeared. I went at once to the tree without removing my eyes from it for an instant. I saw a rise on it covered with moss and lichens, but it differed from the growths often seen on our forest trees, having a perfectly rounded opening, clean and quite smooth. I put a finger into it, and felt the pecking of a bird's bill, then heard a startled cry.

I had, in a word, for the first time in my life, found the nest of our Winter Wren.

After gently forcing the tenant from his premises, I drew out the eggs with a sort of scoop which I formed. There were not more than six. The little bird called to its mate, and their united clamor induced me to leave their treasures with them. But just as I was about to go off, it struck me that I ought to take a description of the nest, as I might not have such an opportunity again. I hope, reader, you will believe that when I resolved to sacrifice this nest, it was quite as much on your account as my own. Seven inches long, four and a half wide, two inches thick with mosses and lichen, it looked like a narrow bag against the bark. It was lined with the fur of a hare, and in the bottom were half a dozen large, downy Grouse feathers. The eggs, of a delicate blush color, resembled the paler leaves of a partly decayed rose, marked with reddish brown dots which were more numerous at the larger end.

Another nest which I found near the Mohawk was discovered by mere accident. One day in early June, about noon, feeling fatigued, I sat down on a rock overhanging the river. There, while resting, I had the pleasure of watching the motions of some fishes in the water. The dampness gave me a sudden chill, and made me sneeze aloud. From beneath the rock a startled Wren flew off. I soon found its nest, attached to the lower part of the rock, and it was like the one I saw in the Great Pine Forest.

In winter, when this Wren takes possession of the wood-pile outside a farm-house, it will challenge the cat in querulous tones. It peeps out here and there as it frisks in safety, wearing out Grimalkin's patience.

Mockingbird

I HAVE observed with astonishment that when those Mockingbirds that arrived in Louisiana after a summer in the Eastern States first returned, the "Southerners" invariably attacked them. For weeks after their arrival, the strangers exhibited much shyness, which, however, like the animosity of the resident birds, eventually disappeared. During winter the tribe is decidedly sociable.

Early in April, or two weeks before, these birds pair and build their nests. Sometimes they select a place with much carelessness. I have found them between fence rails directly by the roadside, and in fields and briers quite open to the view. The coarse nest is made of dried brier sticks, withered leaves, grasses and wool. Inside, it is finished with fibrous roots carelessly arranged in a circle. The female lays four to six eggs the first time, four or five the second, and, when there is a third brood, seldom more than three (only two of which seem to hatch).* The eggs are short oval in form, light green, and blotched and spotted with umber. The young of the last brood cannot fend for themselves until late in the season, when many berries and insects have grown scarce, a fact which has caused some observers to mistake them for a smaller species. The first brood appears in New Orleans about mid-April. Farther up country they are out by mid-May. The second brood is hatched in July, and the third in late September. They appear more plentiful near seashore districts. They seldom penetrate the depths of forests.

The female pays precise attention to the position in which she leaves her eggs when she goes off a short way for exercise and refreshment, to pick up gravel or roll in the dust. She hopes to find them in place, un-

---

* Normal: three to five eggs. A third brood is rare.

touched, but, if she does not, she utters a low, mournful note that brings the male to console her. But it is not true that she abandons the nest; on the contrary, she redoubles her care and scarcely leaves it again for a moment. Only after repeated intrusions does she finally desert it, and then with reluctance. Climbing snakes ascend to the nest to suck the eggs or swallow the young. But not only the pair but many other Mockingbirds of the vicinity fly to the spot, attack the reptiles and force them off if they are fortunate, or else deprive them of life. Prowling house cats, half wild, are also dangerous enemies; they approach unnoticed, pounce on the mother, or at the least destroy the eggs or young, and overturn the nest. Planters usually protect them throughout Louisiana, and give them the freedom of their gardens and buildings. Few Hawks attack them.

While the bird seeks food—insects—on the ground, its motions are light and elegant. It may open its wings as a butterfly does when basking in the sun, move a step or two, and again throw out its wings. In mild winter weather the males often sing with as much spirit as in spring and summer; and the young birds busily practice their notes in preparation for the love season.

The flight is performed by short jerks of body and wings, accompanied by strong twitching of the tail. These motions are even more marked while the bird is walking; it opens its tail and instantly closes it again, like a fan. Its call is a mournful note. It goes from tree to tree, or at most across a field, and scarcely ever rises higher than the top of a forest. During migration its flights are not prolonged; it resorts to the highest part of the woods near water courses, utters its note, roosts in the trees, and travels mostly by day.

I knew of one that was raised from the nest and kept by a gentleman of Natchez. It often flew out of the house, poured forth its melodies, and returned at sight of its keeper. I never heard one produce melodies in captivity, however, in any way comparable to its own natural song, which, unlike its cry, is by no means mournful. The bird's imitative powers are amazing.

The male, which is the smaller of the two, shows more white. In courtship he flies round his mate like a butterfly, his tail spread wide. He ascends, describes a circle, alights, approaches his loved one, and with his beautiful wings raised gently, he bows to her. Then he bounces upwards, opens his bill and pours forth his melody, exulting in his conquest with varied and mellow modulations and gradations all up and down the scale. Probably no bird in the world possesses the musical gifts of this king of songsters, trained by Nature. After the conjugal contract is sealed, he again pours forth his notes with more softness and richness than before, soars higher but glances about with vigilance. After these love scenes, he dances through the air, full of animation and delight, and imitates all the songs which Nature has taught to other species of the grove.

A peculiar note from the female causes him to cease his singing and help prepare the nest. After she lays an egg, he redoubles his caresses. In a fortnight the young brood demands all of their joint care and attention. When the young are two weeks old, they can fly, fend for themselves, and leave their parents.

Thrushes

BROWN THRASHER

PROPERLY CLASSED WITH THE MIMIDS OR MIMICS,
LIKE THE MOCKINGBIRD; NOT A THRUSH.——ED.

My painting of this Thrush shows a male bird courageously defending his nest, and exerting all his powers to extricate his beloved mate from the coils of the vile snake which has already nearly deprived her of life. Another male hears his call and comes swiftly to the rescue. With open bill he prepares to strike a vengeful blow at the reptile. His bright eyes gleam at the foe with hatred. A third male grapples with the snake and tears the skin from its body! The outcome, if victorious for the birds, may prove that innocence, although beset with difficulties, may honorably triumph with the aid of friendship.

The birds in the conflict which I represented did finally conquer the snake, although their nest was upset, their eggs lost, and the female's life imminently endangered. A crowd of Thrushes and other birds held a jubilee over the foe's carcass until the woods resounded with their exultation. I was happy in contributing my share to the general joy, for after I took the almost expiring bird into my hand for a few minutes, she recovered in some degree, and I restored her to her anxious mate.

The Brown Thrush, or Thrasher, is a constant resident of the United States. Immense numbers are found in the South, and in all our Eastern States in spring and summer. I observed none north of Nova Scotia, though they enter the British provinces. Those which breed in the Middle and Eastern districts return south about the first of October after fully six months' absence; but more than half of their number remain there the year round. They migrate by day, silently and singly, as they fly low from one bush to another; their longest flight seldom exceeds the breadth of a field or river, owing perhaps to the shortness of their wings, which contributes to the comparative heaviness of their movements.

If the bird reaches its destination on a fair day, it at once mounts the topmost twig of a tree which is apart from a forest and pours forth its loud, richly varied, and highly melodious song. It may sing for hours at a time, seldom committing errors while repeating the beautiful lessons set to it by Nature, all of which it studies for months during spring and summer. Ah, that I could imitate its loudest notes which are surpassed only by those of that unrivalled vocalist, the Mockingbird! In the South it may enliven an autumnal day by its song, but it is usually silent after the breeding season.

During courtship the male often struts gracefully before the female with his tail trailing like a Pigeon's at that time. Then he perches to sing for her and his body vibrates with vehemence. In Louisiana the Thrasher builds its nest as early as the first of March; in the Middle districts rarely before mid-May; and in Maine seldom before June. It chooses a brier bush, a sumach, or the thickest parts of a low tree, but never in the interior of a forest; and it favors bramble patches along fences or old abandoned fields. Sometimes it nests on the ground. Or it may choose a spot close to a planter's house, in the South, along with the Mockingbird. It is large, made of dry twigs, briers and small sticks, and imbedded in and mixed with dried leaves, coarse grass and other such materials. The thick lining is of fibrous roots, horse-hair, and sometimes rags and feathers. The eggs, four to six, are a pale, dull buff, thickly dotted with brown. Though two broods are usual in the South, there is rarely more than one to northward. The young begin their musical studies in autumn and repeat passages with as much zeal as a Paganini. By the following spring their full power of song is developed.

My friend John Bachman of Charleston gave me the following particulars:

Though good-humored towards the person who feeds them, they are always savage towards all other kinds of birds. I placed three Sparrows in the cage of a Thrush one evening, and next morning I found them killed and nearly stripped of their feathers. So perfectly gentle did this bird become towards me that when I opened its cage it would follow me about the yard and garden. The instant I took up a spade or hoe, it would follow at my heels, and as I turned up the earth it would pick up every insect or worm that it saw.

Ferruginous Thrush
Turdus Rufus —
Magnus François Buffon —

N.° 57

magnus Francis de Buffon —
L. New York May 10th 1841 Jean Jean J. L. Audubon

I kept it for three years. Its affection for me cost it its life. It usually slept on the back of my chair in my study, and one night the door was accidentally left open and a cat killed it.

The Brown Thrush is the strongest of its genus in the United States. Neither the Mocker nor Robin can cope with it. It will chase a dog or cat and tease a raccoon or fox. It will follow and defy the Cooper's Hawk and the Goshawk. Few snakes come off the victor when they attack its nest. The Thrushes will have frequent and severe fights among themselves, but let one of them give the least alarm and the whole party rushes forth to help chase off the common enemy. I have seen two males fight furiously when their nests were placed near each other; the females joined in. One male would approach the other cautiously, spread or jerk his long fanlike tail up, down and sidewise, cry defiance, and perhaps alight on the ground. One or the other attacks, and the fight seldom ends until one Thrush has beaten the other. The vanquished rarely attempts to retaliate, and peace is made.

Thrushes are fond of bathing and dusting in the sand of the roads. They bathe in small puddles during sunlight, then roll in sandy paths, dry their plumage and free themselves of insects. If disturbed at such a time, they run and hide under the nearest bushes, to return as soon as the intruder has retired.

During incubation, the male sings for hours at a time from the tree-tops. It reaches this pinnacle by leaping from branch to branch. It selects several trees for the purpose, none more than a hundred yards from the nest. Then it dives towards its favorite thicket instead of descending via the branches. Both birds sit on the eggs. Their mutual attachment and courage in defending their nest is strong, as country children have discovered. They will even assault a man who may intrude, and scold him with a strong, guttural note resembling *tchai, tcahai,* followed by a plaintive *weō,* until he withdraws. Should he carry off their treasure, they will follow him for perhaps half a mile, each bird crossing his path and reproaching him.

The food of the Brown Thrush consists of insects, worms, berries and other fruits. In winter it eats dogwood berries, sumach and holly.

The young acquire the full beauty of their plumage during the first winter.

WOOD THRUSH

THE Wood Thrush is my greatest favorite of our feathered tribes. To it I owe much. Often when I have listened to its wild notes in the forest, it has revived my drooping spirits. Often, after a night of violent rainstorm, far from my dear home, hungry, wearied, drenched and lonely, I have blessed the Being who formed the Wood Thrush which has consoled me and cheered my depressed mind and made me feel that man ought never to despair, whatever his situation . . . he can never be certain that aid is not at hand.

The Wood Thrush seldom makes a mistake about the weather after a storm such as I have mentioned. No sooner are its sweet notes heard than the heavens gradually clear and the great orb of day at length bursts upon the beholder. The woods echo the joyous thanks of their many songsters. The hunter listens to the Wood Thrush with tranquillity of mind.

The thickest and darkest woods always appear to please it best. The densely shaded borders of murmuring streamlets are its favorite resort. There it is that the musical powers of this hermit of the woods must be heard to be fully appreciated. Though its song has but a few notes, it is nonetheless so powerful, distinct, clear and mellow that it is impossible to convey the effect it produces on the listener. The notes rise in strength, then fall in gentle cadences until they are almost inaudible. Several of these birds may challenge each other, seemingly, from different parts of the forest, especially towards evening, at an hour when nearly all the other songsters are about to retire to rest. Then the notes are doubly pleasing, more than ordinarily effective. These concerts continue for some time after sunset, in June, when the females are sitting.

This species wings swiftly through the woods. It performs its migrations without appearing in open country. It is a regular resident of Louisiana. It reaches Pennsylvania about the first or middle of April, and gradually proceeds northward. Its food consists of berries and small fruits of the woods rather than those of the farmer. Insects and lichens also figure in its diet.

It nests on dogwood branches and also smaller shrubs. The nest is large, well saddled on a horizontal branch, and made up externally of various kinds of dry leaves, with a second bed of grasses and mud, and an internal layer of fine fibrous roots. The situation is often a deep, swampy hollow on a hillside. There are four or five beautiful blue eggs.

On alighting on a branch, this Thrush jets its tail a few times, to a low chuckling note peculiar to itself and very different from those of the Hermit or Tawny Thrush. After standing still for a while with the feathers of the hind part a little raised, it walks and hops along with much ease, and often bends down to peep at objects around it. It frequently alights on the ground and scratches up the dried leaves in search of worms and beetles. Then, on the least alarm, it flies back to the trees. The appearance of a fox or raccoon causes it much anxiety; it will follow the quadruped at a respectful distance while uttering a mournful *cluck*.

The Wood Thrushes never form flocks, but go singly in winter. They pair only in the breeding season. But their song is sometimes heard throughout winter, particularly in sunshine after a shower, in Louisiana.

LOUISIANA WATER-THRUSH

PROPERLY CLASSED WITH THE WOOD-WARBLERS; NOT A THRUSH.—ED.

Much as the song of the Nightingale is admired, I am inclined to think it no finer than that of the Louisiana Water-Thrush, whose notes are as powerful and mellow and at times as varied.

This Thrush resides in the lowlands of Louisiana and Mississippi. Its voice, nearly as loud as that of the Wood Thrush, may be heard in the deepest, swampiest canebrakes, where it perches on the cane tops erectly, while repeating sounds so like the whole two octaves of the pianoforte as almost to induce the listener to imagine he hears the the keys of that instrument. The bird begins on the upper key on down to the bass note which is lost if there is the least breeze. In calm, warm weather you will hear its song even in winter.

I take the liberty of naming this leading songster of our groves after the State which has afforded me my greatest pleasures. It is so gentle and unsuspicious that a person may come within a few yards of it. Its feet are deep blush brown and its tail is forked. Although it is always near and over water, I have never seen it wade through it as the Common Water-Thrush will do. Its flight is easy and continued— among the trees, over the canes and the ground. When it alights, its body vibrates continually, while the tail alternately jerks open and closed. It walks prettily but never hops, as it pursues insects and larvae; these it also takes on the wing, but without the clicking sound heard from the bill of Flycatchers.

The Louisiana Water-Thrush nests in the first days of April, among the roots of a tree, or beside a decayed log in plain view. The outside of the nest is formed of dry leaves and mosses, the inside of fine grasses and a few hairs or the dried fibers of the Spanish moss that resembles horse-hair. The four or five flesh-colored eggs (dark red mottled at the larger end) take fourteen days to hatch. Should the female be disturbed on her nest in the early stage of incubation, she will merely fly off. But towards the end, disturbance will cause her to tumble and roll about, with her wings and tail spread as if she were in the last agonies of despair. To entice the intruder to follow her away from the nest, she employs this ruse—to most piteous sounds.

The young leave the nest in about ten days and follow the parent from place to place on the ground, where they are fed until they can fly.

Warbling Vireo

Wₕᵢₗₑ I was in the little village that is now the city of Camden, New Jersey, where I went to watch the passage of certain Warblers on their way north in May, I took lodgings in a street ornamented with tall Lombardy poplars. One of them almost touched my widow with its branches. In it, too, I had the good fortune of finding the nest of the interesting little Warbling Vireo.

Never before had I seen its nest placed so low. Never before had I an opportunity to examine it, or to observe the habits of the species to such advantage. The nest, unlike others I have since obtained from the tops of tall trees, was fixed to the body of the tree instead of to forks in the top twigs. Its branch jutted off at a very acute angle, and the birds were building it for eight days, working chiefly in the morning and evening. Before they chose this spot, I saw them examining the tree, warbling together as if congratulating each other on their good fortune in finding so snug a place.

One morning I observed both of them at work. They had already attached some slender blades of grass to the knots on the branch and the bark of the trunk, placing them in a circle. They continued to work downwards and outwards, until the nest began to take shape. Before the end of the second day, bits of hornets' nests and particles of corn husks had been pushed between the rows of grass and held by silky substances.

On the third day, the birds were absent, nor could I hear them anywhere in the neighborhood. Thinking that a cat might have caught them from the edge of the roof, I despaired of seeing them again.

On the fourth morning, however, their notes attracted my attention before I rose, and I found them at their labors. Extremely slender grasses were now their material, and they worked it in a circular form within the frame they had already made. The little creatures were absent nearly an hour at a time, and returned together bringing the grass, which, I concluded, they found at a considerable distance.

Going into the street to see in what direction they went, I watched them for some time, and followed them as they flew from tree to tree towards the river. There they stopped, and seemed to be carefully watching me. I retired a small distance, and they resumed their journey. They led me quite out of the village to a large meadow where an old haystack stood. They lighted on it and in a few minutes each had selected a blade of grass. Returning by the same route, they moved so slowly from one tree to another that my patience was severely tried.

Two other days were consumed by them in travelling for the grass.

On the seventh day I saw only the female at work, using wool and horse-hair. The eighth was mostly spent by both in smoothing the inside of the nest, which they would enter, sit in, and turn round to press the lining. This they did, I suppose, a hundred times or more in the course of an hour. The male had ceased to warble. Both birds showed great concern. They went off and returned so often that I actually became quite tired of this lesson in the art of nest-building. Perhaps I would not have looked at them any more that day had not the cat, one belonging to the house, made her appearance just over my head on the roof, within a few feet of the nest. At times the animal came so very near the affrighted and innocent creatures that my interest was at once renewed. I gave chase to Grimalkin and saved the Vireos, at least for that season.

Within five days five eggs were laid, small, white and oval, thinly spotted with reddish black at the larger end. The birds took turns sitting, though not with regularity as to time. On the twelfth day of incubation the young came out. The male would bring insects to the female which she chopped with her beak and placed in the mouths of her young with a care and delicacy as curious as it was pleasing to me.

After three or four days the male also fed them. I thought I could see them growing every time I turned from my drawing to peep at them from my window.

On the fifteenth day, after 8 A.M., the little birds all stood on the edge of the nest and were fed as usual. They remained there the rest of the day, and about sunset they returned to the inner nest. I noticed that the old birds had frequently roosted within a foot of them.

On the sixteenth day after they were hatched, the young ones took to wing, and ascended the branches of the tree with surprising ease and firmness. Next day they were fed on the same tree, where they perched together in a row on a small twig, with their parents just above them. The day after that they flew across the street and betook themselves to a fine peach orchard several hundred yards from my lodging. Never had François Huber, observer of the honey-bee, watched the operations of his creatures with more intentness than I had, and I bade the Vireos adieu at last with great regret.

Their food consisted mostly of black caterpillars which were infesting the poplars in the street that season. The Vireos seldom sallied forth in search of this food more than a few yards, always preferring to remain among the branches. I never saw either of them disgorge pellets as I have seen Pewees do. I saw that now and then they stood stiffly, balancing their body from side to side as if on a hinge, but I could not discover why. During the love season the male spread his little wings and tail and strutted in short circles round the female, pouring out a low warble so sweet and mellow that I can compare it only to the sounds of a good music box. The female received these attentions without coyness; I therefore thought that these birds had been attached to each other before that season.

No better name could have been given to this species than that of the Warbling Vireo. The male sings from morning to night, so sweetly, so tenderly, with such mellowness and softness of tone, and yet with notes so low, that one might think he sang only for his beloved, without the least desire to attract the attention of rivals. In this respect he differs greatly from most other birds. Even its chiding notes—*tsche, tsche*—were low and unobtruding. The nestlings uttered a lisping sound, not unlike that of a young mouse. The only time I saw the old birds ruffled was on discovering a brown lizard ascending their tree. They attacked it courageously, indeed furiously, and although I did not see them strike it, they compelled it to leave the place.

Orioles

BALTIMORE ORIOLE

No traveller with the powers of observation can ascend that extraordinary river, the Mississippi, in early autumn without feeling enchanted by the varied vegetation which adorns its shores. Tall cotton trees descend to the very margin. The arrow-shaped ash mixes its branches with those of the pecan and black walnut. Immense oaks and varieties of hickory cover the densely tangled cane with their foliage. Vines of every kind shoot up, wind round stems, twigs and tendrils, and stretch from one branch to another until they spread a verdant canopy, a solid mass of rich vegetation in the foreground of the picture. Whereever hills are in view, the great magnolias, hollies and noble pines gently wave to the breeze.

The current becomes rapid. Ere long several of the windings of the stream have been met and passed, bringing new scenery. Where the impetuous waters have caused havoc on the banks, the long dangling mosses that spread a ragged veil over the cypress branches give the forest the look of mourning. In his camp the dejected Indian contemplates the melancholy scene as he recalls that he is no longer the sole, peaceful possessor of these lands. A succession of islands appears. At every bend you see boats propelled by steam ascending the rivers; others, without such aid, glide silently with the current.

The traveller's speculations about past, present and future are surprised by the clear, mellow notes that issue from the woods. The brilliant Baltimore Oriole appears before him. He might, in solitude like this, feel pleasure at any sound, even the howl of the wolf or the still more dismal bellow of the alligator.

Once the Mississippi is left behind and the still more enchanting Ohio entered, the traveller is not without the company of the Oriole even for a day. It moves gracefully up and down the pendulous branches of the lofty tulip-trees searching for the caterpillar and green beetle in the leaves and opening blossoms. The twig in my drawing of this bird was not one of these; I cut it in Louisiana.

The Baltimore Oriole arrives from the south—Mexico perhaps, or a more distant region—and enters Louisiana at the beginning of spring. It approaches the planter's house to search his trees for a suitable place to settle, and, I believe, prefers a slope. After choosing a twig, the male flies about most conspicuously in search of the longest, driest filaments of Spanish beard moss. On finding one fit for his needs, he flies to the twig with it, uttering a chirrup all the while in indication of his fearlessness and of his fancy that he is king of the woods. His chirruping becomes louder—even angry—if an enemy approaches, or if a cat or dog surprises him. With bill, claws and an astonishing sagacity, he at once fastens the moss to the twig with as much art as a sailor with his knot. He takes up the other end and fastens it to another twig a few inches off, allowing the thread to float like a swing, its curve perhaps seven or eight inches long. The female comes with another filament, or some cotton thread or fibrous substance, inspects his work, and immediately begins to place each succeeding thread in a direction contrary to those being arranged by her lordly mate. The whole is crossed and recrossed to form an irregular network. Their love, as they see the graceful fabric approaching perfection, increases daily, until their conjugal affection and faith become as complete as in any species of bird with which I am acquainted.

The nest, woven from bottom to top, is so secure that no tempest can carry it off without breaking the branch to which it is attached. This nest contains no warm substance but is almost entirely composed of moss woven to allow the air to pass through easily in the intense heat of the season ahead. Especial care is taken for the same reason to place the nest on the northeast side of the tree. In Pennsylvania or New York, the Oriole lines his nest with the warmest and softest of materials and places it exposed to the sun's rays, the changes of weather early in incubation often proving extreme and dangerous to his brood.

Incubation is fourteen days long. The eggs, four to six, are about an inch long, rather broadly ovate, pale brown, dotted, spotted, and tortuously lined with dark brown. In Louisiana two broods to the season are frequent.

The Oriole's manner of exploring branches of trees differs from that of almost all other birds. It often clings by the feet to reach an insect that is far enough away to require full extension of neck, body and legs without letting go. Its motions are elegant and stately. Its song consists of three or four, or at most eight or ten loud, full, mellow, extremely agreeable notes.

A day or two before the young are quite able to leave the nest, they often cling to the outside and creep in and out of it like young Woodpeckers. After leaving it, they follow the parents for nearly a fortnight and are fed by them. They are fond of ripe mulberries, figs, sweet cherries, strawberries and other fruits. In spring their principal food is insects. These they seldom pursue on the wing, but look for among the leaves and branches. I have seen the young of the first brood out early in May, the second in July. As soon as they are fully able to care for themselves, they usually part from one another and leave the country singly.

The migratory flight of this Oriole is high above the trees, mostly by day. I have seen them alight—always singly—about sunset. They utter a note or two and dart into the lower branches to feed before taking rest. To assure myself that they travel by day, I marked the place where I saw a beautiful male perched one evening. Next morning I heard his first notes at dawn. I saw him search a while for food, then mount in the air and make for a warmer clime in straight, continuous flight.

ORCHARD ORIOLE

THE sociability of the Orchard Oriole is quite remarkable. In this respect it differs much from the Baltimore Oriole, which will not allow any other bird of its species to nest near the spot which it has chosen for its own. Yet I have counted as many as nine Orchard Oriole nests on a few acres of ground, and observed the occupants living in complete harmony. The nest in *The Birds of America*, drawn in Louisiana, was entirely of grass and shows the usual form and construction.

This Oriole is seen in Louisiana from early March until October. It reaches the Middle districts early in April. I have seen it in Maine and at the head-waters of the Mississippi. It is fond of high ground and the neighborhood of mountains during the breeding season, after which it removes to the meadows and prairies to feed on small crickets, ground spiders and small grasshoppers. It also eats different fruits and berries, but not to such an extent as to prove a serious nuisance.

Like its relative, the Baltimore Oriole, it migrates to the North singly and by day. The males appear a week or ten days sooner than the females. Their flight is lower than that of the Baltimore Oriole, and considerably less prolonged. It alights more frequently on tree-tops to rest and feed. There is more wing motion in flight, and more decided jettings of the tail as this bird alights. When they reach their destination, they display much of their natural liveliness and vivacity. The male rises for ten or twenty yards in air, jerks his tail and body, flaps his wings, and sings impetuously, as if in haste and anxious to return to the tree from which he has departed. He descends with the same motions of tail and body and sings as he alights. These gambols and carolings occur often during the day, between his searching up and down the twigs and branches for insects or larvae, his tail jetting and his neck outstretched as he seizes his prey and emits one sweet, mellow note. (His note is much less powerful than that of the Baltimore.) At other times he will bend his body into a curve, with his head inclined upward, to peep under leaves where a grub may be lurking. Or he may spy an insect on the ground and pursue it, or fly towards the blossoms where some of the hundreds of insects which he devours in a day may be lurking. In this he contributes to the welfare of farmers. The Baltimore Oriole often clings by the feet to reach insects.

The arrival of the female during migration is the signal for attention, singing and tricks from the males. A pair will search the meadows for the finest, longest, and toughest grasses and take them to the chosen spot on an apple tree or willow. They attach the grass firmly and neatly to the twigs, twist the filaments, pass them over and under as almost to defy the human eye to follow their weavings and windings. All this is done with the bill of both the Orchard and the Baltimore Oriole in their building. The nest, a hemisphere in shape, is supported by the edge only. It rarely exceeds four inches in depth, and is open almost all the way across. It is finished with long grasses both inside and out in Louisiana; some of the grasses go round the nest several times. In the Middle districts a soft, warm lining is added. The female lays four to six eggs, bluish-white sprinkled with dark brown. There is only a single brood in the season. The young follow the parents for several weeks. Many Orchard Orioles congregate towards autumn, but the males soon separate from the females and set out apart from them—as they arrived in spring.

The plumage of many of our birds undergoes extraordinary changes at times. The male Tanager is a vivid scarlet and velvety black in summer, but a dingy green before it flies southward. The Goldfinch changes from yellow and black to a drab green also. The Rice Bird loses its brightness until spring. Other birds take years to assume their most brilliant plumage . . . the Ibis, the Flamingo and many other waders. The Orchard Oriole's gradual improvement is among the most notable examples. The plumage of the fledglings resembles that of the female bird, and not till the following spring does the male begin to exhibit a bit of black on the chin—the females, never. After two years, a strange mixture of dull orange or deep chestnut peeps through the much increased black feathering of wings and body, as well as a mixed yellowish-green hue held over from the time when the bird left the nest. By the third spring the male is nearer his perfection, the deep chestnut having spread lower, and the black of the upper parts having deepened, as well as that of the whole head, wings and tail feathers. But its final garb is not completed till the fourth spring, as you see it in *The Birds of America*.*

* Final color occurs in second mating season.

Purple Grackle

I COULD not think of any better way to show these birds than in the exercise of their wicked ways. In *The Birds of America* you will notice the delight of the male as he works havoc with the tender, juicy, unripe corn that he stands on. He swells his throat and calls to his companions to come and help him demolish it. The female has fed herself and is about to fly off with her bill well loaded for her hungry, expectant brood. The husk is torn from the ear of corn and the grains are already nearly devoured. This is the tithe that such birds take from our planters and farmers; but it was so appointed and is the will of the Creator.

The Purple Grackle sails along the outskirts of the woods and alights on the newly turned furrows to search for grubs. Its step is elegant and elevated and shows its fearlessness and sense of freedom. The sun shines on its coppery bronze plumage which, at the bird's slightest motion, changes to a deep, brilliant azure, and in the next light to emerald green or sapphire. The farmer, knowing its value well, does not disturb it at this season.

The love season arrives, and the pair seek a safe, agreeable retreat. They visit and examine holes and cavities, some of which were bored in the trees by Woodpeckers. They choose one, fly some dry weeds and feathers to it, and there the female deposits from four to six bluish eggs streaked with brown and black. She sits on them while her mate pours forth his rude notes from the summit of a broken branch, or drives off Woodpeckers and other intruders. The Woodpecker, no match for the Grackle, soon makes off. Or the male roams in search of food for himself and his mate, whose incubation labors he shares.

At length the brood breaks through the shell, and they raise their feeble heads towards their mother who, with intense anxiety, dries and cherishes them. Day by day they grow, until they nearly fill the hole with their bulk. Their parents' industry at feeding and protecting them also grows apace. The rearing of such a family is a sight to gladden the heart—well worth seeing.

Regretfully I must turn to another picture. Hark to the sound of rattles as the farmer's sons and servants halloo and spread across the field! The Purple Grackles cannot heed the slaughter . . . food must be had . . . grubs and worms have already retired to their winter quarters in the earth, and beechnuts and acorns have not yet fallen. Corn is the Grackles' only resource, and the quantity they devour is immense.

The gloom and cold blasts of November drive these birds from the East. They reach Louisiana when the weather is still mild, and the yellow foliage of the fields is filled with myriad birds. In vast flocks the Grackles cover every twig and branch of the forests and begin their choruses and mutual congratulation, until one might think there were twice their number. They feed on the abundant beechnuts and acorns until they gradually clear away the mast, much the way the Passenger Pigeons do. Cold weather sees them frequenting farms—even the cattle pens—for scattered grains. They remain about the farms until early spring.

In the winter of 1821 I caught a number of these birds, as well as other kinds, to send alive to Europe to my scientific friends. I fed and watered them well, and I saw with pleasure that they were becoming more gentle. But as soon as the Grackles became reconciled to confinement, they began to attack other birds in the cage, and to beat and kill one after another so fast that I was obliged to take them out and separate them. Even this did not keep the peace. The strong among them attacked and killed the weaker of their own kind until but a few remained. I look on this remarkable instance of ferocity of the Grackle towards the caged Grosbeaks, Doves, Pigeons, and Blue Jays with special amazement, because I never saw it kill any bird in its free state.

I have been speaking of the Grackle in the South. I shall now speak of those to the North. Most of them leave the South about mid-February in small detached flocks, and reach New York in a straggling manner about mid-May. They migrate in short, undulating lines that resemble small segments of very large circles. Let me explain. Suppose the bird which is poised in air begins to propel itself by flapping its wings strongly, so as to move forward in a curve. It ascends along the curve until it reaches its original level, then it flaps its wings and performs another curve. Thus they accomplish their long journey—to continual, low chattering, as if discussing some important question. You will see them, when they reach Pennsylvania, begin following the farmer's plough, and at a time when those Grackles which remained in Louisiana are feeding their young.

As the farmer turns one furrow after another the Grackle follows him and destroys a far worse enemy of the corn than himself. Every reflecting agrarian knows this well. Were he as merciful towards this bird at a later season, he would prove his grateful recollection of the services it rendered. But man is too often forgetful of the benefits which he has received. His selfishness prevails over reason. No sooner does the corn ripen than he vows to do vengeance against intruders.

In the Northern States they build their nests in a much more perfect and therefore natural way—preferably in a dense pine tree, on a horizontal branch. From the ground the nest might easily be mistaken for the Robin's, were it not so bulky. But it is much larger, and instead of being by itself, it is placed near perhaps a dozen others which appear from tier to tier, from the lowest to the highest branches. The center of the nest is saddled to the bough, so that the middle part is thinner and the opposite sides thicker. The outside diameter is about six inches, the inside four; the depth is also four. Grass, slender roots and mud are lined with hair and finer grasses.

I had a white pine tree on my plantation, "Mill Grove," in Pennsylvania, which many birds nested on each spring. Some mischievous lads sometimes amused themselves by beating the nests down with their fishing-rods, to my great annoyance.

Some of the Pennsylvania farmers have given out the news that these Grackles are fond of pulling up the wild garlic plant which is so injurious to their pastures. I am sorry to say that this assertion is by no means correct; and were these good people to look to the Grackles for the clearing of their fields from that evil, they might wait long enough. The eggs of the Grackle are very delicate food, and I am astonished that those who are so anxious for the destruction of the bird do not gratify their wishes instead by eating the egg.

The Purple Grackle travels very far north. I have found it everywhere during my peregrinations. In one or two instances I have seen its nest in the fissures of rocks.

Dr. Bachman has seen it building in South Carolina in tree hollows and in abandoned nests of Woodpeckers, and carrying grass and mud for the construction of its nest. It breeds in like situations in Louisiana, without using such materials. In the Middle and Northern districts it forms a fine, well-finished nest such as I have described. The eggs measure one and a half inches in length; they are a bluish-white, blotched, streaked, and spotted with brown and black. On the Florida Keys I found the Purple Grackle breeding in low mangroves, in communities, and thought that the glossy richness of the plumage far exceeded that of our Northern birds. Yet I could observe no other difference.

Cowbird

NATURE is evidently perfect in all her parts. The Intellect which planned the grand scheme is infinite in power. Even when we note what to us seems unnecessary or useless, it would be wise to consider it as formed for a purpose, rather than to view it as futile.

The seed of the tree is dropped on the ground. It drinks moisture, swells, and slowly unfolds. Its roots shoot down into the earth as its stem rises towards the sky and the first leaflets appear. It grows as we watch it, year on year. It produces flowers and fruit, and shelters multitudes of beings. At length it becomes the glory of the forest, spreading its huge arms and covering the wild animals that retreat to its foliage for protection from the sun and rain.

Centuries after its birth, the stately tree begins to age. The branches wither, gray and shaggy lichens cover its trunk and limbs, and the Woodpecker hunts beneath its bark. Then, one day, blackness spreads across the heavens and the thunder mutters. Suddenly there comes the rushing noise of the whirlwind which scatters the twigs and foliage before it and brings the patriarch of the forest to the ground. For years the great trunk may lie prone upon the earth, gradually decaying beneath summer's sun and winter's frost, and crumbling to dust that feeds the soil. Thus it finishes its life course.

Look, too, at the egg. It is also a seed, but it gives rise to something very different. Fostered by the warmth of anxious parents, its germ contains the life that swells and finally bursts its fragile cover, and comes tottering into existence. The mother bird seeks food for this helpless being, carefully placing it in its open throat. Under her fostering care, it develops day by day. With all the powers which Nature intended to bestow on it, the young one spreads its pinions to the breeze, and sallies forth as it was destined to do.

How often have I watched over the little bird in its nest, and marked its progress: the coming of its first scanty covering of down, the sprouting of plumelets—all of its growth! With what pleasure I have viewed its changing color and the early signs of its future habits!

Among the wonderful operations of Nature, there is one which has occupied my thoughts ever since I first became acquainted with the Cowbird. Like the Cuckoo of Europe (from which it differs entirely in habits and appearance) it makes no nest of its own, but deposits its eggs, one at a time, in the nests of other birds.* It leaves them to the care of a foster parent.

In the breeding season the males and females arrive together. The males regard the females with little interest, and these birds do not pair. The many carolings, joyous flights, and bursts of ecstatic feeling which other birds display at this season are entirely dispensed with by the Cowbird. The attachment of the two does not continue as with other species for the benefit of their brood, because their young are not reared by them. They are left with other kinds of birds to be hatched and nursed.

When the female Cowbird is about to deposit her eggs, she leaves her companions and perches on a tree or fence, looking uneasy. Should she not see other birds building their nests, she flies off, and moves from tree to tree until she finds what she is looking for. She waits for a proper opportunity to drop one egg in the nest, flies off after she succeeds, and returns in exultation to her companions. She favors the nests of birds smaller than herself, especially the Maryland Yellow-Throat. I have also found her egg in the nests of the Chipping Sparrow, the Bluebird, the Yellow-Bird, several Flycatchers, and the Golden-Crowned Thrush, even though their nests are very different in form, position, size and materials.

It is a very remarkable circumstance that although the Cowbird is larger than those whose nests she chooses for her eggs, the eggs themselves are not much bigger than those of the foster parents, who on all occasions receive it unwillingly. Here we may note the ends and means which Nature has so admirably made, by adapting the size of

* Four or five white, brown-speckled eggs.

Grand Pie Griecka   Sug Raff   Great American Shrike or Butcher Bird N.w.

Lanius excubitor

N° 58.

Washington November 30th
1812.

the egg to the capability of the chosen parents to impart heat to it and hatch it. The intention was not to deceive by similar size and color of the egg, which, if found by the owners in a nest newly finished, they will desert, and build again elsewhere. But if they have already deposited one or more eggs of their own, they will continue their attachment to the nest. There is reason to believe, however, that they are always aware of the Cowbird's intrusion.

The Cowbird never forces an entrance but waits until the nest is deserted by its guardians, then slips to it like one bent on some discreditable deed. When the female of the nest returns and finds an egg different from her own, she leaves it, perches on a branch near it, returns several times in succession, and flies off, calling loudly for her mate. He soon makes his appearance, shows great anxiety at her distress, and they visit the nest together. Then they retire from it and continue chattering for some time. Nevertheless, the hated egg retains its position. The bird continues to lay its eggs and incubation takes place as usual.

After nearly a fortnight the young Cowbird bursts from its grayish-blue oval shell which is sprinkled with dots and streaks. Another remarkable occurrence now takes place. The eggs of the foster bird, not yet hatched, soon disappear. The Cowbird's egg being the first to be hatched, the parents fly off to find food for the helpless creature for whose existence it behooves them to provide. The other eggs are therefore neglected, and the chicks in them perish. Birds probably know an addled or stale egg, for they always remove them from the nest. Such eggs may be seen strewn about near the nest. In the case of the European Cuckoo matters are different, for the young bird very ungratefully jostles all its foster brothers and sisters out to have room enough for himself. Why Nature puts the Yellow-Throat to the trouble of laying all these eggs, if they are, after all, to produce nothing, is a mystery to me. Nevertheless, my belief in her wisdom is not staggered by it.

As the young Cowbird grows up, its foster parents provide well for it, and show all the concern and uneasiness at the intrusion of a stranger that they would for their own offspring. Long after the young fledgling has left the nest, it continues to be led by its affectionate guardians, until it can provide for itself.

Grosbeaks

PINE GROSBEAK

THE Pine Grosbeak is a charming songster. Well do I remember the delight I felt, while lying on the moss-clad rocks of Newfoundland near St. George's Bay, listening to its continuous lay as late as the middle of August, particularly about sunset. I was reminded of the pleasure I had enjoyed on the banks of the clear Mohawk, when I lent an attentive ear to the mellow notes of another Grosbeak, under similar circumstances. But in Newfoundland I was still farther removed from my beloved family, and the scenery was three times wilder and more magnificent. The stupendous, dark granite rocks that faced the north as if to defy the wintry tempests brought a chill to my heart, as I thought of the hardships endured by those intrepid travellers who had braved the horrors of the polar winter for the advancement of science. I was riveted to the spot by the glowing tints of the western sky and by the brightening stars twinkling over the vast waters. The longer I gazed, the more I wished to remain, but darkness was advancing in a mass of damp fog, and the bird ceased its song. All around me seemed transformed into chaos. Silently I groped my way to the beach, and soon reached our schooner, the *Ripley*.

The young gentlemen of my party, accompanied by my son John Woodhouse and a Newfoundland Indian, had gone into the interior in search of deer, but returned the following afternoon, having found the flies and mosquitoes intolerable. My son brought a number of Pine Grosbeaks in moult, their legs covered with sores, due, I believe, to the resin on the fir trees where they feed. One of the figures in my drawing for *The Birds of America* represents the form of these sores, which sometimes cause the back of the lower leg joint to be double the usual size.

The Pine Grosbeak is found in the forest of Newfoundland in considerable numbers, during the most severe cold. A lady who lived there many years, and who was fond of birds, assured me that she had kept several males in cages, which became quite tame. They would sing during the night. They fed on fruits and berries in summer, on seeds in winter.

The flight of this bird is undulating, smooth, high, and in a direct line of groups of five to ten, during migration above the forests. They alight often during the day on trees with opening buds and blossoms, and at such times of migrating are extremely gentle and easily approached. It surprised me, when I fired, to see those that were untouched fly directly towards me until they were within a few feet of where I stood. Then they alighted on the lower branches of the nearest tree, where, standing as erect as little Hawks, they gazed on me as if I were an object quite new, and one of whose nature they were ignorant. In the state of Maine they are easily caught around the wood-cutters' camps by arranging two pairs of snowshoes as a snare.

I once knew one of these sweet songsters which would tune its voice anew the instant the lamp was lighted in the room where its cage was hung.

My kind friend Thomas McCulloch of Pictou in Nova Scotia sent me the following account, which I trust will interest the reader as much as it does me:

Last winter the snow was exceedingly deep here, and the storms so frequent and violent that many birds must have perished, due to the scarcity of food. The Pine Grosbeaks, driven from the woods, collected about the barns in great numbers. They even alighted in the streets of Pictou in search of food.

Being anxious to note their changes of plumage for you, I decided to try to preserve one alive and observe it. I received a male in splendid plumage, but so emaciated that he seemed little more than a mass of feathers. But with cautious feeding he soon regained his flesh, and became so tame that he ate from my hand without the least sign of fear. To reconcile him gradually to confinement, I let him fly about my bedroom. The first thing I did on rising in the morning was to give him a small quantity of seed. But for three mornings in succession I happened to lie rather later than usual, and each morning I was aroused by the bird fluttering on my shoulder and calling for his usual allowance. The third morning I let him flutter about me for some time before showing any sign of being awake, but as soon as I stirred he retired to the window sill and waited patiently till I arose.

As the spring approached he used to whistle occasionally in the morning. His notes were exceedingly rich and full, like those of his relative, the Rose-Breasted Grosbeak. But about the time of migration his tameness entirely disappeared. During the day he never rested a moment, but kept running from one side of the window to the other, seeking a way of escape. Often during the night, when the moonlight would fall upon the window, I was awakened by his dashing against the glass. The desire for liberty seemed at last to absorb every other feeling. For four days I could not detect that he had touched his supply of food. He filled the house with a piteous wailing cry which no person could hear without feeling for the poor captive. Unable to resist his appeals, I gave him his freedom, but when it was attained he seemed very careless about availing himself of it. He perched on the top of a tree in front of the house, arranged his feathers, and looked about him for a short time. He then alighted by the door, and I was at last obliged to drive him away, lest some accident befall him.

An acquaintance of mine kept one of these birds during the summer months. It became quite tame. I was told that the Grosbeak usually sang during a thunderstorm, or when rain was falling on the house.

BLUE GROSBEAK

In the summer of 1829, I accidentally came upon the nest of another of this species, the Blue Grosbeak, in New Jersey, only a few miles from Philadelphia. I was attracted to it by the cries of the parent birds, perched on a tall hickory on barren ground near a swamp which is well known as a haunt of the Woodcock. For some time I looked for the nest, but in vain. The parents left the tree, flew about as if much alarmed and distressed, and at last alighted on the ground not far from me. I followed them gradually, and saw them go up to one of their young nesting in a low dogwood bush. On reaching the place I saw two young ones dead, and one alive, covered with large insects. Presently I heard the chirp of a fourth, which I found a few yards off. Concluding that the insects were the cause of all the distress I saw, I destroyed them and replaced the young birds in the nest, where I left them. Afterwards I visited them repeatedly, and saw them grow apace, until finally they flew off. I cut the twig, then, and drew it with the nest, as you now see it in *The Birds of America*.

My friend John Bachman of Charleston, South Carolina, favored me with the following remarks which I have the pleasure to recommend:

I made considerable effort to find a nest of the Blue Grosbeak, as I wished to raise a young one. I found four nests, one spring, and noticed that two of them had been robbed of their eggs before incubation began. The young of the third nest were destroyed by a snake, which I found in the act and shot from the bush. Those of the fourth nest escaped until nearly fledged. One morning when I drew near it to carry away the young, I heard loud chirping as if they were anxious to be fed. Then I saw a Blacksnake a few yards from me with its head raised high above the ground, as if listening to their cries. It went in a straight line to the bush as if following the sound, and before I came up to the nest it had swallowed one young Grosbeak and was trying to escape with another in its mouth.

I carried the two remaining young ones home, raised these females with ease, and kept them in an aviary for two years. When I took them out of the nest I used a trap cage in which I tried to catch the old ones, both of which were very shy, suspicious and so cautious that only the female entered it. I kept her with her young, but she took no notice of them, and although I kept her for several years she never attempted to build a nest.

I bought a male in full plumage in the market and put him in the aviary. The following spring he mated with one of the young females, and took possession of the nest of a Cardinal Grosbeak which they drove off, carefully repaired it, made it neat and comfortable, and laid two eggs which unfortunately were destroyed by Rats.* In the aviary these birds are generally silent. During rain they appear delighted. They cling to the bars and drive all other birds away, as if determined to enjoy the whole pleasure themselves.

A Blue Grosbeak now in my possession in Edinburgh was raised from the nest. This bird frequently sings in the night and before dawn. He is extremely tame, goes in and out of his cage, perches on the head-dress of my wife or on the heads of other members of the family, alights on the table, and feeds on almost anything given to him. If a gold or silver coin is thrown on the table while he is near it, he goes to it, takes it up in his bill, and tosses it about with apparent pleasure. After bathing he invariably goes to the open fire, and perches on the fender to dry himself. Two or three other birds were put into the cage with him, but were instantly attacked. Now and then he holds his food in his claws like a Hawk.

* Normal: three or four bluish-white eggs.

ROSE-BREASTED GROSBEAK

As for the Rose-Breasted Grosbeak, another of the species, one year in the month of August I was trudging along the shores of the Mohawk River. Night overtook me. Being little acquainted with that part of the country, I decided to camp where I was. The evening was calm and beautiful, and the sky sparkled with stars that were reflected in the smooth waters. The deep shadows of the rocks and trees on the opposite shore fell on the stream, and from afar came the muttering sound of the cataract.

I soon lighted my little fire under a rock, spread out my scanty provisions, and reclined on my grassy couch. As I looked on the fading features of the beautiful landscape, my heart turned towards my distant home, where my friends were doubtless wishing me, as I was wishing them, a happy night and peaceful slumbers. Then I heard the barking of a watchdog, and I tapped my faithful companion to prevent his answering the sound. Thoughts of my worldly mission—to portray all the birds of America—then came upon my mind. I thanked the Creator of all for his never failing mercy, closed my eyes, and was passing away into the world of dreams when suddenly there burst on my soul the serenade of the rose-breasted bird—so rich, so mellow, so loud in the stillness of the night that sleep fled. Never did I enjoy music more; it thrilled through my heart, creating around me an atmosphere of bliss. One might easily have imagined that the Owl remained reverently silent, charmed by this delightful music.

Long after the sounds ceased I continued to enjoy them, and when all was again still, I stretched out my weary limbs and gave myself up to the luxury of rest. In the morning I awoke vigorous as ever, and prepared to continue my journey.

I have frequently observed this beautiful Grosbeak early in March, in lower Louisiana, making its way eastward, high in the air, now and then alighting on the tallest tree-tops as if to rest, and uttering a clear note on the wing. I have seen the same in Henderson, Kentucky, and Cincinnati, Ohio. I have followed it in its migrations into Pennsylvania, New York, and other Eastern States, through the British provinces of

New Brunswick and Nova Scotia, and as far as Newfoundland where many breed, but I saw none in Labrador. I have found them rather plentiful in early May along the steep banks of the Schuylkill River, twenty or thirty miles from Philadelphia, where they fed mostly on the buds of the trees, tender blossoms, and upon insects which they caught on the wing in short sallies. I saw several in the Great Pine Forest of Pennsylvania; but they were more abundant in New York, especially along the banks of the beautiful Mohawk.

I found a nest of this species a few miles from Cincinnati, in the upright forks of a low bush. The nest differed in its composition from those I have seen in the Eastern States, and resembled the nest of the Blue Grosbeak. The three young ones were ready to fly, and the parents fed them soft grains of the late July wheat from a near-by field. Generally, however, the nest of the Rose-Breasted Grosbeak is placed on the top branches of an alder bush, near water, and usually on the borders of meadows or alluvial grounds. It is made of dried twigs mixed with a few leaves and the bark of vines, and lined with fibrous roots and horse-hair. There are seldom more than four eggs, and I believe there is only one brood each season. Both sexes incubate the eggs.

Its flight is strong, even, graceful and sustained. When travelling south towards autumn, about September first, the Rose-Breasted Grosbeak migrates singly, as it does in spring. It passes high over the forest, alights towards sunset on a tall tree, and in a few minutes dives into some thicket for the night.

Present Ranges

AN ALPHABETICAL LIST OF THE BIRDS HEREIN DESCRIBED. AUTHORITY:
AMERICAN ORNITHOLOGISTS' UNION "CHECK-LIST"; FIELD GUIDES BY
ROGER T. PETERSON AND RICHARD H. POUGH

AVOCET, AMERICAN (*Recurvirostra americana*)
Breeds from Washington and Manitoba to California and Iowa. Winters
from California and Texas to Guatemala. Rare east of the Mississippi.
(Plate 318, *Birds of America*: same nomenclature)

BITTERN, LEAST (*Ixobrychus exilis*)
Breeds from North Dakota and Quebec to West Indies and Mexico; from
Oregon to Guatemala. Winters from Georgia and Texas, and from southern
California and Arizona, to Guatemala. Other races occur in South America.
(Plate 210, *Birds of America*: *Ardea exilis*)

CHUCK-WILL'S-WIDOW (*Caprimulgus carolinensis*)
Breeds from Kansas and Maryland to Texas and Gulf states. Winters
from Florida to the Greater Antilles, Central America and Colombia.
(Plate 52, *Birds of America*: *Caprilmulgus carolinensis*)

CORMORANT, EUROPEAN (*Phalacrocorax carbo*)
Breeds from Greenland and Cumberland Sound to the Magdalens; Iceland;
British Isles; and Russia. Winters from Greenland to New York, and the
Canaries. (Plate 266, *Birds of America*: COMMON CORMORANT)

COWBIRD (*Molothrus ater*)
Breeds from British Columbia, Mackenzie and New Brunswick to Mexico
and Tennessee. Winters south to Mexico. (Plate 99, *Birds of America*:
COW BUNTING: *Icterus pecoris*)

CRANE, WHOOPING (*Grus americana*)
Former breeding range from Mackenzie and Hudson Bay to Nebraska
and Iowa; seen in migration from New England to Georgia. Wintered
from Gulf states to Central Mexico. Now reduced to one small flock

under Audubon Society protection. (Plate 226, *Birds of America*: HOOPING [*sic*] CRANE)

DOVES:

MOURNING DOVE (*Zenaidura macroura*)
Breeds from British Columbia and New Brunswick to Mexico and the Bahamas. Winters south to Panama. (Plate 17, *Birds of America*: CAROLINA PIGEON OR TURTLE DOVE: *Columba carolinensis*)

ZENAIDA DOVE (*Zenaida macroura*)
Florida Keys (formerly); the Bahamas; Cuba; Isle of Pines; Haiti; Puerto Rico; Virgin Islands, etc. Common in West Indies. Yucatan coast has allied race. Not recorded in Florida since Audubon's day. (Plate 162, *Birds of America: Columba zenaida*)

DUCKS:

BLUE-WINGED TEAL (*Anas discors*)
Breeds from British Columbia and Maine to New Mexico and New Jersey. Winters from California and South Carolina to Chile and Brazil. (Plate 313, *Birds of America: Anas discors*)

EIDER, AMERICAN (*Somateria mollissima*)
Breeds from Labrador and Greenland to Maine; also on Hudson Bay and James Bay. Winters from Greenland to Virginia (rarely). (Plate 246, *Birds of America: Fuligula mollissima*)

GOLDEN-EYE, AMERICAN (*Glaucionetta clangula*)
Breeds from Alaska and Labrador to British Columbia and the Adirondacks. Winters from Maine to South Carolina, from the Aleutians to Lower California; on the Great Lakes; in the Mississippi and Missouri valleys. (Plate 342, *Birds of America: Fuligula clangula*)

GREEN-WINGED TEAL (*Anas carolinensis*)
Breeds from Alaska and Ungava to California and Quebec. Winters from British Columbia and Chesapeake Bay to Honduras. (Plate 228, *Birds of America: Anas carolinensis*)

MALLARD (*Anas platyrhynchos*)
Breeds from Alaska and Nova Scotia to Lower California and Virginia; also in Europe and Asia. Winters from the Aleutians and Maryland to Panama; also to Africa, India, Burma, Borneo. (Plate 221, *Birds of America: Anas boschas*)

RED-HEAD DUCK (*Aythya americana*)
Breeds from British Columbia and Manitoba to California and Michigan. Winters from British Columbia to Mexico and from Colorado, Illinois and the Chesapeake to the West Indies. (Plate 322, *Birds of America: Fuligula ferina*)

WOOD DUCK (*Aix sponsa*)
Breeds locally in almost every state of the U.S.A. and southern Canada provinces. Winters from British Columbia and Massachusetts to Mexico and Jamaica. (Plate 206, *Birds of America*: SUMMER OR WOOD DUCK: *Anas sponsa*)

EAGLES:
BALD EAGLE (*Haliaetus leucocephalus*)
Breeds from Alaska and Ungava to Lower California and Florida. Exterminated over much of its range. (Plate 11, *Birds of America*: BIRD OF WASHINGTON OR GREAT AMERICAN SEA EAGLE: *Falco washingtoniensis*. Also Plate 31, *Birds of America*: WHITE-HEADED EAGLE: *Falco leucocephalus*)

GOLDEN EAGLE (*Aquila chrysaëtos*)
Breeds from Alaska and Mackenzie to Lower California and Oklahoma; formerly to North Carolina. Winters south casually to Texas and Florida. Seen in some national parks. (Plate 181, *Birds of America*: same nomenclature)

GANNETS:
COMMON GANNET (*Moris bassana*)
Breeds on Bird Rock, Bonaventure and Anticosti islands; on small isles off Newfoundland; British Isles; and Iceland. Winters from Virginia to Cuba and Vera Cruz, the Canaries and Azores. (Plate 326, *Birds of America*: *Sula bassana*)

WHITE-BELLIED BOOBY (*Sula leucogaster*)
Breeds and winters on the Bahamas, some of the West Indies, islands off Central and South America, and Ascension Island. Other races occur in Australia and New Caledonia. Now only casually visits Dry Tortugas, where Audubon saw it. (Plate 207, *Birds of America*: BOOBY GANNET: *Sula fusca*)

GOOSE, CANADA (*Branta canadensis*)
Breeds from Alaska and Baffin Island to California and Tennessee. Winters from south of frost line to Mexico and Florida. Races include: Lesser Canada, White-Cheeked, Hutchins's, and Cackling Geese. (Plate 201, *Birds of America*: *Anser canadensis*)

GRACKLE, PURPLE (*Quiscalus quiscula*)
Breeds from Long Island and the lower Hudson Valley to Georgia, Alabama and Tennessee. Winters mainly south of Delaware Valley. (Plate 7, *Birds of America*: *Quiscalus versicolor*)

GREBE, PIED-BILLED (*Podilymbus podiceps*)
Breeds locally from British Columbia and Nova Scotia to Mexico. Winters from British Columbia and New York southward. (Plate 248, *Birds of America*: AMERICAN PIED-BILL DOBCHICK: *Podiceps carolinensis*)

GROSBEAKS:

BLUE GROSBEAK (*Guiraca caerulea*)
Breeds from Sacramento Valley and Maryland to Mexico and Florida.
Winters south of the U.S.A. (Plate 122, *Birds of America: Fringilla corulea*)

PINE GROSBEAK (*Pinicola enucleator*)
Breeds from Alaska and Newfoundland to New Mexico (in the Rockies),
British Columbia and Cape Breton Island. Winters to New Jersey,
Minnesota, British Columbia, etc. American races: 7 described; one occurs
in Europe. (Plate 358, *Birds of America: Pyrrhula enucleator*)

ROSE-BREASTED GROSBEAK (*Hedymeles ludovicianus*)
Breeds from Mackenzie and Cape Breton Island to Kansas and Georgia.
Winters from Mexico to Ecuador. (Plate 127, *Birds of America: Fringilla ludoviciana*)

GROUSE, RUFFED (*Bonasa umbellus*)
Ranges from Alaska and Nova Scotia to Colorado and Alabama. (Plate 41,
Birds of America: Tetrao umbellus)

GULL, GREAT BLACK-BACKED (*Larus marinus*)
Breeds from Labrador and Greenland to Maine; also British Isles, Scan-
dinavia and Russia. Winters from Greenland to the Great Lakes and
Delaware Bay; and to the coast of Senegal. (Plate 241 *Birds of America*:
same nomenclature)

HAWKS (True): (*See also* Osprey or Fish Hawk; Sparrow Hawk)
BROAD-WINGED HAWK (*Buteo platypterus*)
Breeds from Alberta and Cape Breton Island to the Gulf coast and Texas,
mainly east of the Mississippi. Winters from Florida and Mexico to Peru.
Other races occur in the Lesser Antilles. (Plate 91, *Birds of America: Falco pennsylvanicus*)

COOPER'S HAWK (*Accipiter cooperii*)
Breeds from British Columbia and Prince Edward Island to northern
Mexico. Winters from British Columbia and southern Maine to Mexico.
(Plate 36, *Birds of America*: STANLEY HAWK: *Astur stanleii*)

DUCK HAWK (*Falco peregrinus*)
Breeds from Alaska and Greenland to Lower California, Mexico and
Tennessee. Winters from Vancouver Island and Massachusetts to the
West Indies and Panama. (Plate 16, *Birds of America*: same nomenclature)

RED-SHOULDERED HAWK (*Buteo lineatus*)
Breeds from Ontario and Prince Edward Island to North Carolina,
Tennessee, Kansas, and west to edge of the Great Plains; also in California
(Red-Bellied race) and Texas. Winters from Iowa and New Hampshire

to Mexico and the Gulf Coast; also in California. (Plate 56, *Birds of America: Falco lineatus*)

RED-TAILED HAWK (*Buteo jamaicensis*)
Breeds from Alaska and Newfoundland to Lower California and Florida. Winters from British Columbia and Maine to Guatemala and the Gulf. Races are known as Krider's and Harlan's Hawks. (Plate 51, *Birds of America: Falco borealis*)

HERONS:

GREAT BLUE HERON (*Ardea herodias*)
Breeds from Alaska and Nova Scotia to Mexico and Bermuda. Winters from Alaska and New York southward. Races include: Ward's, Treganza's, Northwest Coast, and California Herons. (Plate 211, *Birds of America: same nomenclature*)

GREAT WHITE HERON (*Ardea occidentalis*)
Ranges Florida bays, keys and shallows. (Plate 281, *Birds of America: same nomenclature*)

LOUISIANA HERON (*Hydranassa tricolor*)
Breeds from North Carolina and Lower California to West Indies and Central America. Winters from Lower California and South Carolina southward. Related races occur in South America and Trinidad. (Plate 217, *Birds of America: Ardea ludoviciana*)

HUMMINGBIRD, RUBY-THROATED (*Archilochus colubris*)
Breeds from Alberta, North Dakota and Cape Breton Island to Texas and Florida. Winters from Florida and Louisiana to Panama. (Plate 47, *Birds of America: Trochilus colubris*)

IBIS, WHITE (*Guara alba*)
Breeds from Lower California and South Carolina to Peru and Venezuela. Winters from Mexico and Florida southward. (Plate 222, *Birds of America: Ibis alba*)

JAY, BLUE (*Cyanocitta cristata*)
Breeds from Nebraska, Alberta and Newfoundland to Texas and Florida, ranging farther south in winter. (Plate 102, *Birds of America: Corvus cristatus*)

KINGFISHER, BELTED (*Megaceryle alcyon*)
Breeds from Alaska and Labrador to California and the southern border of the U.S.A. Winters from British Columbia and Virginia to South America. (Plate 77, *Birds of America: Alcedo alcyon*)

MAN-O'-WAR BIRD (*Fregata magnificens*)
Breeds in West Indies; Bahamas; islands along west coast of Mexico; and the Galápagos archipelago. Winters in breeding area and adjacent seas.

Seen casually far northward. (Plate 271, *Birds of America*: FRIGATE PELICAN: *Tachypetes aquilus*)

MOCKINGBIRD (*Mimus polyglottos*)
Ranges chiefly from California, Wyoming and New Jersey to Mexico and Florida. Introduced into Bermuda. (Plate 21, *Birds of America*: *Turdus polyglottus*)

ORIOLES:
BALTIMORE ORIOLE (*Icterus galbula*)
Breeds from Wyoming, Alberta and Nova Scotia to Texas and Georgia. Winters from southern Mexico to Colombia. (Plate 12, *Birds of America*: *Icterus baltimore*)

ORCHARD ORIOLE (*Icterus spurius*)
Breeds from North Dakota and Massachusetts to Mexico. Winters from Mexico to Colombia. (Plate 42, *Birds of America*: same nomenclature)

OSPREY (*Pandion haliaetus*)
Breeds from Alaska and Labrador to Lower California and Florida. Winters from Lower California and Florida to the West Indies and Central America. Other races occur in the Bahamas, Europe, Asia, Australia, etc. (Plate 81, *Birds of America*: FISH HAWK: *Falco haliaetus*)

OWLS:
BARRED OWL (*Strix varia*)
Breeds from Wyoming and Saskatchewan and Newfoundland to Texas and Florida. (Plate 46, *Birds of America*: *Strix nebulosa*)

GREAT HORNED OWL (*Bubo virginianus*)
Breeds from Alaska and Ungava to Lower California and Florida. Many races have been named. (Plate 61, *Birds of America*: *Strix virginianus*)

LITTLE SCREECH OWL (*Otus asio*)
Ranges from Alaska and New Brunswick to Mexico. (Plate 97, *Birds of America*: MOTTLED OWL: *Strix asio*)

SAW-WHET OWL (*Cryptoglaux acadica*)
Breeds from Alaska and Nova Scotia to Mexico, Nebraska and Maryland. Winters to southern California and Virginia. (Plate 199, *Birds of America*: LITTLE OWL: *Strix acadica*)

SNOWY OWL (*Nyctea scandiaca*)
Breeds from the Bering Sea and northern Greenland to Keewatin and Ungava; also in northern Europe and Asia. Winters from Arctic coast to southern prairie provinces. Enters the U.S.A. at times in numbers. (Plate 121, *Birds of America*: *Strix nyctea*)

PARAKEET, CAROLINA (*Conuropsis carolinensis*)
Extinct in North America since 1904. Formerly occurred from Gulf states

to Colorado, Nebraska and New York; only parrot of eastern North America. (Plate 26, *Birds of America*: CAROLINA PARROT: *Psitacus carolinensis*)

PIGEON, PASSENGER (*Ectopistes migratorius*)
Extinct. Last known Passenger Pigeon died in Cincinnati Zoo in 1914. (Plate 62, *Birds of America: Columba migratoria*)

PELICAN, BROWN (*Pelecanus occidentalis*)
Breeds from California and North Carolina to Brazil. Winters from British Columbia and Florida southward. (Plate 251, *Birds of America: Pelecanus fuscus*)

PHOEBE (*Sayornis phoebe*)
Breeds from Mackenzie and Prince Edward Island to New Mexico and Georgia. Winters in the U.S.A., mostly south of Lat. 37° south to Mexico. (Plate 120, *Birds of America*: PEWIT FLYCATCHER: *Muscicapa fusca*)

PRAIRIE CHICKEN (*Tympanuchus cupido*)
Ranges from Alberta, Manitoba and Indiana to New Mexico and Louisiana, but exterminated over much of its range. Its eastern race, the Heath Hen: extinct. (Plate 186, *Birds of America*: PINNATED GROUSE: *Tetrao cupido*)

PUFFIN, ATLANTIC (*Fratercula arctica*)
Breeds from Greenland and Ungava to Maine, also from Norway and the British Isles to Portugal. Winters to New York, and in Morocco and the Azores. (Plate 213, *Birds of America*: PUFFIN: *Mormon arcticus*)

RAVEN (*Corvus corax*)
Ranges from Alaska and Greenland to Nicaragua and Georgia. Allied races occur in Europe and Asia. (Plate 101, *Birds of America*: same nomenclature)

SPARROW-HAWK (*Falco sparverius*)
Breeds from Upper Yukon and Newfoundland to Mexico and Florida. Winters from British Columbia and Massachusetts to Panama. (Plate 142, *Birds of America*: same nomenclature)

SWALLOWS: (*See also Swift*)
BARN SWALLOW (*Hirundo erythrogaster*)
Breeds from Alaska and Quebec to California, Mexico and North Carolina. Winters from Mexico to northern Argentina and Central Chile. (Plate 173, *Birds of America: Hirundo americana*)

CLIFF SWALLOW (*Petrochelidon albifrons*)
Breeds from Alaska and Cape Breton Island to Guatemala. Winters in South America, where range is unknown. (Plate 68, *Birds of America*: REPUBLICAN CLIFF SWALLOW: *Hirundo fulva*)

PURPLE MARTIN (*Progne subis*)
Breeds from Alaska and Nova Scotia to Mexico and Florida; also Lower California. Winters in Brazil. (Plate 22, *Birds of America: Hirundo purpurea*)

SWAN, TRUMPETER (*Cygnus buccinator*)
Formerly ranged as far south as Missouri. Now to be seen in Yellowstone Park region and Canada. (Plate 376, *Birds of America*: same nomenclature)

SWIFT, CHIMNEY (*Chaetura pelagica*)
Breeds from Montana, Alberta and Newfoundland to Texas and Florida. Winter range unknown. (Plate 158, *Birds of America*: AMERICAN SWIFT: *Cypselus pelasgius*)

TEAL (*See* Ducks)

TERNS:

ROSEATE TERN (*Sterna dougallii*)
Breeds locally from Nova Scotia to Venezuela and British Honduras; in Europe from Lat. 57° N. to the Mediterranean; in Africa, Ceylon and China. Winters from Louisiana to Brazil. Allied races occur in Australia and the Indian Ocean. (Plate 240, *Birds of America: Sterna Dougalii*)

SOOTY TERN (*Sterna fuscata*)
Breeds from Bahamas and Dry Tortugas to Venezuela. Winters from Louisiana to the Falkland Islands. (Plate 235, *Birds of America: Sterna fuliginosa*)

THRASHER, BROWN (*Toxostoma rufum*)
Breeds from Montana, Alberta and Quebec to the Gulf. Winters from Missouri and North Carolina to Texas and Florida, and occasionally as far north as New York, etc. (Plate 116, *Birds of America*: FERRUGINOUS THRUSH: *Turdus rufus*)

THRUSH, WOOD (*Hylocichla mustelina*)
Breeds from South Dakota and New Hampshire to Texas and Florida. Winters from Mexico to Panama. (Plate 73, *Birds of America: Turdus mustelinus*)

TURKEY, WILD (*Meleagris gallopavo*)
Ranges from Pennsylvania and Oklahoma to central Mexico; formerly to South Dakota and Maine. (Plate 1, *Birds of America*: GREAT AMERICAN COCK: *Meleagris gallopavo*)

VIREO, WARBLING (*Vireo gilvus*)
Breeds from British Columbia and Nova Scotia to Lower California and North Carolina. Winters south to Guatemala. (Plate 118, *Birds of America*: WARBLING FLYCATCHER: *Muscicapa gilva*)

WATER-THRUSH, LOUISIANA (*Seiurus motacilla*)
Breeds from Nebraska and New England to Texas and Georgia. Winters from Mexico to Colorado, and in the West Indies. (Plate 19, *Birds of America: Turdus aquaticus*)

WATER-TURKEY (*Anhinga anhinga*)
Breeds from Arkansas and North Carolina to Argentina, and winters in about the same area, north to California and occasionally South Carolina. (Plate 316, *Birds of America:* BLACK-BELLIED DARTER: *Plotus anhinga*)

WHIP-POOR-WILL (*Caprimulgus vociferus*)
Breeds from North Dakota, Manitoba and Nova Scotia to Arizona and Georgia. Winters from South Carolina and the Gulf states to Central America. (Plate 82, *Birds of America: Caprimulgus vociferus*)

WOODPECKERS:

IVORY-BILLED WOODPECKER (*Campephilus principalis*)
Virtually extinct. Florida and South Carolina only. Formerly ranged from Oklahoma, Illinois and Indiana, south to the Gulf. (Plate 66, *Birds of America: Picus principalis*)

PILEATED WOODPECKER (*Ceophloeus pileatus*)
Ranges from British Columbia, Mackenzie and Nova Scotia to California and Florida. (Plate 111, *Birds of America: Picus pileatus*)

RED-COCKADED WOODPECKER (*Dryobates borealis*)
Ranges from South Atlantic and Gulf states north to Virginia, Tennessee, Kentucky and Missouri. (Plate 389, *Birds of America: Picus querulus*)

WRENS:

BEWICK'S WREN (*Thryomanes bewickii*)
Breeds from British Columbia and Pennsylvania to Lower California and Georgia. Winters from near the northern limit of its range to California and Florida. (Plate 18, *Birds of America:* BEWICK'S LONG-TAILED WREN: *Troglodytes bewickii*)

CAROLINA WREN (*Thryothorus ludovicianus*)
Ranges from Nebraska and Connecticut to Mexico and Florida. (Plate 78, *Birds of America:* GREAT CAROLINA WREN: *Troglodytes ludovicianus*)

HOUSE WREN (*Troglodytes aedon*)
Breeds from British Columbia and New Brunswick to Lower California and South Carolina. Winters from California and the Gulf states to Mexico. (Plate 83, *Birds of America:* same nomenclature)

WINTER WREN (*Troglodytes troglodytes*)
Alaska, Alberta and Labrador to California, Michigan and New England, and southward in mountains to Georgia. Winters to Texas and Florida. (Plate 360, *Birds of America: Sylvia troglodytes*)

Bibliography

FIRST EDITIONS

Audubon, John James. *The Birds of America*, 4 vols.: 435 hand-colored copper-plate engravings, double elephant folio. London, published by the Author, 1827-1838. First 10 plates engraved in Edinburgh by W. H. Lizars in 1826 and retouched by R. Havell & Son in London in 1827; from June 1830 the plates were engraved by R. Havell, Jr.

Audubon, John James. *Ornithological Biography* . . .
Vol. I: text for above folio plates 1-100. Edinburgh, 1831; Philadelphia, 1831, 1835, with same text and pagination.
Vol. II: text for plates 101-200. Edinburgh, 1834; Boston, 1835, same.
Vol. III: text for plates 201-300. Edinburgh, 1835. No American edition. 9 woodcut engravings: anatomical drawings by William MacGillivray.
Vol. IV: text for plates 300-387. Edinburgh, 1838. No American edition.
Vol. V: text for plates 387-435. Edinburgh, 1839. No American edition. 98 wood engravings of anatomical drawings by MacGillivray.
Total pages: 2,139 (text) and 140 (introductory). No illustrations by Audubon.

Audubon, John James. *The Birds of America*. 7 vols.: roy. 8vo. New York and Philadelphia, Audubon and Chevalier, 1840-1844. Text that of *Ornithological Biography,* with deletions, some additions, and minor corrections and revision. *Episodes* omitted. Follows order of Audubon's *A Synopsis of the Birds of North America* (Edinburgh and London, 1839). 500 plates in 100 parts, lithographed by J. Bowen and staff, Philadelphia, from camera lucida drawings by John Woodhouse Audubon of 435 folio plates by J. J. Aububon, and from additional drawings by Audubon with certain new botanical accessories by Maria Martin.
For more data see F. H. Herrick: *Audubon the Naturalist*: I, 401-405: New York, D. Appleton-Century, 1917; 1938.

Audubon, John James. *The Birds of America*. Introduction and notes by William Vogt, editor. 500 color plates. New York, Macmillan, 1937. (Reissued 1941, 1946, 1953, with 435 color plates.)

Audubon, John James. Introduction and notes by Ludlow Griscom, editor. 288 color plates. New York, Macmillan, 1950.